Food Engineering Operations

Second edition

Food Engineering Operations

Second edition

by

J. G. Brennan
J. R. Butters
N. D. Cowell
A. E. V. Lilly

National College of Food Technology
University of Reading

with a foreword by
Professor E. J. Rolfe

APPLIED SCIENCE PUBLISHERS LIMITED

LONDON

APPLIED SCIENCE PUBLISHERS LTD
RIPPLE ROAD, BARKING, ESSEX, ENGLAND

First edition 1969
Second edition 1976
Reprinted 1979
Reprinted 1981

ISBN: 0 85334 694 1

WITH 18 TABLES AND 233 ILLUSTRATIONS

© APPLIED SCIENCE PUBLISHERS LTD 1976

Printed in Great Britain by Galliard (Printers) Ltd Great Yarmouth

FOREWORD TO THE FIRST EDITION

Since the time when man first killed animals and harvested plants he has been faced with the problem of preserving his food from season to season, and from periods of glut to those of famine. Drying is probably the earliest form of preservation he used, and salting is another ancient process. In more recent times there has arisen a greater requirement for preserved foods, not only because of the massive increase in population of the world but also because of the accompanying shift from rural to urban districts and towns. Industrialisation has led to the massing of people into towns and cities, and this situation demands an ample supply of stable foods which can be stored and transported, but they must also be palatable and in general must closely resemble the original fresh foodstuff. It is not surprising therefore that food has become a major present day industry. In Britain the total food bill for 1964 was £5557 m of which more than a half was for food processed in some way.

Such a large industry cannot be supported by processing methods based on art and empiricism. It is essential to employ safe and reliable methods which consistently produce palatable stable foods of uniform quality, a goal which has been achieved through the study and understanding of the foodstuffs themselves and of the processing operations. A fascinating example of the development of a process from the art to the modern scientifically based procedure is the preservation of food by heating in sealed containers. The method was discovered by Nicholas Appert (a report of the process was published in 1810), but it was not until 1895 that the results of Pasteur's discoveries concerning the spoilage of wine by micro-organisms were applied to explain the spoilage of canned foods. Now our understanding of bacteria and their relation to food processing together with other basic knowledge concerning e.g., heat transfer, has permitted the growth and development of a large canning industry.

Our vast food industry needs a constant supply of knowledgeable and trained manpower, and to meet this need at least in part, several universities now have teaching departments in food science and technology. Such systematic teaching is of recent introduction, and consequently there exists a shortage of suitable texts to assist the student in his (or her) studies. The object of this volume is to bring together information on one restricted but appropriate field, *i.e.*, principles of food engineering and the plant used in the processing of foodstuffs. The treatment is such that the material can form part of a first degree course in food science and technology. It is hoped that this work will become a useful book of reference not only for students in the UK but also for those overseas, particularly in countries where so much remains to be done in order to establish a food industry adequate to the needs of the community.

E. J. ROLFE

Principal, National College of Food Technology

FROM THE PREFACE TO THE FIRST EDITION

This book is largely based on the lecture course in Food Engineering given at the National College of Food Technology (University of Reading) to undergraduate students reading Food Technology. The basic purpose of the work is, therefore, to provide an undergraduate text. A knowledge of simple calculus and some applied physics is assumed. While no exhaustive bibliography of the topics discussed is attempted, the reader is referred throughout to special texts, review articles and selected research papers to encourage a deeper study of the subject and to make the work more generally useful to the practising Food Technologist.

The authors must acknowledge the considerable help they have received both from those in the food and food machinery industries and from the Principal and staff of the National College. In particular, thanks are due to Mr. S. Green, and to Mr. H. D. G. Roper for his suggestions and advice.

Readers should note that throughout this work the common logarithm is denoted by log ( ), the Napierian logarithm by ln ( ) and exponentiation by exp ( ).

J.G.B.
J.R.B.
N.D.C.
A.E.V.L.

PREFACE TO THE SECOND EDITION

In preparing the second edition, the whole work has been revised and more extended treatments given in some places. New sections have been added, *e.g.* on membrane separation and thawing, and one new chapter on solid–liquid extraction and expression. However, the guiding principle in this edition has been the same as in the first: to produce an undergraduate textbook giving a basic coverage of the subject and, through selected references, directing the reader's attention to more extensive or detailed treatments of specific topics.

The SI system of units has been used throughout, but in certain circumstances, particularly when discussing topics where these units are not yet extensively used, quantities expressed in SI units are accompanied by their equivalents in more conventional terms.

The authors acknowledge with gratitude the assistance given by Mr I. F. Davison in the preparation of this second edition.

J.G.B.
J.R.B.
N.D.C.
A.E.V.L.

CONTENTS

PART II—CONVERSION OPERATIONS

PART I
PRELIMINARY OPERATIONS

CHAPTER 1

THE RAW MATERIAL AND THE PROCESS

1.1. INTRODUCTION

Food processing is seasonal in nature, both in the demand for its output and in the availability of its raw materials, many of which have to be imported. In common with any other manufacturer the food processor would prefer his raw materials: to be continuously available in sufficient quantity and quality to enable him to operate on a planned year-round basis; to be stable in storage; to be of uniform characteristics and to be of predictable price. In practice few, if any, of these criteria are satisfied and it is the purpose of this chapter to identify the particular raw material requirements of the food industry, to indicate some of the problems of supply and to show how the industry and its suppliers respond to these.

In general, the process suitability (S) of a food raw material is determined by a balanced assessment of its properties such as: its availability (a); its geometric (g), physical (p), functional (f), growth (gr) and mechanical (m) properties and its thermal (t) and electrical characteristics (e), etc.

Thus:

$$S = \varphi(a + g + p + f + gr + m + t + e + \cdots) \qquad (1.1)$$

The relative importance of these factors in their contribution to the suitability index will, of course, vary depending on the raw material, the process applied to it and the end product made from it.

1.2. GEOMETRIC PROPERTIES OF THE FOOD

Foods of regular geometry are best suited to high speed mechanised processes. Potato varieties of smooth shape and with shallow eyes are preferred for mechanical peeling and washing. Again, smooth-skinned tomato varieties are more easily washed than ribbed varieties (which also tend to harbour insects such as *Drosophila*). Other examples of shape selection are pigs with long lean backs for bacon and straight runner beans for mechanical snipping (*i.e.* topping and tailing) and slicing. Thus, shape, uniformity of shape, freedom from surface irregularities and size are important processing indices.

1.2.1. SHAPE

The dimensional relationships of a food unit are important: in packaging; in controlling fill-in weight; in freezing; in canning and other heat processes; and in determining the way in which materials behave during pneumatic conveying and bulk storage.

Measurement of a set of specimens enables the magnitude of the contribution of each dimensional variable to the overall process suitability to be estimated. Griffiths and Smith[1] found that the volume of quartzite pebbles could be estimated simply from the relationship:

$$\log \text{volume} = b_1 \log \text{major axis} + b_2 \log \text{minor axis}$$

Mohsenin[2] describes the application of this technique to the measurement of the volumes of irregularly shaped maize kernels and other foods.

1.2.2. UNIFORMITY OF SHAPE

This is of importance during: filling into containers; conveying; heat treatment; freezing; dehydration; and during sorting and grading operations.

The roundness of biscuits and hamburgers; the sphericity of apples or potatoes; pears which are of uniform pyriform shape and cucumbers of regular fusiform shape are examples of desirable shape-uniformity characteristics. Shape classifications for UK varieties of fruits and vegetables are discussed by Arthey,[5] and Mohsenin[2] describes procedures whereby roundness and sphericity may be measured and lists data for US varieties of apples and other fruits. Information of this type enables the processor to select cultivars for particular purposes.

1.2.3. FREEDOM FROM SURFACE IRREGULARITIES

Clearly, surface projections and depressions occurring in a food unit present cleaning and processing problems. The food industry is relatively labour and energy intensive and raw materials account for a large proportion of the cost of processed foods.[3] Surface imperfections removed either intentionally or during processing contribute significantly to these costs. Specific varieties must be selected or developed to minimise these defects.

1.2.4. SIZE AND WEIGHT OF FOOD UNITS

Optimum dimensions exist for each process and raw materials complying with these specifications must be provided. Whilst sorting (*see* Chapter 3) can assist in size and weight control, raw materials containing oversize and undersize materials present the processor with economic and disposal problems. Sampling and testing before acceptance must be carried out to ensure conformity with processing requirements.

1.2.5. SPECIFIC SURFACE OF FOOD UNITS

This raw material property is important in processes involving gas/solid and liquid/solid reactions such as respiration, extraction, smoking, brining and oxidation. It is also an important economic factor in determining peel and core to fruit or vegetable ratios and washing losses. The specific surface properties of particulate foods are also of importance in fluidised processing and movement (*see* Appendix I).

Surface areas may be determined by peeling followed by measurement of the peel area using a planimeter. Simple relationships between the surface area (A) and the weight (W), of the form $A = K_1 + K_2 W$ (where K_1 and K_2 are constants) are available in the literature for varieties of apples, pears and plums.[2]

1.3. OTHER PHYSICAL PROPERTIES OF THE RAW MATERIAL

Many physical properties, in addition to geometric properties (Section 1.2) warrant consideration when selecting food raw materials. These include: colour; texture; resistance to mechanical stress; aero- and hydrodynamic properties and frictional characteristics.

1.3.1. COLOUR PROPERTIES

In low temperature processes (*e.g.* freezing or freeze drying), colour changes during processing are minimal, so the colour of the raw material is a reasonable index of its suitability for these processes. In heat processes (*e.g.* canning and dehydration), the fresh-food colour is not a reliable index of suitability. Thus, some varieties of apples and pears develop a pink tinge on canning, whilst rhubarb and some cherry varieties become bleached due to migration of colour into canning syrups. Again, chlorophyll is converted into brown-green phaeophytin during the heat processing of green vegetables. Potatoes pose special problems; varieties exhibiting minimum browning are necessary for canning or dehydration whereas for potato chip processing, some degree of browning is necessary.

Colour control is best exercised by selecting varieties of known processing performance, by using the correct pretreatment procedures such as blanching (*see* Chapter 10) and by using process conditions designed to retain the natural food colour. The use of added colourings, preferably those of natural origin, or in the limit, artificial colours in the permitted list[4] may be necessary. Methods of colour sorting are discussed in Chapter 3.

1.3.2. TEXTURAL PROPERTIES

The textural characteristics of the raw material are of great importance. The first requirement is that the raw material must be sufficiently robust to withstand the mechanical stresses to which it is subjected during preparative operations. Secondly, the raw material must withstand the processing conditions so as to yield a final product of the desired texture. Fruit and vegetable varieties with improved mechanical strength have been developed, such as tough-skinned peaches and tomatoes suited to mechanised washing, peeling and sorting. Other examples include the selection of blackcurrant varieties suitable for mechanical strigging (*i.e.* stalk removal) and pea and bean varieties which will withstand mechanical podding.

The evaluation of textural characteristics is based either on sensory testing using trained panels or on instrumental procedures.[5] The well known Tenderometer, and other machines such as the Maturometer, the General Foods Texturometer* and the Instron Food Texture Tester† are typical instruments used in this field. Whilst the

* General Foods Corp., N.Y., USA.
† Instron Ltd, High Wycombe, Bucks., England.

correlation between that perceived and that measured is not easy, instrumental procedures are of considerable assistance in the prediction of the behaviour of raw materials during processing.

1.3.3. AERO- AND HYDRODYNAMIC PROPERTIES

Differences in these properties between the desired and undesired parts of a raw material may be used to clean, sort and grade the raw material (*see* Chapters 2 and 3). In addition, air and water are frequently used to convey, mix and process materials. Thus, aerodynamic and hydrodynamic properties are important raw material characteristics.

Reference to Appendix I relating to fluid flow will indicate that many of the physical properties discussed in this chapter, such as size, shape, uniformity of shape and surface properties are operative in determining how particulate foods behave in fluid flow. Additional material properties involved include density and porosity.

Data regarding these material properties are reported in the literature[2] and the subject of pneumatic conveying is discussed in Chapter 19.

1.3.4. FRICTIONAL PROPERTIES

Before grain can slide down a chute or discharge from a bulk bin the forces of static friction due to interparticle action and particle–wall friction must be overcome. Once the material begins to flow, the coefficient of dynamic friction must be exceeded in order that flow should continue. A simplified treatment of the more recent concepts of friction theory is included in Chapter 19. For a more detailed discussion including design data, the reader is referred to the excellent treatment by Mohsenin.[2]

Differences in frictional properties may be used to effect separation of contaminants in cleaning processes (Chapter 2) and to sort out blemished or damaged units from sound material (Chapter 3).

1.4. FUNCTIONAL PROPERTIES OF FOOD RAW MATERIALS

A raw material of ideal functionality is one which may be processed to give a first quality product whilst permitting maximum process effectiveness. Clearly, the functional properties required of a material will vary depending upon the process to which it is to be subjected.

Many examples of varieties developed for special purposes are common knowledge, *e.g.* sheep bred for wool or meat and cattle for meat or milk. Special wheat varieties yield soft, low protein flour suitable for biscuits and cakes whilst other, high protein wheats are used for bread flours. Similarly, the dry solids content of potatoes, which may vary between 16 and 22% is of great importance to the potato processor and the development of suitable, high solids content varieties has received much attention.[6, 7]

Selection of raw materials on a functional basis usually involves process-testing of varieties. In some cases it is possible to assess function by chemical or physical testing or combinations of these. An example of this is the evaluation of cereal flours for bread, cake or biscuit manufacture using specially designed apparatus such as the 'Research' Dough Testing Equipment* and the Brabender Farinograph.†

1.4.1. FLAVOUR PROPERTIES

Flavour, perhaps more than any other property, is a matter of personal preference. In serving a mass market, extremes of flavour must be avoided. In some cases, the flavour of the processed food is more a function of additives than of the raw material. Examples of this are the use of strongly flavoured syrups in some canned fruits and of protein hydrolysates and yeast extracts in meat soups.

In general, therefore, varieties selected for processing should impart only flavours which are characteristic of the food and these flavours should be neither too powerful nor too weak. For these reasons, flavour is of less importance than other factors (*e.g.* colour and texture), in determining the suitability of a variety for processing.

1.4.2. RESISTANCE TO PROCESSING STRESSES

Apple varieties vary widely in suitability for processing. Some dessert varieties lose their rigidity on processing and are, therefore, unsuitable. Firm, white-fleshed, acid varieties are preferred for canning and freezing. Again, clingstone peaches have excellent texture when canned. For this reason this variety is used, almost exclusively, in preference to the better flavoured but more delicate freestone and

---

* Henry Simons Ltd, Stockport, England.
† C. W. Brabender Instruments Inc. (N.J., USA).

white peach varieties. Similarly, the relatively tough Marrowfat pea varieties are used for canned, processed peas whilst the more tender pea varieties are used for canned and frozen garden peas.

Bartlett pears of high acidity and tannin content are reported to give a pink colour when canned. The growing conditions and soil types were shown to be of importance in controlling this defect and pink colour formation could be eliminated by using high pH fruit.[8]

These examples are typical and illustrate the importance of adequate pilot-testing before approving raw materials for processing purposes.

1.4.3. FREEDOM FROM DEFECTS

Food manufacture, unfortunately, is a low profit activity, and based as it is on raw materials of natural origin, these representing a major cost factor, it is vital to procure low defect-level input materials. Cleaning, sorting and grading generate labour and plant costs and may cause product damage, producing material defects. These preparatory procedures are essential steps in processing but the plant used must be carefully designed and the operators thoroughly trained if defect levels are to be controlled. The literature contains numerous references to defects produced in the field or orchard, to the sowing of varieties which are insufficiently disease resistant and to harvesting and handling damage. The combined effect of these defect-producing activities is evidenced by the large output of waste from most food factories. Clearly, the plan must be to start with the best and then to treat it with loving care.

Defects which affect processing suitability include the following:

(i)   Geometric deformities and unequalities.
(ii)   Mechanical damage due to impact, puncture or abrasion.
(iii) Colour defects.
(iv)   Insect, animal, fungal and microbial damage.
(v)   Extraneous matter contamination.
(vi)   Textural and functional defects.
(vii) Immaturity or over-maturity

1.5.   GROWTH PROPERTIES OF THE RAW MATERIAL

It will be apparent from the foregoing that the food manufacturer is vitally concerned with the characteristics of natural or nature-derived raw materials. It is not surprising, therefore, that the modern processor regards his factory as extending back to the growing area. Thus the processor becomes involved in many aspects formerly the concern of the supplier, such as contract buying, growth programming, transportation and storage.

1.5.1. CONTRACT PURCHASING OF RAW MATERIALS

Purchasing of raw material produce in the open market is substantially outmoded. These days, the food processor contracts ahead with the farmer or grower for a definite acreage of produce. Under this system the processor may do any or all of the following:

(i)   Agree the sowing plan.
(ii)   Supply seed of selected varieties, fertiliser and sprays.
(iii) Indicate expected harvest date.
(iv)   Provide technical advice *via* his field men.
(v)   Provide harvesting or vining equipment and, sometimes, labour.
(vi)   Arrange or provide transport keyed to his production and handling systems.

This system is applied to an ever growing list of food raw materials from wheat, barley and rye, to vegetables such as potatoes, peas and beans. It is a most effective method of assuring supplies of the required materials at the required time and in the required quantity.

1.5.2. SELECTIVE BREEDING OF RAW MATERIALS

Any improvement in the suitability of the raw material for its intended purpose, or in the spreading of the season over which the raw material may be harvested, results in improved processing efficiency and plant utilisation. The development of varieties for food processing involves consideration of all those attributes of the raw material which are reflected in the quality of the finished product (Chapter 3). The development of suitable varieties for processing requires close cooperation between breeders, research stations and processors and considerable progress has been made.

Selective breeding of processing raw materials is now commonplace. Typical examples include: high dry-matter content potatoes, tomatoes and onions; tomatoes giving puree of improved colour and flavour; brussels sprouts of improved freezing properties; and bitter-free cucumber varieties.

The widespread adoption of mechanical harvesting has stimulated the breeding of varieties with suitable growth habits. For example, pea varieties are now available which have a low, upright, firm growth bearing tangle-free pods. Again, fruit varieties which may be easily plucked or shaken free by mechanical harvesters have been developed.

1.5.3. MATURATION PROPERTIES

The maturity of the raw material is important in controlling both the quality of the final product and the effectiveness of processing. Processing varieties are required to mature both uniformly (to facilitate mechanical harvesting) and predictably, to permit adequate planning.

Over-maturity results in a high proportion of reject material, excessive product damage and spoilage during storage. Sterilisation efficiency may be reduced due to the high microbiological loads often encountered with over-mature materials. Under-maturity implies a reduced yield and the final product is liable to have substandard colour, flavour and texture.

In some foods (*e.g.* meat, cheese, wines), a period of maturing is essential whilst, in others (*e.g.* eggs), maturing is undesirable. Fruits and vegetables may be harvested over a range of maturities, depending on their destined end-use. Peas are a particular example and much work has been carried out relating canning and freezing properties to maturity.[9, 11] As a result of this work, it is possible to harvest peas at their optimum maturity for any desired purpose. Since, in many cases, the optimum is reached and passed in a matter of a few hours, this is a matter of great importance to the processor. Similar work has been carried out with broad beans.[10]

1.5.4. PREDICTION OF MATURITY

Forecasting of harvest dates is of great value to the planner. In many commodities (*e.g.* meat, milk, eggs), harvest patterns are well established. For peas and beans, the Heat Unit System[12] has proved to be useful in predicting maturity. This system is based on the fact that attainment of maturity is a function of growth temperature. Armed with specific growth data on the variety of crop and a knowledge of the average meteorological records of the growing area, it is possible to make a long-range forecast of the probable harvest date for any sowing. Corrections can then be made, during the growing period, for the actual weather conditions and the long range forecast may be adjusted accordingly. For example, peas are assumed not to grow at all below 40 F (4·5 C). In any one day of growth, the difference between 40 F (4·5 C) and the average temperature throughout that day is known as the number of 'degree days' or accumulated heat units (AHU's). The AHU measurements of many pea and bean varieties are now available from the seed supplier so that reasonably reliable harvest forecasts may be made using this method.

1.5.5. EXTENSION OF HARVEST SEASON

The use of early, middle and late varieties has done much to spread the season over which food raw materials become available for processing. The widespread adoption of the broiler and battery systems has extended the availability of chicken meat and eggs. The broiler system is now being used in the production of beef and promising results are being obtained. Pea varieties have been the subject of much investigation regarding the spread of harvest season.

Availability may be extended by using preserved raw materials such as brined, dried or pulped crops or by storing part-processed or raw foods. Usually, increased costs are incurred with these procedures and their economic feasibility must be considered carefully before adoption.

Fish pose special problems as a result of the steeply rising harvesting costs, the depletion of fish stocks and the consequent political problems. Fish farming would appear to offer an attractive prospect.[13] Currently, rainbow trout weighing around 5 kg at very competitive prices are being farmed in the UK. Investigatory work involving salt water fish is proceeding apace.[14]

Hydroponics, *i.e.* soilless culture, also presents interesting future possibilities for spreading harvests. This system, using solar-actuated climatic control, permits simplified disease control, water economies and concentrated planting. Soilless culture is now an established commercial practice in many countries.[15]

1.6. MECHANISATION AND THE RAW MATERIAL

The food industry, faced with soaring labour costs and low profitability has mechanised its operations wherever practicable. Mechanisation, whilst offering undoubted advantages, unless carefully engineered, can cause excessive product damage.

1.6.1. PRODUCT DAMAGE

The main causes of damage during food preparation are: operator damage caused by careless manipulation; unsuitable mechanical handling procedures; poor equipment design and incorrect containerisation.

Damage occurs at every stage of the manufacturing chain starting with the grower or breeder and extending through processing to packaging and distribution. It has been stated that an apple may be handled thirty times between the tree and the consumer and that bruise damage in the US apple industry exceeds ten million dollars a year.[16]

Damage manifests itself in many ways: the appearance of the food is affected; mould and rot infections invade bruised and punctured areas; infestation by insects and vermin occurs and enzymatic and chemical spoilage is accelerated. Damage spoilage spreads to adjacent material causing financial loss and impairment or invalidation of process effectiveness. In the extreme this represents a positive health hazard.

Produce is damaged: by impact with other produce or hard surfaces; by excessive pressure caused by overlying food; by puncturing by sharp projections and by abrasion caused by movement and vibration.

A detailed discussion of the mechanics of damage is inappropriate here but the reader is referred to the literature on the subject.[2]

1.6.2. MECHANICAL HARVESTING

The change from selective to mechanical harvesting of the 'once-over' or destructive type has produced substantial reductions in labour costs but has many disadvantages. Amongst the more important of these are excessive damage and consequent quality reduction and increased capital investment and maintenance costs. Additionally, this system requires careful coordination between the field and the factory. Frequently, this involves the manufacturer in process alterations and in changes in his handling, containerisation and storage arrangements.

In the UK the combine harvester, the pea viner, the bean harvester and various harvesters for root crops are familiar. In the USA there has been considerable development of harvesters for many other crops (*e.g.* berry fruits, asparagus, sprouts, cucumbers, cabbage, spinach and tomatoes). Apples and citrus fruits may be harvested using tree shakers and blowers.[17,18]

Currently, mechanical harvesting machines utilise one or more of the following seven principles:[19]

(i) Shaking of trees or bushes carrying crops (sometimes used in conjunction with abscission promoting sprays).

(ii) Combing of berry fruits such as blueberries and strawberries.

(iii) Cutting of cabbages, lettuces, cauliflowers, etc., the plant being severed at ground level.

(iv) Pulling of carrots, radishes and celery in which the stems are gripped by opposing, driven belts.

(v) Stripping of cucumbers and maize ears using differentially driven soft rubber rollers.

(vi) Vining of peas and beans involving either stripping, pulling or cutting of the vines followed by podding.

(vii) Mechanical digging of root crops such as potatoes or onions.

Frequently, harvesting machines carry out other preparative operations such as aspiration, screening, destoning and colour sorting.

Mechanical harvesting, therefore, requires a multi-disciplinary approach with breeders, farmers, food technologists, engineers and economists working in close cooperation.

1.6.3. DESIGN OF TRANSIT CONTAINERS FOR RAW MATERIALS

In-transit damage due to impact, abrasion and pressure, frequently is the result of incorrect containerisation. O'Brien *et al.*[20] demonstrated substantially lower damage when tomatoes were harvested into shallow lug-boxes compared with collection in bulk bins whereas Pearl,[21] only one year earlier, had shown the reverse to be true. O'Brien's work suggested that fruit to fruit contacts are more damaging than fruit to container-surface impacts, whereas Pearl's findings indicated that fruit to container-surface impacts cause more damage than fruit to fruit contacts, there being less damage in the case of the deeper containers with a higher tomato to container-surface ratio. Evidently, consideration must be given to other factors such as: the type and variety of fruit; its maturity; its shape; its size (as affecting its kinetic energy when falling) and the nature of the container surface (*e.g.* its hardness and texture). The warning is clear, each situation calls for its own investigation and of interest in this respect is the work of O'Brien and Guillou[22] who have developed an in-transit vibration simulator for fruit handling studies and Hammerle's[23] work on the evaluation of abrasion resistance in fruit and vegetables.

Pressure damage caused by overlying material in containers which are too deep or by overfilling of open top containers which are then stacked is all too common. Some apples will not withstand an overlying static weight in excess of 4 kg whilst peaches are even more fragile. Pressure damage is cumulative, a pyramid of damage emanating from the original pressure point. Damage of this latter type is likely to be more extensive in shallow containers with a high exposed-surface to fruit ratio than when deep containers are used.

1.6.4. TRANSPORTATION OF RAW MATERIALS

Arranging to have available raw materials of the proper quality in the required amounts and at the correct time is mandatory to any process. In the food industry particular problems of supply exist. Raw foods sensitive to microbiological, insect and chemical spoilage and, in many cases, still continuing to respire, become available over a relatively short period at harvest. Delivery delays disorganise production and impair raw material quality. Proper scheduling is vital and the processor should either specify delivery procedures in the buying contract (including a penalty clause in the event of default) or, alternatively, exclude delivery from the supplier's liability and accept responsibility for transport himself.

Particular care must be exercised in the correct choice of container (Section 1.6.3) and in maintaining these in a sound and clean condition so as to avoid contamination of the raw material with wood fragments, nails, etc. Where transportation takes place in bags or sacks, careful sack cleaning and examination is necessary. Second-hand sacks which may have contained fertilisers or spray materials are sometimes pressed into service in an emergency, occasionally with dire consequences.

Transportation vehicles require special attention. They should be properly maintained so as to avoid tainting or discoloration of the food by exhaust gases or fuel. Vehicles should give a smooth, uninterrupted ride to their contents and be well-ventilated to allow product heat to dissipate during the journey. Above all, vehicles should be thoroughly clean and insect free. Contract transport is notoriously difficult to control in these respects and, all too frequently, outbreaks of insect infestation are traceable to foods being transported in a vehicle which has been incompletely cleaned after carrying infested material for another customer.

Finally, it is important to ensure, as far as possible, that the transportation operation, as a whole, is integrated with the handling system in use in the factory. Rehandling is expensive and inevitably causes raw material damage.

1.6.5. RAW MATERIAL STORAGE

Ideally, all raw materials are processed immediately on arrival at the factory. In practice this situation seldom exists so that some provision must be made for on-site storage of raw materials and part-processed products. In this way, delivery delays, plant breakdowns and bumper harvests may be accommodated and, occasionally, the store can be an asset allowing forward-buying when advantageous market conditions exist.

Reference to Chapter 16 will indicate that, for most food materials, storage conditions are highly specific with respect to temperature, humidity and surrounding atmosphere. Storage of any type ties up capital and is costly to provide and operate. With the demanding conditions imposed by many foodstuffs these factors warrant the most careful consideration when planning the provision of storage facilities. More often than not emergency situations may be resolved by overtime working or by temporary hiring of storage space. Provision of emergency storage capacity should therefore be on a minimal basis.

REFERENCES

1. Griffiths, J. C. and Smith, C. M., 'Relationships Between Volume and Axes of Some Quartzite Pebbles'. Am. J. of Sci., **262**(4), 497–512 (1964).
2. Mohsenin, N. N., 'Physical Properties of Plant and Animal Materials' Vol. 1. (Gordon & Breach, New York: 1970.)
3. Thijssen, H. A. C., 'Process Engineering in the Food Industry'. Chem. and Ind. (12), 501–4 (1975).
4. Anon., 'The Colouring Matter in Foods Regulations 1973. No. 1340'. (HMSO, London.)
5. Arthey, V. D., 'Quality of Horticultural Products'. (Butterworths: 1975.)
6. Irving, G. W. and Hoover, S. R. (Eds), 'Food Quality. Effects of Production Practices and Processing'. (American Association for the Advancement of Science. Pub. No. 77: 1965.)
7. Talburt, W. F., and Smith, O., 'Potato Processing'. 3rd ed. (AVI. USA: 1975.)
8. Luh, B. S., Leonard, S., and Patel, D. S., 'Pink Discolouration in Canned Bartlett Pears'. Fd Technol., **14**(1), 53–6 (1960).
9. Adams, W. B., 'The Quality of Fruit and Vegetables for Processing', *in* Hawthorn, J., and Muil Leitch, J. (Eds), 'Recent Advances in Food Science'. Vol. 2 (Butterworths: 1962.)
10. Arthey, V. D., and Webb, C., 'The Relationship between Maturity and Quality of Canned Broad Beans'. J. Fd Technol., **4**(1), 61–74 (1969).

11. Arthey, V. D., and Gent, G. P., 'The Suitability of Pea Varieties for Canning and Quick Freezing: 1965 Tests'. Tech. Memo. No. 67. Fruit Veg. Preserv. Res. Ass. (1966).

12. Seaton, H. L., 'Scheduling Plantings and Predicting Harvest Maturities for Processing Vegetables'. Fd Technol., **9**, 202–9 (1955).

13. Brown, E. E., 'Mariculture and Aquaculture'. Fd Technol., **37**(12), 60–66 (1973).

14. Richardson, I. D., 'Marine Fish Farming Experiences in the UK'. Biologist, **18**(1), 10–14 (1971).

15. Stoughton, R. H., 'Soilless Cultivation and its Application to Commercial Horticultural Crop Production'. (FAO, Rome: 1969.)

16. Anon., 'A Review of Literature on Harvesting, Handling, Storage and Transportation of Apples'. ARS 51–4. (1965). US Department of Agriculture. Agricultural Research Service.

17. Ryall, A. L., and Pentzer, W. T., Handling, Transportation and Storage of Fruits & Vegetables. (AVI: 1974).

18. Smith, M. D., 'Mechanisation for Production, Harvesting and Handling of Canning Crops'. Fd Trade Rev., **38**(2), 46–51 (1968).

19. Hawkins, J. C., 'Fruit and Vegetables: Mechanised Harvesting in the USA'. Span, **13**(2), 116–9 (1970).

20. O'Brien, M., York, G. K., McGillivray, J. H., and Leonard, S., 'Bulk Handling of Canning Tomatoes'. Fd Technol., **17**(8), 96–101 (1963).

21. Pearl, R. C., '1961 Tomato Mechanical Harvesting Research in California'. Fd Technol., **16**(7), 54–6 (1962).

22. O'Brien, M., and Guillou, H., 'An In-Transit Vibration Simulator for Fruit Handling Studies'. Trans. Amer. Soc. Agric. Engng, **12**(1), 94–7 (1969).

23. Hammerle, J. R., 'A Technique for Evaluating Fruit and Vegetable Abrasion Resistance'. Trans. Amer. Soc. Agric. Engng, **13**(5), 672–5 (1970).

CHAPTER 2

CLEANING OF RAW MATERIALS

The preliminary preparative operation of cleaning, together with the operations of sorting and grading dealt with in Chapter 3, are conveniently regarded as separation operations.

Cleaning separates contaminants from the raw materials.

Sorting separates the raw material into categories of different physical characteristics such as size, shape and colour.

Grading separates the raw material into categories of different quality.

This classification is useful but not rigid, since cleaning and sorting operations result in up-grading of quality, and grading always involves sorting of some kind. However, the terms are meaningful, providing they are applied to the primary purpose of the activity.

2.1. THE FUNCTIONS OF CLEANING

In cleaning his raw material, the processor has two main objectives: (i) the removal of contaminants which constitute a health hazard or which are aesthetically unacceptable; (ii) the control of microbiological loads and chemical and biochemical reactions which impair subsequent process effectiveness and product quality.

An acceptable cleaning process must satisfy the following requirements:

(i)   The separation efficiency of the process must be as high as possible consistent with minimum wastage of good material.

(ii) The contaminant must be removed completely after separation so as to avoid recontamination of the cleaned food.

(iii) The process and equipment should be so designed as to limit recontamination of the cleaned food, *e.g.* by flying dust or by contaminated wash water from previous batches.

(iv) The cleaning process must leave the cleaned surface in an acceptable condition.

(v) Product damage must be avoided.

(vi) Volumes and strengths of liquid effluents must be kept to a minimum and disposed of effectively.

Completely clean raw materials are an unattainable ideal. In practice a balance has to be struck between cleaning costs (as reflected in reject material and labour and process charges) and the need to produce good quality food. Thus, 'acceptable' standards of raw material cleanliness must be specified for each end-use, taking into account the extent to which raw material contamination will be reflected in the final product.

Inefficient removal and disposal of the contaminant, once it is separated, results in product recontamination. Occasionally, gross recontamination occurs when some, or all, of the contaminant from a large quantity of cleaned material is redeposited in a small quantity of following material, resulting in a localised concentration of the contaminant.

The condition in which the cleaning operation leaves the surface of the material is a matter of great importance to the food processor. Roughened surfaces are unattractive in appearance and, in fruits and vegetables, the damaged outer cells lead to rapid browning. Again wet, bruised or damaged surfaces provide excellent breeding grounds for micro-organisms and insect pests such as vinegar flies and weevils.

The prevention of recontamination of the cleaned food is a vital consideration which is often neglected both in the design and operation of food cleaning plant. Again, reliable removal of the contaminants both from the cleaned food raw material and from the processing area is an important step controlling the effectiveness of the subsequent preservation operations. In canning, heat processes are calculated assuming a standard initial microbiological load. In freezing preservation where there is no attempt to obtain sterility, freezing results only in a decrease in the number of vegetative organisms.[1] Similarly, dehydration processes, especially with the trend towards low temperature methods such as spray drying and freeze drying, result in relatively small decreases in the micro-organism population.

It should be clear, therefore, that the utmost care must be taken to observe the proper adherence to the criteria previously stated. This is not always easy since the cleaning area, by the very nature of its function, often is the dirtiest part of the factory.

Cleaning plant must be carefully designed and constructed. The use of suitable materials of construction, the application of proper sanitary design and careful finishing are obvious requirements which are not always observed. Additionally, the process should be sufficiently flexible to allow for the wide variability in the extent and types of contaminants encountered in natural materials.

2.2. CONTAMINANTS IN FOOD RAW MATERIALS

The types of contaminant most frequently encountered are:

(i) *Mineral* —soil, sand, stones, grease, metallic particles and oil.
(ii) *Plant* —twigs, foliage, stalks, pits, skins, husks, rope and string.
(iii) *Animal* —excreta, hairs, insect eggs, body parts.
(iv) *Chemical* —spray residues and fertilisers.
(v) *Microbial* —micro-organisms and their by-products.

The growth of mechanisation in the harvesting, processing, handling and storage of foods has increased, rather than reduced the occurrence of mineral, plant and animal contaminants in foodstuff raw materials. Similarly, the rapid extension in the use of agricultural sprays provides an added hazard in food processing.

The importance of microbiological cleanliness has been stressed already and it is important to appreciate that practically all the ingredients used in the food industry—water, sugar, starches, spices, colouring matter and even containers—are capable of causing microbiological contamination of food products. Hersom and Hulland[2] deal with typical examples of microbiological contents of food raw materials, whilst Gillespy[3] discusses the effects and control of initial infection in vegetable canning.

Incorrect storage of raw materials awaiting processing, delays between harvesting and processing and damage in transit may introduce contamination as a result of biochemical reactions. A typical example of this is the development of off-flavour in peas which makes them inedible if they are not processed within a maximum of 4 hours after harvesting.

2.3. CLEANING METHODS

The wide variety of contaminant encountered in raw food materials and the low tolerances permitted for these contaminants calls for a variety of cleaning methods to be adopted. The methods in use fall into two groups:

(i)   *Dry cleaning methods*—Screening, brushing, aspiration, abrasion, magnetic separation.

(ii) *Wet cleaning methods*—Soaking, spraying, fluming, flotation, ultrasonic cleaning, filtration, settling.

These processes are used, almost invariably, in combination—the methods employed depending on the nature of the raw material, the contaminants to be removed and the desired condition of the cleaned material. It is impracticable, within the narrow confines of this chapter, to deal fully with this wide range of equipment. However, the following examples should serve to indicate the more important features of these two groups of cleaning equipment.

2.3.1. DRY CLEANING METHODS

These methods have the advantages of relative cheapness and convenience whilst the cleaned surface is left in a dry condition. However, unless considerable care is taken to minimise the spread of dust, recontamination can occur. Further, the dusty conditions encountered during dry cleaning can give rise to fire and explosion hazards. Dust explosions are a real and continuous hazard in food processing. H.M. Factory Inspectorate lists no fewer than 64 food materials which either have initiated or are capable of initiating a dust explosion.[4] Fortunately, the dust concentration which has to be achieved before a dust explosion can occur is ~ 30 mg/litre which is above that usually regarded as tolerable in a working environment (~ 10 mg/litre). However, dislodgement of dust from rafters, tops of doors and window sills by a small primary explosion or disturbance may create a situation which then needs only a spark of around 100 mJ intensity (*e.g.* from a falling tool or a faulty electrical connection) to cause a major explosion.[5]

Careful control of dust is important in the food industry generally (in milling, high-speed conveying, etc.) but especially so in dry cleaning where dusty conditions are present in conjunction with potential spark generators such as stones, and tramp metal occurring as extraneous matter in the raw material. Remedial measures include: dust-proofing of equipment; dust extraction; rigorous housekeeping and, with high-risk equipment, spark-proofing and the fitting of special relief systems which, instantaneously, vent the primary-explosion shock waves outside the building.

2.3.1.1. Screening. Primarily, screens are size separators which fall into the class of sorting machines (Chapter 3). However, screens may be used as cleaning equipment, removing contaminants of different size from that of the raw material.

In its simplest form a screen is a perforated bed supported on a frame and screens of this elementary pattern are still in use in the food

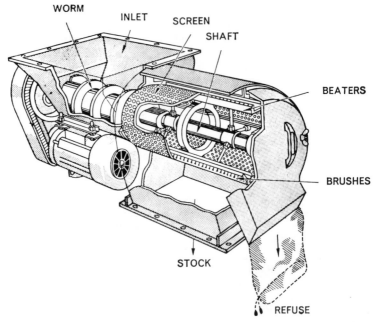

FIG. 2.1.   Diagram of the Le Coq Sifter. (By courtesy of Simon Barron Ltd.)

industry. Such discontinuous screens have now been largely replaced by continuous types of which the drum screen (Fig. 2.1) and the flat-bed screen (Fig. 2.2) are typical.

Rotary drum screens, variously referred to as trommels, centrifugal screens or reels, are continuous units which find numerous applications in the food industry. Cleaning may be carried out so as to retain undesired oversize material such as string, bag-hairs, etc., from flour, salt or sugar, whilst discharging a cleaned product. Alternatively, the screen may be arranged to retain the cleaned material as oversize whilst discharging undesired material, *e.g.* in the removal of weed-seeds, grit and small stones from cereals.

Screens of this type have good capacity and they are relatively inexpensive to install, maintain and operate. Disadvantageously, unless carefully designed, they are difficult to clean and recontamination may occur. Rotary drum screens exhibit speed criticality (see Chapter 4).

Flat-bed screens, in general, consist of one or more flat screen-decks fixed together in a dust-tight casing, the assembly being shaken by a variety of devices. It is usual to include hard rubber tapper-balls

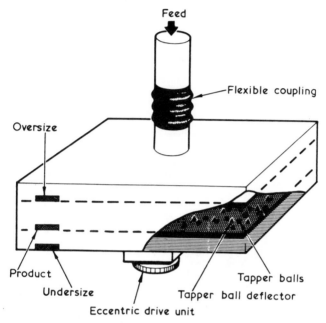

Feed

Flexible coupling

Oversize

Product

Undersize

Tapper balls

Tapper ball deflector

Eccentric drive unit

FIG. 2.2.   Diagram of a flat-bed screening unit. The eccentric drive unit imparts a gyratory motion to the box containing the screens.

between the decks to minimise blinding of the screen apertures with fine materials. Flat-bed screens are excellent for cleaning fine materials such as flour and ground spices, since they are not easily blinded. They must be easily accessible for frequent cleaning. Large pieces of foreign matter trapped in the screen may be pulverised by abrasion, this resulting in the spreading of contamination.

The abrasion and impact caused by moving bed screens, although useful in loosening adherent soil, may damage sensitive foods. Often it is found that the small, repetitive impacts encountered in equipment of this type cause greater damage than one or two heavier collisions. Damage appears to be dependent on the total energy transferred.

Screening effectiveness is a function of the shape-regularity of the working substance (Chapter 1). Spherical materials may be sorted accurately on screens whereas other shapes are sorted, usually, on a minimum-dimension basis. Screening, therefore, tends to give incomplete separation although it is of wide application in the preliminary stages of cleaning and sorting chains.

2.3.1.2. Abrasion cleaning. Abrasion between food particles or between the food and moving parts of cleaning machinery is used to loosen and to remove adhering contaminants. Trommels, tumblers, vibrators, abrasive discs and rotating brushes are used for this purpose. Scrupulous attention to dust removal is necessary in order to limit recontamination, to protect operators and to prevent dust explosions.

2.3.1.3. Aspiration cleaning. Aspiration (or winnowing) finds wide application in removing debris differing in buoyancy, *i.e.* in aerodynamic properties (see Chapter 1), from the desired material. In principle, the material to be cleaned is fed into a stream of air at controlled velocity when separation into two or more streams (*e.g.* light, middle and heavy) is effected. It is usually arranged for the

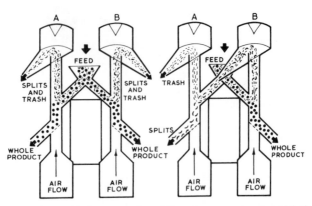

FIG. 2.3.   The Sortex Air Separator. A and B are two separators in which the solid material is removed from the air stream. Separator B has a swivelling discharge to allow the plant to be used as a two- or three-way separator, as shown. (By courtesy of Gunson's Sortex Ltd., London.)

cleaned product to be discharged as the middle stream leaving heavy debris (*e.g.* stones, pieces of metal or wood) behind whilst floating off light debris such as stalks, husks and hairs.

One machine which uses this principle is shown in Fig. 2.3. This is suitable for two- or three-stream separation of cereals, nuts and similar foods.

Aspiration, as a cleaning stage, is used extensively in combine-harvesters, in pea-viners, in bean-harvesters and in similar machines. The aspiration principle is used to clean onions, melons, eggs and other foods which are not amenable to wetting. The soil is loosened by abrasion, using brushing or by contacting with rotating rubber fingers (pintles), and the debris is then removed, selectively, by air streams.[6] Aspirators are capable of very precise adjustment. They may be used to remove bran particles from flour and even to discriminate between protein and starch fragments in the production of protein enriched flours. One such machine claims to separate within the range of 3–60 μm.[7] Aspirators use large quantities of low-pressure air and, hence, consume much energy. Careful dust-control is necessary for safety and health reasons and to prevent the spread of contaminants. The method should not be used with oxidation-sensitive materials.

2.3.1.4. Magnetic cleaning. This involves, at its simplest, cascading the contaminated product stream over one or more magnets which are usually located in the conveyor trunking. Magnetic separators may also take the form of rotating or stationary magnetic drums, magnetised belts, magnets located over belts carrying the food or staggered magnetised grids through which the food is passed.[8]

Both permanent magnets and electromagnets are used. The latter are more suitable for foodstuff cleaning, the adhering metallic particles being removed easily by switching off the current. The frequent removal of the screenings is vital since, if a build-up occurs, then the particles may be swept off by the product stream, causing gross recontamination. Electromagnets are considerably more expensive than permanent magnets and are subject to power failure.

Separators of this type may be followed by an electronic metal-detector which monitors the product for both ferrous and non-ferrous particles.[8] Such detectors generate a powerful electromagnetic field through which the food is passed. The presence of a metallic inclusion distorts this field; the disturbance is amplified and the resulting signal is utilised to sound an alarm or activate an automatic reject device. Electronic detectors can also detect certain other inclusions such as clinker, some stones, carbonised grease and metal-impregnated grease.

2.3.1.5. Miscellaneous dry-cleaning principles. Theoretically, any procedure which can detect a property difference can be used to effect separation and, hence, clean, sort, and, possibly, grade materials. Increasing labour costs in the food industry have encouraged research into the field of mechanised separation. Interesting developments in this direction include the following.

Electrostatic cleaning takes advantage of differences in electrostatic charging of materials under controlled humidity conditions, charged particles being removed by oppositely-charged or earthed rollers, grids, etc. This procedure is used in dust extraction and in other processes such as the cleaning of tea.[9] In this application, tea-fannings are cleaned of dust, stalks, etc., by flowing the material over a roller charged to a potential of 5–20 kV and rotating at 70–350 rev/min. The tea is adjusted to a moisture content of 3–4% and the separated matter is removed from the roller, continuously, by rotating brushes.

Radio-isotope separation of clods of earth and stones from potatoes using low-energy gamma radiation, is being investigated by The Scottish Institute of Agricultural Engineering.[10] The potatoes are distinguished from rubbish by differences in opacity to gamma rays emitted by [241]Am. The differences are sensed by a Geiger–Muller detector, the signals from this being used to actuate a mechanism which rejects the rubbish. The prototype machine is reported to remove 90% of the contaminants.

X-ray separation of stones, glass and metal fragments in foods such as confectionery is well established. The food is conveyed through an X-ray scanner and the image is viewed on a fluorescent screen by an operator who stops the conveyor when an inclusion is seen.

Mechanisation of this process has proved difficult but a machine capable of detecting inclusions in pickles has been reported.[15] In this machine, a difference in contrast between the optical and X-ray images of jars of pickles is used to generate an electrical signal which triggers an ejection device.

Application of this principle to bulk-food cleaning is still awaited but the ability to remove non-metallic inclusions from food presents an attractive prospect.

2.3.2. WET CLEANING METHODS

Wet cleaning is effective in removing firmly-adherent soils and in allowing the use of detergents and sanitisers. Unfortunately, the method has a number of disadvantageous features. First, it uses large amounts of high-quality water, which is becoming increasingly costly, and regenerates this as troublesome effluent. The volumes of effluent produced are considerable (∼ 15 000 litres/tonne of canned food), it is highly polluting and requires expensive waste treatment before disposal. Second, wet surfaces spoil more rapidly, thus wet cleaning often involves final de-watering to provide cleaned material suitable for processing or storage. When wet processes are used, careful attention must be paid to water conservation and management,[11, 12] to plant sanitation and to water quality (Chapters 17 and 18). The theory of wet cleaning is discussed by Krochta and Bellows.[16]

2.3.2.1. Soaking. This is the simplest method of wet cleaning and is often used as a preliminary stage in the cleaning of root vegetables and other foods which are heavily contaminated. Adhering soil is softened and some is removed, together with stones, sand and other abrasive materials which would damage the machinery used in the later stages of cleaning. Soak tanks are made of metal, smooth concrete or other materials of construction suitable for regular cleaning and disinfection. Absorbent materials such as wood should not be used. Gridded bottom outlets are provided for the removal of heavy soil and side outlets should be fitted to allow the removal of light debris which would otherwise be drained back into the cleaned material.

The efficiency of soaking is improved: (i) by moving the water relative to the product by means of caged propeller-stirrers built into the tank; (ii) by moving the product relative to the water either by means of slow-moving paddles or by feeding the raw material into a horizontal perforated drum which rotates whilst partially submerged in the soak tank. These procedures tend to cause damaging of delicate materials. Agitation may also be produced by sparging compressed air through the tank.[13] This procedure can be used for delicate materials, *e.g.* strawberries and asparagus, or for materials like spinach or celery which trap dirt internally.

Warm water improves the efficiency of soaking but the rate of spoilage of foods may be increased thereby. The use of detergents is increasing, especially in foods contaminated by spray residues and mineral oil.[14, 17] Care is necessary, however, in the selection and use of such agents, since the appearance and texture of the food may be affected. Examples of this are the softening effects of sodium hexametaphosphate on peas and the toughening effect of some metal ions on peas and peaches destined for canning.

Frequently, soak tanks are supplied with lightly contaminated water from subsequent washing stages. In this way, water economies are effected and effluent volumes are reduced. With such counter-current re-use of water it becomes especially important to exercise careful microbiological control and for regular changing of soak water to be carried out.

Chlorination is used to decrease bacterial loadings in soak tank water but its high chemical oxygen demand (C.O.D.) rapidly removes active chlorine so that high concentrations of this are necessary. At high levels of chlorine the food may be affected, *e.g.* potatoes may develop blackened flesh.[6] Nevertheless, used with a full understanding of its advantages and limitations, chlorine is a valuable cleaning aid.[18]

2.3.2.2. Spray washing. This is probably the most widely used method of wet cleaning, the surfaces of the food being subjected to water sprays.

The efficiency of spray washing depends on: the water pressure employed; the volume of water used; the water temperature; the distance of the food from the spray origin; the time of exposure of the food to the sprays and the number of spray-jets used. A small volume of water, at high pressure, is the most effective general combination.[19] However, damage may be caused to ripe soft-fruits such as strawberries and to delicate vegetables like asparagus. Sometimes high pressure sprays are used to cut out damaged parts in peaches and tomatoes and to remove adherent soil, *e.g.* black moulds on citrus fruits.

Spray drum washers. The spray drum washer consists of a reel constructed of metal slats or rods, spaced so as to retain the food whilst allowing debris to be washed through. The drum, which rotates slowly, is inclined to the horizontal. The speed of rotation and angle of inclination control both the movement of the food within the drum and the duration of the washing cycle. The washer is equipped with a central spray-rod which is fitted with jets or slots through which water is sprayed (Fig. 2.4). Whilst the abrasion which occurs in this washer is useful in loosening dirt, it may cause damage to some foods.

Spray belt washers. This type of spray washer is simply a conveyor (*e.g.* a perforated belt) which carries the food beneath banks of water sprays. With roughly spherical foods such as apples, contact is improved by using roller conveyors which cause the fruit to spin beneath the sprays (Fig. 2.4). For smaller foods, movement under the sprays may be produced by using a vibratory conveyor.

The problems of water conservation and effluent generation, already referred to, have spurred research into many aspects of food processing. Examples include the development of reduced-water blanching (Section 10.5) and peeling processes. A recent development in the field of wet cleaning is the U.S.D.A. Rubber-Disc Cleaner.[17] In this process, tomatoes are first freed of gross contamination in a soak tank and are then conveyed mechanically into a shallow channel, 10 m long by 0·3 m wide, in which adherent soil is removed in 15–25 s by exposing the fruit to the brushing action of soft rubber discs spinning axially at 450 rev/min. The specially profiled discs, which are ∼ 11 cm in diameter, are mounted at 8 cm spacing on driven shafts which taper inwards from inlet to outlet end. The discs are staggered and overlap slightly. Thus, the wet fruit is brushed as it is conveyed along the channel, the soil being flung off as a mud into the base of the channel

Water sprays

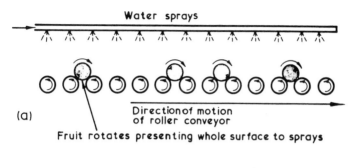

(a)

Direction of motion
of roller conveyor

Fruit rotates presenting whole surface to sprays

Rotating drum

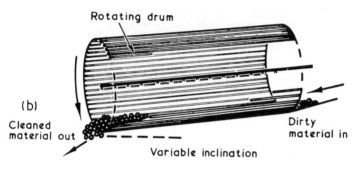

(b)

Cleaned
material out

Dirty
material in

Variable inclination

(c)

FIG. 2.4. Spray washers. (a) Diagram of a belt-type spray washer. (b) Diagram of a spray drum washer, partly cut away to show the spray-rod. The drum may be made of perforated metal or from slats. Alternatively, non-blocking wedge-wire drums may be used (shown diagrammatically at (c)).

where it is removed. The residual soil is removed by spraying briefly with water into which detergents or detergent foams may be incorporated. Substantial reduction in water consumption and effluent volume are claimed, the disc-cleaner using around 20 litres of water per tonne of fruit compared with 1500–5000 litres/tonne for conventional cleaning processes. Average removals of soil, bacteria and spores were 99%, 94% and 97% respectively.

2.3.2.3. Flotation washing. This method depends on a difference in buoyancy between the desired and undesired parts of the food to be cleaned. Thus bruised or rotten apples, which sink in water, may be removed by fluming the fruit into a tank and collecting the overflow of sound fruit.

Heavy debris can be removed by fluming dirty produce over a series of adjustable weirs arranged in series. The less buoyant contaminants are trapped by and remain behind the weirs. The product, now contaminated by material of the same or higher buoyancy, is further purified by passage over a vibrated screen where water sprays remove the fine contaminants.

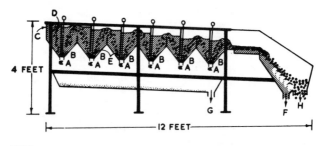

KEY

A. Quick release valve   E. Dirt and stones collected in base cones

B. Plunger   F. Water and refuse outlet

C. Water entry   G. Trough outlet

D. Product entry   H. Product outlet

Fig. 2.5. A flotation separation system. (By courtesy of Chisholm-Ryder International Manufacturing Ltd., Middlesex, England.)

The flotation washer illustrated in Fig. 2.5 effectively removes stones, dirt and plant debris from peas, beans, dried fruits and similar materials at rates of 3 tonnes/h. Water flow rates in the range of 200–500 litres/min are necessary, *i.e.* a consumption of 4000–10 000 litres of water for each tonne of product. At this rate of use, water recirculation is necessary.

Froth flotation, depending on the principle of differential wetting of the food and its contaminants, is an elaboration of the flotation procedure. Neubert[20] describes a method of freeing peas from weed-seeds which are not effectively removed by normal flotation methods. The contaminated peas are immersed in a dilute, mineral oil-detergent emulsion through which air is blown. The contaminants float on the foam where they may be removed. The cleaned peas are then given a final wash to remove the emulsion contaminant.

2.3.2.4. Ultrasonic cleaning. Ultrasonic waves are sound waves of frequencies above those detectable by the human ear, *i.e.* frequencies above about 16 kHz.[21] Insonation of a fluid with ultrasonic waves at frequencies of 20–100 kHz produces a rapidly alternating pressure in the path of the waves and this leads to the rapid formation and collapse of bubbles in the fluid. Cavitation and decavitation, as these effects are called, result in the release of energy in the system and this energy causes violent agitation of particles immersed in the fluid (see Chapter 5).

This phenomenon may be utilised to effect the loosening of contaminants, *e.g.* grit in vegetables, grease or wax on fruits[22] or dirt on eggs.[23] The contaminants after loosening are removed by conventional methods. Ultrasonic cleaning, using water or detergent solutions, finds many applications in the engineering industry, but application in the food industry at present appears to be limited to experimental development. The method would appear to have much to commend it to the attention of food technologists.

2.3.2.5. Dewatering. Wet cleaning, more often than not, leaves the cleaned product contaminated with excess water. Dewatering may be affected by passage of the food over vibrated screens, or by the use of dewatering reels, *i.e.* specially designed rotary screens. In some cases, *e.g.* cleaned peas for freezing or washed wheat for milling, dewatering centrifuges may be used (see Chapter 7). Occasionally it is necessary to resort to drying procedures, for instance with washed cereals or with wet-cleaned fruit which is to be stored or is to be sold as a finished foodstuff.

2.3.3. COMBINATION CLEANING PROCEDURES

As remarked earlier, cleaning methods are generally used in combination. Many cleaning machines involve several stages combined as a single unit. Thus, bean- or pea-washers often consist of a soak tank linked to a spray drum washer followed by a dewatering screen. Again, cleaning screens are often associated with an aspiration device and with a magnetic separator. A typical example of a combination procedure is the cleaning process used for producing cleaned wheat for milling into flour. The stages involved in this process are illustrated in Fig. 2.6. In cleaning chains, such as this, inter-stage handling methods require careful design and selection in order to control material damage, effluent volumes (*e.g.* in hydraulic transfer) and handling costs (Chapter 19).

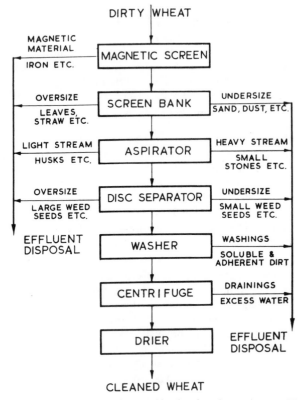

FIG. 2.6.   A typical cleaning combination for wheat prior to milling.

REFERENCES

1. Tressler, D. K., and Evers, C. K., 'The Freezing Preservation of Foods'. Vol. 1. 3rd ed. (AVI. U.S.A.: 1957).
2. Hersom, A. C., and Hulland, E. D., 'Canned Foods'. 6th ed. (Churchill: 1969).
3. Gillespy, T. G., 'Significance and Control of Initial Infection in Canned Vegetables'. Rep. Fruit Veg. Cann. Quick Freez. Res. Ass. (1948).
4. Anon., 'Dust Explosions in Factories', SHW 830 (H.M.S.O. London: 1968).
5. Rose, H. E., 'Dust Explosion Hazards'. Brit. Chem. Engng, **15**(3), 371–5 (1970).
6. Ryall, A. L., and Lipton, D. J., 'Handling, Transportation and Storage of Fruits and Vegetables'. (AVI: 1972).
7. Anon., 'Air Separation for Fine Powders'. Fd Process. Ind., **43**(513), 28 (1974).
8. Anon., 'The Automatic Detection of Foreign Matter in Food'. Brit. Fd J., **68**(806), 33–4 (1968).
9. Anon., 'Improving Tea Quality and Stalk Extraction by Electrostatic Means'. Fd Trade Rev., **38**(2), 58 (1968).

10. Anon., 'Clods and Spuds'. Bull. Inst. Phys., **26**, 523 (1975).
11. Weisse, H. J., 'Fundamentals of Mechanical Recirculation Cleaning. I, High Pressure-Low Volume Cleaning'. Journal of Milk and Food Technology, **32**(9), 346–347 (1969).
12. Whitehead, D. B., 'Fundamentals of Mechanical Recirculation Cleaning. II, Recirculation Cleaning'. Journal of Milk and Food Technology, **32**(9), 347–49 (1969).
13. Jacquel, A., 'Préparation Industrielle des Fruits Destinés à la Conserve'. Inds aliment. agric. 84ᵉ Annee (9–10), 1299–1312 (1967).
14. Emery, A. W., 'Produce Washing—Which Detergent For?' Fd Engng, **36**(12), 68–70 (1964).
15. Anon., 'X-ray Unit Detects Minute Glass Particles, Metal, Stone'. Fd Process. (Chicago), **34**(6), 47–8 (1973).
16. Krochta, J. M., and Bellows, R. J., 'Cleaning of Food'. Fd Technol., **28**(2), 34–37 + 47 (1974).
17. Krochta, J. M., Graham, R. P., and Rose, W. W., 'Cleaning of Tomatoes Using Rotating Rubber Discs'. Fd Technol., **28**(12), 26–34 (1974).
18. Malpas, J. F., 'The Use of Chlorine for Water Disinfection in Industry'. Chem. and Ind., 111–5 (1971).
19. Irving, G. W., and Hoover, S. R., 'Food Quality' (Publication No. 77. American Association for the Advancement of Science, USA: 1965).
20. Neubert, A. M., 'Using Froth Flotation to Clean Vined Canning Peas'. Fd Ind., **19**(6), 85–8 (1947).
21. Blitz, J., 'Fundamentals of Ultrasonics'. (Butterworths: 1971).
22. Anon., 'Ultrasonics in Food Processing'. Fd Process. Packag., **31**(375), 456 (1962).
23. Dawson, L. E., Hall, G. W., Farrer, E. H., and Mallman, W. L., 'Ultrasonic Energy for Cleaning Eggs'. Poult. Sci., **41**(2), 620–6 (1962).

CHAPTER 3

THE SORTING AND GRADING OF FOODS

As stated in Chapter 2, sorting and grading may be regarded as separation operations; sorting being separation into groups with differing physical properties and grading being separation into groups with differing quality characteristics.

3.1. SORTING AND GRADING—GENERAL CONSIDERATIONS

3.1.1. PRODUCT DAMAGE

The causes and effects of product damage are referred to in Chapter 1 (Section 1.6). The control of damage is important at all times but is particularly so during sorting and grading. First, the food, having been grown, harvested, transported to the factory and cleaned, has accumulated appreciable labour and process charges. Damage during sorting and grading, where the material has a relatively high value, therefore results in a substantial economic loss to the processor. Secondly, sorting and grading are the last separation stages before processing. Damage and its consequent spoilage, therefore, are likely to be transmitted to the finished product, affecting its quality and the effectiveness of the process to which it is submitted.

3.1.1.1. Drop damage. The emptying of containers (dumping) on to sorting belts and falls from sorters can cause extensive product damage. Many devices are used for minimising damage of this type, ranging from simple padded collecting chutes to more complex arrangements such as that illustrated in Fig. 3.1. In this machine, the size-sorted fruit is fed *via* a canvas chute into a spring-loaded tray which is free to rotate within the bin. The influx of the fruit causes the tray to rotate slowly and, as the loading increases, the tray sinks, limiting the drop distance to a minimum.

Damage caused by emptying containers on to conveyors may be controlled by simple devices such as that depicted in Fig. 3.2. This

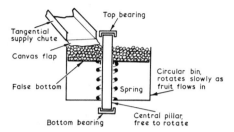

FIG. 3.1. A pivoted bin-discharge arrangement for a sorting machine.

consists of a frame in which the full container is placed. The frame is fitted with a padded, spring-loaded hinged lid and is pivoted above the conveyor so as to limit the drop to a minimum. Tipping the loaded frame is assisted by a coil spring, the flow of food being controlled by the hinged lid.

Dumping into water reduces drop damage but the product must be conveyed away immediately, either mechanically or by water-fluming, otherwise damage as a result of material to material impacts may occur.

Studies aimed at controlling drop damage aerodynamically showed typical values for the terminal velocities of fruits as given in Table 3.1. Since falls of only a few centimetres are sufficient to damage many raw materials, these figures suggest that air-cushioning, to be fully effective, would require upward air streams of similar magnitudes to the terminal velocities. The conclusion was that the provision of this would probably be too costly but this interesting concept would, possibly, repay further investigation.

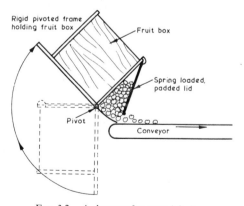

FIG. 3.2. A dumper for crated fruit.

3.1.1.2. Operator damage. The operation of sorting machinery and the grading of food require much human intervention and are monotonous occupations. Inattention reduces effectiveness of grading and causes malfunctioning of sorting equipment. Careful study of the ergonomics involved, *i.e.* the relationship between the operator, his machine and the surroundings, is important in

TABLE 3.1
Typical values for terminal velocities of various fruits

	Terminal velocity (m/s)
Apples	44
Apricots	35
Blackberries	19
Cherries	25
Peaches	44
Plums	35

After Quackenbush *et al.*[1]

controlling this variable. Thus the correct working height and location of machinery, the lighting and colour scheme of the work area and the relief of tedium by the use of background music are often useful in improving efficiency.

Efficient training of operators is also of great importance. For instance, considerable damage can be caused by picking up several fruits at a time instead of singly, each contact point being a potential damage area. Again, overlong finger nails can cause puncture damage and produce infection.

3.1.2. REASONS FOR SORTING

Sorting plays an important part in controlling the effectiveness of many food processes. Sorted foods have the following desirable attributes:

(i) They are better suited to mechanised operations such as peeling, blanching, pitting and coring.

(ii) They are necessary in processes in which uniformity of heat transfer is critical (*e.g.* sterilisation and pasteurisation) and they are advantageous in processes in which uniformity of heat transfer is desirable (*e.g.* dehydration and freezing).

(iii) They give better control over the weights filled into standard sale containers.

(iv) In consumer use, sorted products are more attractive to the eye and allow the serving of uniformly sized portions. This latter point is of particular importance in catering packs.

3.2. WEIGHT SORTING

Concurrent with increasing raw material costs is the demand for sorting equipment of improved efficiency. Since the weight of a food unit is proportional to the cube of its characteristic dimension, weight sorting is capable of more precise separation than is dimensional sorting. For this reason weight sorting devices are replacing size sorters increasingly. Meat cuts, fish fillets and similar materials which are to be sold by weight may be weighed manually or, more generally, weighed on a computing-type scale. This automatically records the piece-weight, computes the price and delivers a printed, adhesive ticket which is affixed to the pack.

In another system,* food units are weighed on a computer-controlled weighing head. The computer selects the best combination of items to make up a required weight and groups these together on a conveyor for processing or packaging. The machine assembles about 30 groups of items each minute and substantial reduction in over-weighting losses are claimed.

Many fruits (*e.g.* apples, pears and citrus fruits) and vegetables (*e.g.* potatoes, carrots and onions) are sorted by weight.[4] Typical weight-sorting machines carry fruits in tared canvas pockets attached to pivoted beams fitted with counterbalance weights. As the beams pass along the sorter, the beam fulcrum is moved towards the counterbalance weight until such time as the weight of the fruit causes the beam to tip, discharging the fruit into padded chutes in weight categories.

In the UK, eggs, almost invariably, are sorted by weight. Weighings are carried out on a 6–12 station beam balance. Each balance has a counterweight which is pre-set to deliver eggs of a predetermined weight. Unsorted eggs are carried on a conveyor synchronised with the weighing assembly, the eggs being picked up in fingers attached to the weighers. The beam is raised with the conveyor stopped, heavy eggs are discharged into collecting chutes whilst light eggs are lowered back on to the conveyor for passage to the next weigher and the operation is repeated. Machines of this type are capable of weighing to considerable accuracy (0.5 g) at high speeds ($10\,000$ eggs/h).

Recent developments in weight-sorting machines involve the use of electro-mechanical and hydrostatic transducers to sense weight

* Precision Engineering Products Ltd, Suffolk, England.

differences and improved devices, often computer-controlled, for directing the weighed units into collection chutes.

A novel approach to the problems of high-speed weighing is represented by a machine which measures, electronically, the cross-section dimensions of potatoes at $\frac{1}{4}$ in intervals along their length axes. These dimensions are converted into weights by a computer which then sorts the potatoes into 4 weight categories at rates up to 4500 kg/h.[2]

Weight-sorting using a catapult principle[3] is claimed to sort apples, accurately and without damage, at rates of 6000 fruits an hour into 12 weight categories. The fruits are fed, singly, into adjustable spring-loaded catapult arms which hurl the fruit into one of twelve padded collection-chutes carried on a momentum-absorbing frame. The height of the trajectory of the fruit and hence the position of the chute which collects it is related to the weight of the fruit.

3.3. SIZE SORTING

Screens of various designs are widely used to effect size separation of foods. The engineering considerations relating generally to screens are dealt with in Chapter 4, whilst reference is made to the use of screens for cleaning in Chapter 2. The screen designs most commonly encountered in food sorting are classified in Fig. 3.3.

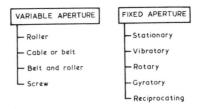

Fig. 3.3.   Types of screen used in food sorting.

3.3.1. FIXED APERTURE SCREENS

Screens of this type are permanently clad with screen beds having apertures of fixed size and shape. Various types of bed material may be used depending on the application. Metal sheets perforated with holes, slots or other shapes, mesh-wire, wedge-wire, cloth and silk of various weaves are used.[4] Movement of the food on the screen bed may be produced by rotary, vibratory or gyratory movement of the frame carrying the screen bed. Fixed aperture screens in general use for food sorting fall into two groups—flat-bed and drum types.

3.3.1.1. Flat-bed screens. This type of screen in its simplest form, as a pitched, stationary frame clad with a screen bed, still finds application for preliminary sorting of potatoes, carrots and turnips on the farm. Multideck flat screens (described in Section 2.3.1.1) find extensive use in the size sorting of raw materials (*e.g.* cereals and nuts) and of part-processed and finished foods, such as flour, sugar, salt, herbs and ground spices.

3.3.1.2. Drum screens. One type of drum screen has been described in Section 2.3.1.1 as a cleaning screen, but drum screens are used extensively as size sorters for peas, beans and similar foods which will withstand the tumbling action produced by the drum rotation. Drum sorters are usually required to separate the feedstock into more than two streams, so that two or more screening stages are required. This may be effected by arranging the screens to function concentrically or consecutively.

The concentric drum screen (Fig. 3.4) has the advantage of compactness but, since the feed enters at the centre, this results in the highest product loading on the smallest screen area. *The series-consecutive drum screen* (Fig. 3.5(a)) has the disadvantage of

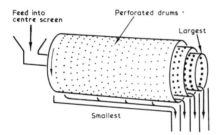

Fig. 3.4. Diagram of a concentric drum screen.

requiring a large floor area. More seriously, since the feed enters at the end which has the smallest aperture screen, the screen tends to become overloaded at the inlet end and inefficient sorting results.

The parallel-consecutive type (Fig. 3.5(b)) overcomes this disadvantage by first contacting the inlet material with the large-aperture screen, leaving the following, smaller-aperture screens to deal with a reduced quantity of near and undersize material. This procedure is repeated at each stage and results in more accurate sorting than is possible with a similarly sized, series screen. Conveying between the screens in the parallel system is usually by water-fluming.

Another type of drum screen which is reported to reduce damage during pea sorting, uses spaced, circumferential, wedge-section rods

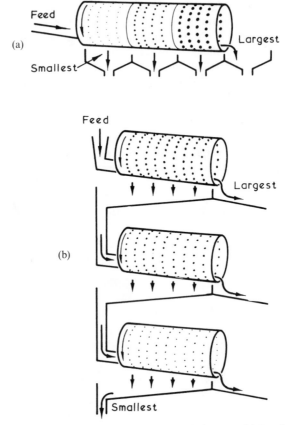

FIG. 3.5.   Consecutive drum screens. (a) Series type. (b) Parallel type.

instead of perforated-screen drums.* The spacing of these rods increases in steps from inlet to outlet giving a series-consecutive system. Built-in flights ensure smooth transfer of the peas through the sorter.

3.3.2. VARIABLE APERTURE SCREENS

Size sorters of this type have apertures which may be either continuously variable or stepwise variable. In the former group are included roller, cable and belt sorters, the food being passed along a

* Mather and Platt Ltd, Radcliffe, Manchester, England. Publication No. Q.P. 2697.

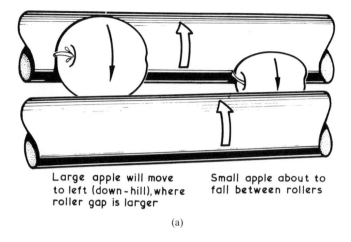

Large apple will move
to left (down-hill), where
roller gap is larger

Small apple about to
fall between rollers

(a)

Direction of roller conveyor

(b)

FIG. 3.6.   Roller sorters. (a) Inclined roller type showing the position of apples during sorting. (b) Operating principle of a Mather and Platt 'Grovesend' Grader.

continuously diverging slot. The latter group includes some types of roller sorters and screw sorters.

3.3.2.1. Sorting screens with continuously variable apertures. The simplest design is that of a pair of inclined driven rollers with an adjustable fall from inlet to outlet. The aperture between the rolls is adjustable and a continuously variable slot is thus presented to the food. The rotation of the rollers orients the food in the position of most regular shape. For example, apples are aligned with the stem–calyx axis parallel to the rolls (Fig. 3.6(a)). Padded collection chutes, located at intervals below the rollers, collect the size-sorted food.

Roller sorting using variable pitch rollers (Fig. 3.6(b)) is the principle involved in the patented Grovesend Grader.* This consists of a roller conveyor in which the gap between the rollers is arranged to

* Mather and Platt Ltd, Radcliffe, Manchester, England. Publication No. Q.P. 2697.

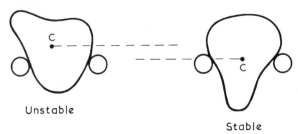

Fig. 3.7. The position of pears on a rope sorter. C—the centre of gravity of the fruit.

increase regularly from inlet to outlet end of the conveyor. The food (*e.g.* fruit or root vegetables) remains on the conveyor until it encounters a gap in the rollers through which it falls into a padded collection chute. The roller pitch may be adjusted as required.

In *rope or cable sorters* a diverging aperture is produced by two driven inclined cables or ropes. The cables can be driven at the same or different speeds. Separation takes place on the basis of most stable position, *e.g.* in the case of pears as illustrated in Fig. 3.7. Sorting is, therefore, on a minimum-dimension basis.

Belt sorters (Fig. 3.8) function similarly, the food being carried along a continuously diverging slot produced by driven inclined belts. There is a tendency for the food to slip through sideways, leading to

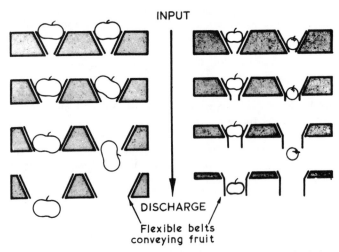

Fig. 3.8. The behaviour of fruit during belt sorting. (Left) The diverging belt system where the fruit sinks in the channel throughout the process, producing a tendency for it to slip sideways. (Right) The Jansen 'Fruitsizer' where the fruit remains at a constant depth until sorted.

uneven sorting. This can be corrected, partially, by driving the belts at different speeds. Belt sorters of these types are gentle with the food compared with drums and moving screen sorters and, providing drop damage is minimised, little bruising of fruits is caused. They are widely used in fruit-packing houses where ripe fruits are handled in quantity. Belt sorting efficiency has been improved substantially by the patented system used in the Jansen Fruitsizer.* Here, the fruit is carried on endless felt belts which travel along either side of a 'vee'-shaped channel. The base of the 'vee' is cut away at an incline which slopes upwards from the inlet end of the sorter. Thus an inclined slot of a width which increases continuously from inlet to outlet is produced. The belts are driven at different speeds to produce correct orientation of the units. The fruits, after passing through a short stabilising section, move along the sorter at constant depth in the 'vee', depending on their size. The fruit thus retains its correct orientation until it meets a position in the channel which permits it to fall through to a receiving chute. With diverging belt-sorters, in which the fruit sinks as it moves along, differences in friction between the fruit and the belt produce a tendency for the fruit to slip through sideways (Fig. 3.8).

3.3.2.2. Sorters with stepwise-variable apertures. This group includes some special types of roller sorters, belt and roller sorters, and screw sorters.

Stepwise variation of apertures in roller conveyor type sorters may be arranged by having two banks of driven rollers located one above the other. The top bank of rollers have a fixed spacing which is greater than the diameter of the largest item to be sorted. The bottom rolls are arranged to give a stepwise-variable gap between the two roller banks

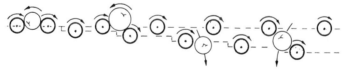

FIG. 3.9.   The operating principle of a stepped roller sorter.

(Fig. 3.9). The food is both conveyed and rotated by the friction-driven rollers. Cucumbers, gherkins and similar foods with one long dimension may be width-sized on this type of sorter.

The *belt and roller sorter* (Fig. 3.10) consists of a belt conveyor inclined across its width towards driven rollers. The gap between each roller and the belt is adjusted to give the required size categories. The

* Jansen Patents Ltd, Reading, Berks., England.

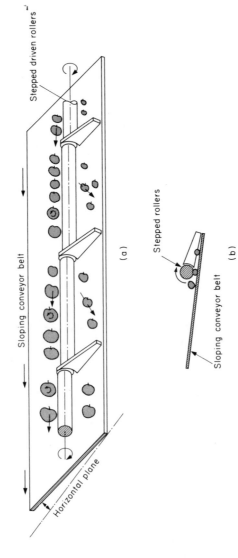

Stepped driven rollers

Sloping conveyor belt

Horizontal plane

(a)

Stepped rollers

Sloping conveyor belt

(b)

FIG. 3.10.   The operating principle of a belt and roller sorter. (a) Oblique view. (b) Section across conveyor belt.

FEED

Pieces being sorted   Direction of motion of pieces

FIG. 3.11.   A diagrammatic plan view of a screw sorter.

driven rolls cause the fruit to rotate in the position of most uniform shape, *e.g.* apples with their cores parallel to the rollers. This is an effective high-speed sorting machine but some bruising of delicate fruit is encountered.

The *screw sorter* (Fig. 3.11) carries the food on two partially-intermeshing helices, one of which is continuous whilst the other is divided into sections. The sorting gap between the sections and the continuous helix may be adjusted to give a stepwise increase in aperture. The rotation of the spirals both conveys the food and orients it in the position of most regular dimensions. The helices, which are usually felt covered, rotate relatively slowly and gentle handling of the fruit results.

Sorters such as those described above where a tumbling action is involved tend to damage the product. This is minimised by the use of felt-covered or soft rubber rollers.

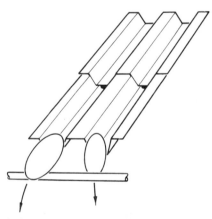

FIG. 3.12.   Method of operation of a Sortex 'Polygrada' length sorter. Food pieces pass down the channels in a vibratory feeding table. The step in the table helps break clusters and ensure that the pieces reach the sorting bar in a single stream, one after the other. Short pieces are unable to bridge the gap between the table and the bar while longer pieces can pass over the bar. (By courtesy of Gunson's Sortex Ltd, London.)

Length and width sorting may be carried out by conveying the food along slotted channels arranged in cascade. The gaps between the channel-ends increase in steps so that food units unable to bridge these gaps fall through and are thereby sorted on a length basis (Fig. 3.12). Vibration is a convenient method of conveying in these sorters.

Photoelectric size sorting on length or width bases may be effected by electronic measurement of the time required by an object, travelling at constant speed, to pass a photocell.[5] The food units, *e.g.* cucumbers or potatoes, are aligned in vibrated channels for scanning.

3.4. SHAPE SORTERS

In some foods, cleaning, followed by size sorting or weight sorting, may still leave the food containing undesirable constituents. For example, cleaned and sorted wheat may still contain weed-seeds of similar size and weight to the wheat. In these circumstances it may be possible to separate on the basis of shape, *e.g.* the combination of length and diameter.

The disc sorter (Fig. 3.13) is an example of shape sorting. It functions by collecting materials of desired shape in indentations on both sides of rotating, vertical discs. Banks of such discs are mounted on a driven, horizontal shaft and the lower ends of the discs run in a trough of the unsorted food. Foods of the correct shape are held in the indentations until the disc reaches the top of its rotation when the collected material is discharged into troughs. The material in the feed-trough is moved down the machine and, eventually, is discharged. Standard discs are available for wheat, oats, rice and barley and specially indented discs can be made for specific purposes. Standard disc sorters are available with capacities of between $\frac{1}{2}$ and 6 t/h.

The cylinder sorter functions on the same principle as the disc sorter but in this case the internal surface of a rotating, horizontal cylinder is machined with shaped indentations. Foods of the desired shape are picked up by these pockets and are discharged at about top dead-centre into a centrally located channel inside the drum whence the separated material is conveyed away. Thus the material remaining in the drum becomes enriched, progressively, with food-pieces which are unable to enter the shaped indentations.

Shape sorting may also be effected by taking advantage of the propensity of spherical particles to travel down an inclined surface. Thus, spherical seeds may be separated by feeding the food on to an inclined driven belt when spherical units run down against the belt travel, the separated material being carried upwards by the belt and discharged upstream of the feed. This principle has been used to

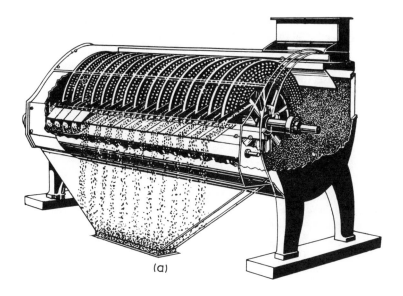

(a)

(b)

FIG. 3.13.   A disc separator by Henry Simon Ltd, Stockport, England. (a) A cut-away drawing of the machine. (b) Cross-sections of a wheat disc (left) and a seed disc (right).

separate snails from blackcurrants and spherical weed-seeds from wheat, barley and other cereals. Similarly, peas may be separated from vine dross and pea viners are often fitted with separators of this type which is generally called a *draper separator*. Other shape-sorters which use sphericity differences to effect separation include: machines in which the material is fed, at a controlled rate, onto a horizontal rotating disc, the more spherical particles being ejected peripherally; equipment comprising a horizontal plate which is shaken or bumped at low frequency and which retains non-spherical components of a material fed onto it.

3.5. PHOTOMETRIC SORTING

The reflectance and transmittance characteristics of foods are important indicators of their processing suitability. Reflectance properties are used to indicate: raw material maturity (*e.g.* the colours of fruit, vegetables, meat, etc.); the presence of surface defects (*e.g.* worm-holed cereals or bruised fruits); the extent of processing (*e.g.* of biscuits, bread and potato crisps) and so on. Transmittance measurements of foods are used to determine their internal properties such as ripeness or core defects in fruits, extraneous matter inclusions and blood spots in eggs. When these measurements are used to actuate separation mechanisms then photometric sorting is effected and, if multiple-property assessment is carried out, quality separation, *i.e.* grading (Section 3.6) may be achieved.

3.5.1. REFLECTANCE SORTING

When a material is scanned, that which is seen may range from simple specular reflectance to a complex combination of radiation, scattering and reflection, depending upon the nature of the scanned surface. Thus, a glossy apple provides a different stimulus from that generated by a matt-surfaced apple of the same basic colour. This situation makes colour comparison, in practice, a matter of some difficulty.[6] In many respects, the eye, backed by the discriminatory ability of the brain, is superior to machines but unless provided with a set of comparison standards it is unable to make reliable quantitative assessments. The provision of permanent, truly representative standards represents a major problem in this type of sorting.

Visual colour-sorting is used extensively in the food industry in spite of its limitations. Permanent comparison standards in the form of coloured plastic strips, colour photographs, etc., are used, the food being sorted manually on a conveyor belt. The advantages and limitations of this procedure are discussed more fully in Section 3.6.

Mechanised colour-sorting functions on the basis of photometric scanning of the surface of each food unit as it falls past, or is rotated before a photocell. The signal generated by this photocell is compared, automatically, with an adjustable, pre-set standard signal.

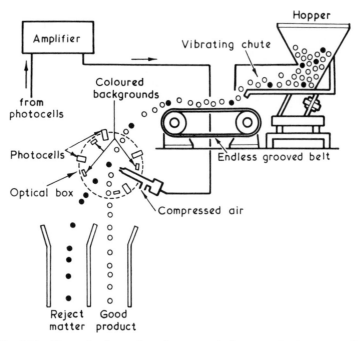

FIG. 3.14.   The mode of operation of a pneumatically operated colour sorter. (By courtesy of Gunson's Sortex Ltd, London.)

Imbalance between these two signals is then amplified and used to actuate sorting gear. A typical sorter of this type is shown diagrammatically in Fig. 3.14. Mechanised colour-sorters are widely used to sort, clean and grade foods such as: nuts, cereals and coffee beans containing worm-holes or other defects; diced vegetables, whole potatoes, onions or fruits which are incompletely peeled; citrus fruits and tomatoes exhibiting maturity differences and finished products like jams, peanut butter, butter, crisps, etc., which may have been incorrectly processed.[9] Mechanisation has conferred many advantages compared with manual colour-sorting, notably in reducing labour costs, in increasing throughput and in improving sorting efficiency by eliminating the boredom which impairs the performance of human sorters.

Rejection systems of various types are used. For small, particulate foods, pneumatic procedures as shown in Fig. 3.14 are employed, the signal from the discriminator being used to operate an air jet which deflects substandard material into the reject chute. With larger food units, such as diced vegetables or whole fruits which are presented for scanning individually carried on a vacuumised pick-up wheel, mechanical displacement is used. In the case of foods composed of small particles in which individual treatment would be impractical, a mechanical gate is used to deflect a small amount of the material containing substandard matter. Electrostatic separation may be used, also, the reject material being charged by an electrode and then withdrawn from the bulk of the product by an oppositely-charged electrode or deflector.

3.5.2. TRANSMITTANCE SORTING

Non-destructive internal examination of solid foods and monitoring of opaque, liquid foods by transmitted electromagnetic radiation offer attractive prospects to food processors. Application is complicated by the fact that relatively small amounts of the incident energy are transmitted by other than thin sections of many food materials. The transmitted energy may amount to as little as 0.1% of the incident energy so that very sensitive detection systems are necessary, *e.g.* in the examination of fruit or vegetable tissue.[4]

Manual procedures using this principle are exemplified by the candling of eggs which is described in Section 3.6. A further example is the use of a fluorescent screen to visualise X-ray transmission through solid foods followed by manual operation of reject devices. A study aimed at using this concept for automatic in-line sorting[7] reports satisfactory discrimination with thin or low-density products such as foil sachets of dried soups or packets of potato crisps but poor performance with thick food sections or dense products like fruit cake or canned meat. However, successful machine-sorting using this principle in one application has been reported (Section 2.3.1.5) and it is to be expected that further developments in X-ray sorting will be forthcoming.

Instrumental measurement of the transmittance of whole apples to light at 692 ± 3 nm was reported to be related to the chlorophyll content of the flesh of the fruit and, hence, to their maturity.[8] This work led to the development of the USDA Difference Meter which is now used to measure the internal properties of a wide variety of fruits and vegetables.[6] More recently, a fully mechanised transmittance sorting system has been developed. This machine uses electronic interpretation of the information generated by a photometer to actuate a sorting device.[10]

Other sorting procedures which do not fall conveniently into the classifications already discussed in this chapter include devices used in seed cleaning[11] which, although not of wide application in food processing, are worthy of mention as providing practical sorting principles. Examples include separations based on surface property differences such as roughness or stickiness. Thus, *dodder-mills* may be used to separate seeds with rough skin-coats which are preferentially retained when passed through an inclined rotating cylinder lined with muslin, velvet or flannel. Again, certain weed seeds, *e.g.* buckthorn become sticky when damp and may be removed, as agglomerates, by screening. In another machine, material is fed to the upper end of an inclined, porous deck through which air at controlled velocity is passed; this provides an inclined air-slide. Separation then takes place on the basis of the combination sphericity and aerodynamic properties of the mixture components.

Also of interest is the principle involved in a sorter designed to remove worm-holed or cracked peas from sound material. This is done by feeding the raw material into a slowly-rotating, inclined drum which is lined with fine needles which project inwards. Damaged peas are picked up by the needles and are then discharged into a collecting trough located inside the drum below top dead-centre. The whole peas are swept aside by the needles and travel slowly down the base of the drum under the influence of gravity to the discharge point located at the lower end of the drum.[12]

3.6. GRADING OF FOODS

Grading, or quality separation, depends on an overall assessment of those properties of the food which affect its acceptance as a food or as a working substance for the food processor.

3.6.1. THE GRADING OPERATION

The term 'quality' has different connotations for different commodities and the relative importance of the component material properties which contribute to the overall suitability index (*see* Chapter 1) of a food ingredient depend on its destined end-use. Grading, therefore, involves overall, balanced assessment of all those properties of a material which affect its acceptance as a food and as a working substance for the processor. More often than not, grading involves simultaneous evaluation of multiple properties so that mechanical grading is a matter of some complexity. For this reason, grading is frequently carried out manually.

Whilst separations based on size, shape, colour, etc., discussed under sorting (Section 3.5), up-grade the material it is seldom that any one of these is sufficient, by itself, to determine quality. It is for this reason that it is considered worthwhile to differentiate between separation on the basis of single properties and to call this sorting and separation on multiple properties (*i.e.* quality) and to call this grading.

3.6.2. GRADING FACTORS

In general terms, the properties of a food which determine its quality fall conveniently into four groups. These are properties controlling: (i) process suitability; (ii) consumer safety; (iii) conformity with legal requirements and (iv) consumer acceptance.

There are at least as many grading standards as there are materials to be graded but grading statements commonly specify the following:

(i)   *Size and shape:* as functional and acceptability factors.
(ii)   *Maturity:* freshness of eggs; ripeness in fruit; ageing in meat.
(iii)   *Texture:* crumb structure in bread and cakes; crispness in celery and apples; viscosity of cream.
(iv)   *Flavour and aroma.*
(v)   *Function, i.e.* the suitability of the food for its end use, *e.g.* the milling and baking properties of flour; the canning and freezing properties of fruits and vegetables.
(vi)   *Freedom from blemish:* cloudy yolks, blood spots or shell cracks in eggs; bruises in fruits; insect holes in coffee beans.
(vii)   *Colour:* as affecting process and consumer acceptance.
(viii) *Freedom from contaminants:* rodent hairs and insect parts in flour; soil and spray residues on fruit; micro-organisms and their by-products in meat; toxic metals in shellfish, etc.
(ix)   *Freedom from undesired parts of the raw material:* bone fragments in meat products; leaf or pod residues in peas and beans; stalks or stones in fruit.
(x)   Conformity with legal standards or codes of practice.

Quality standards are the responsibility of a number of regulatory bodies at national, continental and world-wide levels.[13] National standards are imposed: by statutory regulations; by codes of practice (*e.g.* The Fruit and Vegetable Canners Code, 1965, in the UK) and by independent bodies such as The British Standards Institution (BSI). Continental regulations may also be effective, *e.g.* those set up by the UN Economic Commission for Europe (ECE) or by the European Economic Community (EEC). These latter provisions apply to both international and domestic trading and although national standards may still apply, in all cases, these must either comply with, or be improvements upon, the EEC standards. Thus, with the entry of the UK into the Common Market in 1973, Britain is required to comply with EEC standards established up to that date and with all subsequent regulations (over which the UK will exercise some control). World-wide standards are being established for many processed foods. This is the responsibility of the Codex Alimentarius Commission which in 1971 represented 89 member-countries. The aims of this body are to harmonise national and international standards and to facilitate international trade.

3.6.3. GRADING METHODS

These fall into two groups: (i) procedures in which the quality is determined by laboratory tests on samples drawn statistically from a batch of food, (ii) procedures which result in the physical separation of the total quantity of the food into quality categories. The first group is, properly, the province of quality control and is outside the province of this book.

The second type of grading may be carried out manually or, in a few cases, by specialised machines. In either case, the food units must be presented singly to the grader for assessment.

3.6.3.1. Presentation for grading. At its simplest, presentation may be arranged by aligning the food on an inspection belt which is often located at the end of a sorting machine. More sophisticated presentation devices are represented by the roller-table, operating on the principle illustrated in Fig. 2.4, and by the spiral-roller table.[14] The latter comprises pairs of longitudinal, driven rollers fitted with helical grooves. The pairs of rollers provide pockets in which the food-pieces are rotated whilst being conveyed along the inspection table. It is usual to divide tables of these types into lanes by fitting longitudinal rods or partitions. Other inspection procedures include the use of vibratory tables or channels and rotating wheels equipped, peripherally, with vacuum ferrules which pick up food-pieces, rotate them for viewing and then release them at a given signal. Specialised alignment gear may be employed such as that used to inspect peeled peach-halves for defects like peel and pit residues, colour defects and blemishes. The peach-halves are fed on to an inclined vibrating table at the end of which are located comb-like projections with either rectangular or 'vee'-shaped cross sections. In passing through these projections, the fruit-halves are aligned, first cup-up and then cup-down, allowing all-round inspection of the food (Fig. 3.15). Another

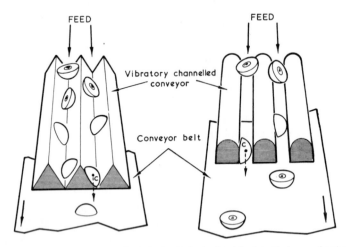

FIG. 3.15. Alignment devices for bringing halved, pitted fruit to the 'cup-up' or 'cup-down' positions. The devices ensure that on discharge from the vibratory conveyor the centre of gravity (C) of the piece lies to the appropriate side of the point of contact of the fruit-half and the conveyor belt.

alignment device in common use is the unscrambling table, as used in some types of colour sorter. The food is fed, at a controlled rate, to the centre of a slowly rotating horizontal disc. Above, and just clear of the disc, is fitted a helical guide-rail. Friction between the food, the disc and the guide-rail results in the food being transformed from a pile in the centre of the disc to a single row of food units at the edge of the disc. Deflection on to an inspection band or through a mechanical scanner then permits individual inspection (Fig. 3.16).

3.6.3.2. Manual grading. Much grading is carried out by trained human operators who are able to assess a number of grading factors simultaneously. The grader forms a balanced judgement of the overall quality and physically separates the food into quality categories. Comparison is made using permanent colour standards in the form of plastic strips or models or coloured representations either printed or photographed onto cards. Apples may be graded using colour cards depicting various grades in terms of: proportion of the surface showing characteristic fruit colour; extent of russeting; variation in discoloration; surface imperfections and shape conformity. Cherries grown in Canada are compared against models made from spheres of plastic, fitted with nylon stems, which are dipped into specially formulated lacquers coloured to reproduce the appearances of fruits

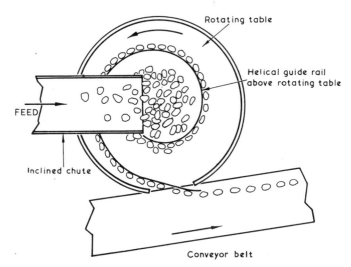

FIG. 3.16.   Diagrammatic plan view of an unscrambling table.

at different stages of maturity. Permanent standards are available for a wide variety of raw and processed foods but although these are useful and sometimes indispensable they have limitations. Differences in colour sensation as a result of the different surfaces provided by the food and the standard (resulting in different degrees of reflectance and scattering) and shape variations (*e.g.* a spherical fruit surface as against a flat comparison surface), introduce inaccuracies.

Eggs are graded manually by '*candling*'. This is a non-destructive examination of the egg contents through the translucent shell when the egg is spun in front of a powerful light in a darkened booth. The presentation of each egg is automatic and a candling operator can separate several thousand eggs an hour into 3–4 grades, taking into account up to 20 grading factors. In certain cases, light at specific wavelengths may be used. Thus, blood spots in eggs are best detected when light at 577 and 597 nm is used whilst green rot is revealed by fluorescence at 490 and 510 nm.[9]

Meat carcases are graded by inspectors whose training enables them, almost at a glance, to assess quality in terms of maturity, the likely eating qualities of the meat and the bone to flesh ratio of the carcase.

Manual grading has many disadvantages, the most important being the high cost of labour and its availability, particularly in the case of seasonal foods, when manpower is in high demand elsewhere. Additionally, boredom and fatigue, even though offset by the means indicated in Section 3.1.1.2, lead to reduced grading efficiency and corresponding financial loss.

3.6.3.3. Machine grading. In some cases it is possible to combine a group of sorting operations so as to separate foods on a quality basis. Thus wheat of a particular variety (which determines its 'function', as defined in Section 3.6.2) may be graded by a combination procedure such as that set out in Fig. 2.6 (Chapter 2).

In other cases, it is possible to take advantage of the fact that a single property of the food is an index of its quality. Thus, small peas are recognised to be the most tender and of highest quality,[13] so that size sorting of cleaned peas results in quality grading. Again, there is good correlation between the density of peas and their tenderness[15] so that they may be graded by flotation in brines of varying densities. A continuous brine-grader using this principle has been described[16] and an industrial machine marketed.*

In potatoes, high solids content (which is reflected in high density) is desirable in the manufacture of dehydrated mashed potato, potato crisps and french fries so that brine separation may be used to quality grade potatoes.[4]

Transmittance differences may be used to sort foods (Section 3.5.2). Additionally, these procedures indicate other internal properties such as scald, core defects and internal damage in apples, and black-heart in potatoes and, hence, function as grading procedures.

Considerable research effort is being devoted to the search for single material properties which reflect overall quality. One notable development is the correlation of the ultrasonic characteristics of animal tissues to the eventual yield and quality of the carcase. Instruments using this principle are now available which provide reliable prediction of carcase quality.[17] Other interesting possibilities include the correlation of tomato quality (colour, firmness and pH) with the distortion produced in an electromagnetic field when the fruit is passed through this,[18] and studies on the vibrational response properties of tomatoes.[19]

Clearly, mechanised grading has many advantages compared with

---

* The Key Brine Grader. Key Manufacturing Co., USA.

manual grading, such as speed, reliability and low labour costs. It is to be expected that efforts will continue to develop mechanised grading principles similar to those indicated, in order to replace manual methods.

REFERENCES

1. Quackenbush, H. E., Stout, B. A., and Reis, S. K., 'Pneumatic Tree Fruit Harvesting'. Agric. Engng, **43**, 388–393 (1962).
2. Anon., 'Tubers Measured in 3D', American Vegetable Grower, **23**(1), 30 (1975).
3. Maggs, D. H., 'Catapult Fruit Grading—Tests of a Commercial Machine'. Fd Technol. Aust., **25**(11), 554–8, 560–1 (1973).
4. Ryall, A. L., and Lipton, D. J., 'Handling, Transportation and Storage of Fruits and Vegetables' (AVI: 1972).
5. Asti, A. R., Baxter, J. R., Hansen, R., and Robe, K., 'Photoelectric Grader Doubles Pickle Production While Cutting Labour Needs in Half'. Fd Process., **30**(8), 48–9 (1969).
6. Francis, F. J., and Clydesdale, F. M., 'Colour Measurement of Foods I–XXXVIII'. Fd Prod. Dev., **2** (1968) to **7** (1973).
7. Preece, K., 'Detection of Foreign Bodies'. Fd Mf., **47**(9), 21–2, 51 (1972).
8. Yeatman, J. N., and Norris, K. H., 'Evaluating Internal Quality of Apples with New Automatic Fruit Sorter'. Fd Technol., **19**(3), 123–5 (1965).
9. Francis, F. J., 'Continuous Colour Measurement'. Fd Technol., **26**(12), 48, 59 (1972).
10. Rosenthal, R. D., and Webster, D. R., 'On-Line System Sorts Fruit on Basis of Internal Quality'. Fd Technol., **27**(7), 52, 4, 6, 8, 60 (1973).
11. Hall, C. W., 'Processing Equipment for Agricultural Products' (AVI: 1963).
12. Anon., 'Sorting by Colour, Air and Diameter'. Fd Process. Ind., **43**(513), 23 (1974).
13. Arthey, V. D., 'Quality of Horticultural Products'. (Butterworths: 1975.)
14. Allshouse, G. W., and Stephenson, K. Q., 'Development of a Handling and Sorting System for Certain Fruits and Vegetables'. Transactions of the ASAE, **12**(3), 290–4 (1969).
15. Makower, R. U., 'The Determination of Density and Evaluation of Quality in Peas Preserved by Freezing', Fd Technol., **11**(2), 126–9 (1957).
16. Martin, T., 'Quality Grading of Peas by Brine Separation', Fd Pckr, **25**(5), 34–6 (1944).
17. Johnson, A. H., and Peterson, M. S., 'Encyclopedia of Food Technology'. Encyclopedia of Food Technology & Food Science Series. Vol. 2 (AVI: 1974).
18. Veal, C. D., 'Use of Radio Frequency Waves for Evaluation of Tomato Maturity'. Dissertation Abstracts International, Section B, The Sciences and Engineering, **31**(3), 1238 (1970).
19. Stephenson, K. Q., Byler, R. K., and Wittman, M. A., 'Vibrational Response Properties as Sorting Criteria for Tomatoes'. Transactions of the ASAE, **16**(2), 258–260, 265 (1973).

PART II
CONVERSION OPERATIONS

CHAPTER 4

SIZE REDUCTION AND SCREENING OF SOLIDS

4.1. GENERAL PRINCIPLES

4.1.1. INTRODUCTION

The breakdown of solid material through the application of mechanical forces is a frequent requirement in many food processing operations. The reasons for size reduction are varied.

(a) Size reduction may aid the extraction of a desired constituent from a composite structure, *e.g.* flour from wheat grains or juice from sugar cane.

(b) Reduction to a definite size range may be a specific product requirement, *e.g.* as in the manufacture of icing sugar, in the preparation of spices and in chocolate refining.

(c) A decrease in particle size of a material leads to an increase in surface of the solid. This increase in surface is of assistance in many rate processes, *e.g.*

(i) the drying time for moist solids is much reduced by increasing the surface area of the solid.

(ii) the rate of extraction of a desired solute is increased by increasing the contact area between solid and solvent.

(iii) process time required for certain operations—cooking, blanching, etc.—can be reduced by cutting, shredding or dicing the process material.

(d) Intimate mixing or blending is usually easier with smaller size ranges of particles, an important consideration in the production of formulated, packaged soups, cake mixes, etc.

4.1.2. NATURE OF FORCES USED IN SIZE REDUCTION

Three types of force are generally recognised. In a comminution operation more than one type is usually present.

The types of force predominating in some of the mills in common use in the food industry are summarised as follows.

Force	*Principle*	*Machine*
Compressive	Compression (nutcracker)	Crushing rolls
Impact	Impact (hammer)	Hammer mill
Shear (attrition)	Attrition (grindstone)	Disc attrition mill

Compressive forces are used for the coarse crushing of hard materials. Impact forces can be regarded as general purpose forces and are used for coarse, medium and fine grinding of a variety of food materials. Attrition or shear forces are extensively used in machines for the comminution of softer, non-abrasive, materials in the smaller size ranges, *i.e.* in fine grinding.

The term crushing is often applied to the reduction of coarse material down to a size of about 3 mm. Grinding is the term commonly used for the production of powdered material. Crushing is more often associated with the application of compressive forces and grinding with attrition forces.

4.1.3. NUMBER OF REDUCTION STAGES FOR A GIVEN PROCESS

In a comminution process the product particles from a mill will often vary widely in size. It is often necessary to classify these particles into particular ranges of sizes. A product specification will commonly require a finished product not to contain particles greater than (or less than, depending on the process) some specified size. In comminution studies particle size is frequently referred to as screen aperture size (Section 4.7.1).

The complexity of a size reduction plant, that is, the number of individual units and intermediate size separation stages required, varies with the feed and desired product size ranges. For the reduction of relatively large, solid lumps to finely divided powder, several stages will be required, each stage capable of handling a given size reduction. Figure 4.1 shows a flow sheet for a typical size reduction plant employing three reduction stages.

4.1.4. REDUCTION RATIO (R.R.)

The ratio,

$$\frac{\text{Average size of feed}}{\text{Average size of product}}$$

is known as the reduction ratio and can be of use in predicting the likely performance of a particular machine. Coarse crushers have size reduction ratios of below 8:1, but for fine grinding, ratios as high as 100:1 can be realised. Much depends on the particular machine and feed material. The values for average size of feed and product depend

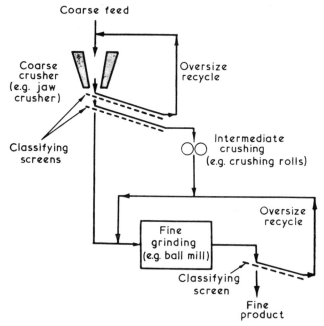

FIG. 4.1.   A typical size reduction flow sheet.

on the method of measurement. Commonly used is the true arithmetic average diameter, obtained from screen analyses on samples of the feed and product streams.[1, 2]

4.2.   CONSIDERATIONS GOVERNING EQUIPMENT SELECTION

The aim of an economic size reduction process is to achieve the desired reduction at minimum cost. Capital, operating and maintenance costs all play a part in determining the profitability of a process and these charges, for the various possible alternatives available, must be carefully considered before selecting a particular comminution line. Consideration of the alternative machines, when working to the particular process requirement, is imperative. In general, a knowledge of the characteristics of the feed material, possible machines and of the product material will be necessary. One of the first steps in specifying size reduction equipment is to find out as much as possible about the characteristics of the feed material. North lists a number of characteristics which may require to be considered.[3] These include: hardness; toughness; abrasiveness; stickiness; softening or melting temperature; structure; specific gravity; free moisture content; chemical stability; homogeneity; and purity. Those properties of importance in any particular process vary widely. Some properties likely to be important in food processing are discussed below.

4.2.1. HARDNESS AND ABRASIVENESS OF FEED

Although not normally a primary consideration in food processing operations, a knowledge of the hardness of the feed material can be important in selecting comminution equipment. In general, hard materials are more difficult to comminute. More energy is required and residence times in the 'action zone' must be longer. This may necessitate either (a) a slower throughput for a given mill or (b) a larger capacity mill to satisfy a particular duty. Hard materials are usually abrasive so wear of working surfaces can be pronounced. These surfaces should be fabricated in hard wearing materials of construction, such as manganese steel, and should be easily replaceable. To reduce wear, a mill for reducing the size of a hard material is relatively slow moving. It will also be of robust construction to withstand the mechanical stresses developed. For these reasons maintenance on these machines is sometimes overlooked.

4.2.2. MECHANICAL STRUCTURE OF FEED

A knowledge of the mechanical structure of the feed material can indicate the type of force most likely to effect disintegration. If the material is friable, or has a crystalline structure, fracture may occur easily along cleavage planes, larger particles fracturing more readily than smaller ones. In these cases, crushing, using compressive forces is employed.

If few cleavage planes are present and new crack tips have to be formed, impact and shear forces may be better. Many food materials have a fibrous structure and are not easily disintegrated by compressive or impact forces so shredding or cutting is required.

4.2.3. MOISTURE

The presence of water can both aid and hinder a comminution process. With many materials, moisture content in excess of 2% to 3% can lead to clogging of the mill. Throughput and grinding efficiency may suffer. Agglomeration or 'balling' can also occur in the presence of moisture. This is undesirable if a free flowing, finely powdered food material is required. Dust formation, arising during the dry milling of many solids, can cause problems.

(a) Prolonged inhalation of otherwise non-toxic dusts can lead to dangerous respiratory diseases and operatives must be protected against such possibilities.

(b) Many solid food materials are, in a finely divided condition, extremely inflammable and dust explosions are not unknown in the food industry.[4, 5]

The presence of small quantities of water has been found useful in the suppression of dust and, in applications where the presence of water is acceptable, water sprays are often used to reduce dust formation.

In some applications, large excesses of water are introduced into the milling system. The water transports the solid particles through the action zone in the form of a free flowing slurry. This wet milling is widely used in corn milling.[6]

4.2.4. TEMPERATURE SENSITIVITY OF FEED

In the action zone of a mill, inter-particle friction arises. Particles can also be stressed within their elastic limits without fracture, the strain energy absorbed being released as heat when the stress is removed. Heat arising from both these sources can lead to a considerable rise in temperature of the material being processed and degradation could occur.

Besides a knowledge of the chemical stability of heat sensitive materials their softening or melting temperatures are also of importance. If heat generated leads to the development of a sticky charge, clogging of the mill and a reduction in the efficiency of the process may well result. Cooling facilities—jackets, coils, etc.—may be required round the action zone if heat sensitive materials are being handled.

4.3. SIZE REDUCTION EQUIPMENT

Machines of various types and sizes are available for the comminution of food materials.

Larger types of coarse crushers such as jaw crushers and gyratory crushers[1] are not normally encountered in the food industry.

The more common types of machines used are discussed below.

4.3.1. CRUSHING ROLLS

In this machine, two or more heavy steel cylinders revolve towards each other (see Fig. 4.2). Particles of feed are nipped and pulled through the rolls, experiencing a compressive force which crushes them. In some machines a differential speed is maintained between the rolls and shearing forces also arise.

The throughput of these units is governed by roller length and diameter and by the speed of rotation. With larger diameters, speeds of 50–300 r.p.m. are usual. Size reduction ratios are low—usually below 5. The diameter of the rolls, differential speed of the rolls and the 'nip', the spacing between the rolls, can be varied to suit the feed size and throughput rate required. An overload compression spring protects the roller surface from damage, but hard foreign bodies should be removed before crushing.

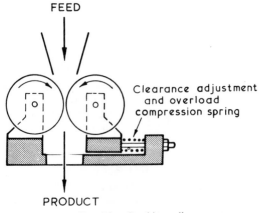

FEED

Clearance adjustment and overload compression spring

PRODUCT

FIG. 4.2. Crushing rolls.

4.3.1.1. Angle of nip. The angle formed by the tangents to the roll faces at the point of contact between a particle and the rolls, the 'angle of nip', is of importance in specifying the size of a pair of crushing rolls for a given duty.

If A is the angle of nip, D_f the average diameter of the feed particles, D_p the average diameter of the product particles, D_r the diameter of the rolls, it can be shown[1] that

$$\cos\frac{A}{2} = \frac{D_r + D_p}{D_r + D_f} \qquad (4.1)$$

For the limiting case when the particle is just pulled into the rolls by friction:

$$\tan\frac{A}{2} = \mu \qquad (4.2)$$

where μ is the coefficient of friction between the particle and the rolls.

4.3.1.2. Capacity of crushing rolls. The theoretical capacity of these units is the volume of the continuous ribbon of product discharged from the rolls.

For a machine with roll diameter D_r m, and length of face l m, when the nip is D_p m and the roll speed is N rev/min, the volumetric capacity (Q) is given by

$$Q = \frac{ND_rD_pl}{60}\,\text{m}^3/\text{s} \qquad (4.3)$$

Knowing the bulk density of the discharge stream the approximate mass flow rate may be estimated. In practice the actual capacity is found to lie between 0·1 and 0·3 of the theoretical capacity.

Crushing rolls are used for intermediate crushing and find wide application in the milling of wheat[7] and in the refining of chocolate.[8] In other modifications the roll surfaces may be studded or fluted to aid friction and nip.[9] Single roll crushers which compress the feed between the roll and a stationary breaker plate find use in the crushing of more friable materials.

4.3.2. HAMMER MILL

This type of impact, or percussion, grinder is common in the food industry (Fig. 4.3).

A high speed rotor carries a collar bearing a number of hammers

FEED

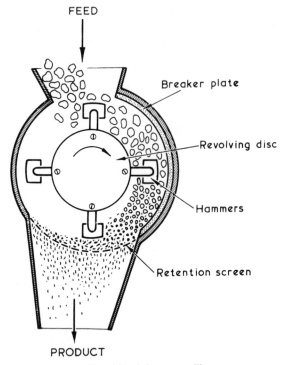

FIG. 4.3.   A hammer mill.

around its periphery. When the rotor turns, the hammer heads swing through a circular path inside a close fitting casing containing a toughened breaker plate. Feed passes into the action zone where the hammers drive the material against the breaker plate. Reduction is mainly due to impact forces, although under choke feeding conditions (Section 4.4.3) attrition forces can also play a part in the size reduction. The hammers are often replaced by cutters, or by bars as in the beater bar mill. The hammer mill may be regarded as a general purpose mill, handling hard crystalline solids, fibrous materials, vegetable matter, sticky materials, etc. In the food industry it is extensively used for grinding peppers and spices, dried milk, sugars, etc.

4.3.3. DISC ATTRITION MILLS

Mills utilising attrition or shear forces for size reduction play a major part in fine grinding. Since much of the milling carried out in the

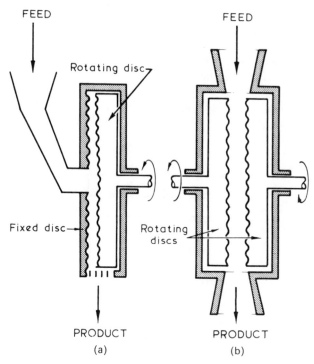

FIG. 4.4.   Disc mills. (a) A single disc mill. (b) A double disc mill.

food industry is for the production of very small particle sizes, this type of mill finds extensive application. Two types of disc mill are shown in Fig. 4.4.

4.3.3.1. Single disc mill. In this device the feed stock passes into a narrow gap between a high speed, rotating grooved disc and the stationary casing of the mill. Intense shearing action results in comminution of the feed. The gap is adjustable, depending on feed size and product requirements.

4.3.3.2. Double disc mill. In this modification the casing contains two rotating discs. The discs rotate in opposite directions giving a greater degree of shear than that attainable in the single disc mill. In yet another modification to this basic principle, the Foos mill, the discs carry studs which aid disintegration. This type of disc attrition mill is widely used in cereal preparation, corn and rice milling.[10]

The pin-disc mill, popular in the food industry, carries pins or pegs on the rotating elements. In this case impact forces also play a significant part in the breakdown of particulate matter.

4.3.3.3. Buhr mill. This is an older type of disc attrition mill, originally used in flour milling.

Two circular stones are mounted on a vertical axis. The upper stone, which is often fixed, has a feed entry port (Fig. 4.5). The lower

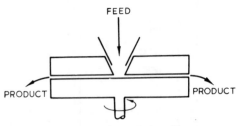

FIG. 4.5. A Buhr mill.

stone rotates. Feed material passes to the gap between the upper and lower stones. The material, after subjection to the shearing force developed between the stones, is discharged over the edge of the lower stone. In some models both stones rotate, in opposite directions. In modern machines, toughened steel stones are replacing the traditional 'natural' or 'composition' stones.[10]

This type of mill is still being used in the wet milling of corn for the separation of starch gluten from the hulls.[6, 11]

Other variations of this type of grinding mill are extensively used in chocolate manufacture. For example, cacao nibs are crushed in horizontal triple stone grinding machines, although here again more modern processes are utilising hardened steel, toothed discs in place of stones.[8]

4.3.4. TUMBLING MILLS

A mill extensively used in many process industries for fine grinding is the tumbling mill.

Two basic types, the Ball mill and the Rod mill, are available.

4.3.4.1. Ball mills. In the ball mill (Fig. 4.6) both shearing and impact forces are utilised in the size reduction.

The unit consists of a horizontal slow speed rotating cylinder containing a charge of steel balls or flint stones. As the cylinder rotates balls are lifted up the sides of the cylinder and drop on to the material being comminuted, which fills the void spaces between the balls. The balls also tumble over each other, exerting a shearing action on the feed material. This combination of impact and shearing forces brings about a very effective size reduction. Ball sizes are usually in the range 25–150 mm (1–6 in). Small balls give more point contacts but larger balls give greater impact. As with all grinding mills, working surfaces gradually wear, so product contamination must be guarded against.

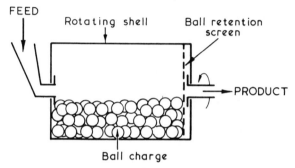

FIG. 4.6. A ball mill.

At low speeds of rotation the balls are not lifted very far up the walls of the cylinder. The balls tumble over each other and shear forces predominate. At faster speeds the balls are lifted further and the impact forces increase. Attrition and impact forces play a part in reduction. At high speeds the balls can be carried round at the wall of the mill under the influence of centrifugal force. Under these conditions grinding ceases. For efficient milling the critical speed should not be exceeded. This is defined as the speed at which a small sphere inside the mill just begins to centrifuge. It can be shown[1] that the critical speed N_c, in r.p.m., is given by

$$N_c = \frac{42 \cdot 3}{(D)^{1/2}} \tag{4.4}$$

where D is the diameter of the mill, in metres.

In practice, the optimum operating speed is about 75% of the critical speed and should be determined under the plant operating conditions.

A variation of the conventional ball mill finding increasing use for very fine grinding is the vibration ball mill. In this device the chamber containing the grinding media is caused to vibrate by means of out of balance weights attached to each end of the shaft of a double-ended electric motor. The energy imparted by the walls of the grinding chamber is transmitted to the media and the material to be ground. The latter fills the interstices between the grinding media. The void space in these mills can be varied by using different shaped media. In the Vibro Energy[16] mill using spheres the void space is about 37% whereas with cylinders it falls to 25%. At lower voidages the layers of trapped material become thinner and conditions for ultrafine grinding improve. The media vibrate without appreciable relative movement so shearing forces are minimal, the force developed being essentially that of impact. Vibration mills are also finding use in mixing and dispersing applications.

4.3.4.2. Rod mills. In the rod mill, the balls are replaced by high carbon steel rods. Impact and attrition forces still play a part but the effect of impact forces is less pronounced. Rod mills are recommended for use with sticky charges where balls can be trapped in the mass of the charge and become ineffective. The rods run the full length of the mill and, as with a ball charge, occupy about 50% of the mill volume.

4.4. MODES OF OPERATION OF SIZE REDUCTION PLANT

Several operating methods can be considered. Not all will be applicable for a given feedstock and process requirement. Ideally, the object is to achieve the desired size reduction at minimum cost.

4.4.1. OPEN CIRCUIT GRINDING

This is the simplest method of operating a mill (Fig. 4.7). No ancillary classifying systems (vibrating screens, etc.) are used so the capital outlay for the plant is low. Feed enters the mill, passes through the action zone and is discharged as a product. No recycle of oversize particles (having a size range greater than that desired) is possible. Since some large particles pass rapidly through the mill and other small particles have long residence times in the mill, a wide size distribution in the product results. Power utilisation is poor, since acceptable sizes of particles are still further reduced due to the excessive retention period in the action zone.

4.4.2. FREE CRUSHING

With this method of operation residence time in the action zone is kept short. When used in conjunction with open circuit grinding, this is commonly accomplished by allowing the feed material to fall through the action zone under gravity. Unnecessary breakdown of small particles is limited so the formation of undersize particles (particles smaller than the desired size range) is reduced. This mode of operation is more economic on power consumption but, since some

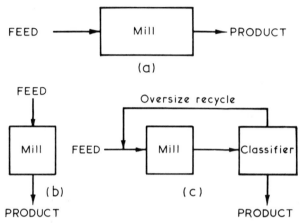

FIG. 4.7. Methods of mill operation. (a) Open circuit grinding. (b) Free crushing. (c) Closed circuit grinding.

large particles rapidly pass through the action zone, a wide size range of product can result.

4.4.3. CHOKE FEEDING

In choke feeding the discharge of product is restricted by inserting a screen in the outlet from the machine. For a given feed rate, material remains choked in the action zone of the mill until reduced to a size capable of passing the screen. Since residence times can be long, excessive grinding of smaller particles is likely, so undersize particles are produced at the expense of a high power consumption. Choke feeding is useful when a finely divided product is required. It affords a fairly large size reduction ratio from a single machine.

4.4.4. CLOSED CIRCUIT GRINDING

The method of operation is shown diagrammatically in Fig. 4.7c. The residence time of material in the mill is kept short, either by gravity fall, or by rapid transport through the action zone in an air or water stream. The discharge stream from the mill passes to a classifying system where oversize material is removed and recycled back to the mill. In this way the mill works on bigger particles, so wasteful power consumption is minimised. The classification methods employed depend on the mode of transport. With a gravity or mechanical conveyor flow, vibrating screens are commonly used. With hydraulic or pneumatic transport, cyclone separators are often used.

4.4.5. WET MILLING

If the feed material is wet, or can be wetted without harm, this method of operation may be considered. The feed stock is ground as a suspension in a carrier liquid stream—often water. Dust problems associated with dry milling are overcome and hydraulic classification techniques such as elutriation, sedimentation and centrifugation may be employed for separating desired size fractions.

Very often in food processing the milling is part of an extraction process, a soluble constituent of the feed being transferred to the liquid stream for recovery by evaporation, as in corn milling.[6, 11]

Experience shows that power consumption is generally high with wet grinding. Mill wear may also be increased. Wet-milling tends to produce finer particles than those obtainable with dry milling operations. For this reason this mode of operation finds extensive application in ultrafine grinding applications (see also Section 5.2.2.3).

4.5. DISINTEGRATION OF FIBROUS MATERIALS— SLICING, DICING, SHREDDING AND PULPING

4.5.1. INTRODUCTION

The foregoing principles of size reduction are applicable to frangible materials requiring reduction to granular or powdered forms when the feed is either dry, or contains little liquid. A wide range of substances fall into this category, including sugars, spices, peppers, nuts, cereals and dried foods. Many other foodstuffs requiring comminution (*e.g.* meat, fresh fruits and vegetables) have a fibrous structure and contain appreciable quantities of liquid. Being non-crystalline, the direct application of compressive forces may contribute little to their disintegration. Compressive forces do play a part in expression, another unit operation involving size reduction in which the object is to extract liquid (*e.g.* fruit juice) from the body of the material (Chapter 8).

In general, impact and shearing forces, often applied via a cutting edge, are used in the disintegration of fibrous materials. Much of the equipment used is similar to that used for dry, powdered materials. For example, hammers in a percussion mill can be replaced by a series of knives which apply the impact force along a thin cutting edge. Again, disc attrition mills may carry studs or serrations on the faces of the discs: these impart a tearing action.

In more specialised size reduction operations a uniformly sized and specific shape of particle may be required to simplify handling, aid rate processes such as dehydration or heat treatment, or to improve product appearance. Again, fibrous solids may require conversion into soft, semi-solid pulps, a common requirement in jam manufacture. These more specialised size reduction operations usually employ specially designed equipment. One of the commonest of these more specialised cutting operations is slicing.

4.5.2. SLICING

Sliced fruits are much in demand as a dessert dish. They present an attractive appearance, the portions produced being of a convenient size for eating. Rotary cutting knives are usually employed, the knives being set to cut the material being presented to them—often on a vibrating belt—into parallel slices of the desired thickness. In other fruit slicing operations the fruit is forced through a tube containing stationary knife edges arranged radially along the length of the tube. This type of assembly can produce decored, wedge shaped sections from firmer fruits such as apples.

4.5.3. DICING

Dicing—the cutting of material into cubes—usually follows a preliminary slicing operation which produces slices of the desired thickness. These slices are then fed onto a conveyor belt containing a series of studs which hold the slices in position as the belt carries them against a rotary knife assembly which cuts them into strips. The strips then pass through a further cutting zone at right angles to the stripping section. This produces the required cube.

4.5.4. SHREDDING

In shredding, the food material is torn into small fragments, the average size of the pieces depending on the type of machine and on residence time in the action zone. Shredding often precedes dehydration, the increase in surface aiding the rate process. Hammer mills are commonly used as shredders. The rotating shaft carries a number of discs, each having a series of impact edges around its periphery. The hammers can also be pivoted so as to produce a flailing action. Squirrel cage disintegrators—twin concentric cylindrical cages having their surfaces built up of cutting edges running along the length of the cylinders—are useful for shredding fibrous materials.[1] The feed material is introduced into the inner cage and passes into the action zone between the cages, which rotate in opposite directions. The material is torn apart by the intense shearing and cutting action to which it is subjected, the shredded material passing through the outer cage to a product hopper.

4.5.5. PULPING

Pulping is another comminution operation, widely used in the processing of lower grade fruits separated during grading (Chapter 3). The fruit, which is edible but unacceptable for whole fruit processing, may be used in jam manufacture. A combination of pulping and sieving is used with many fruits and vegetables. A common form of pulper consists of a cylindrical perforated screen containing high speed rotating brushes. Material is fed to the inside of the cylinder, the brushes forcing pulped material through the perforations. Stalks, skins and stones pass over the screening surface as reject (Section 4.7.1). An alternative form of this machine has high speed paddles to help the breakdown of fruit. Screen sizes vary with the particular product requirement; finely dispersed, solid-liquid pulps being obtained with correct choice of perforations. Some fruits are softened by heating before pulping, the softening often leading to higher pulp yields.

4.5.6. ENERGY REQUIREMENT FOR A CUTTING OPERATION

Little work has been carried out on the energy requirement for a cutting operation. Friction and deformation of the material during cutting both play a part in the wasteful dissipation of energy during breakdown (Section 4.6). Well maintained cutting edges will reduce these losses.

4.5.7. MAINTENANCE OF CUTTING EDGES

Besides limiting energy losses, well sharpened knives also reduce the incidence of poor quality (*i.e.* badly bruised and torn) material which commonly arises when blunt or damaged cutting surfaces are used. For extended cutting edge life, knives should be made of hardened alloy steel or similar material and all foreign matter (stones, metal scrap, etc.) likely to damage the knives should be removed during the cleaning stage. Blade assemblies carried on high speed rotating shafts may well be in balanced pairs so their removal, sharpening and replacing should be performed with care.

4.6. ENERGY REQUIREMENTS FOR COMMINUTION OF SOLIDS

Little fundamental work on the energy consumption in such disintegration operations as cutting, shredding and dicing has been carried out. Somewhat more is known of the breakdown of frangible materials. Two stages of breakage are recognised:

(1)   initial fracture along existing fissures or cleavage planes in the body of the material.
(2)   the formation of new fissures or crack tips, followed by fracture along these fissures.

It is generally accepted that little of the input energy to a comminution plant is usefully utilised in the breakdown operation. Only a small percentage of the energy supplied to the machine appears as increased surface energy in the solids. Figures of less than 2 % are quoted,[12] so grinding is a very inefficient process. Much of this input energy is lost in deforming the particles within their elastic limits and through friction between particles. This wasted energy appears as heat which, as we have seen, can lead to heat damage (Section 4.2.4).

Theoretical considerations suggest that the energy dE required to produce a small change dx in the size of unit mass of material can be expressed as a power function of the size of the material. Thus

$$\frac{dE}{dx} = -\frac{K}{x^n}$$

This equation has been used by a number of workers.

4.6.1. RITTINGER'S LAW (1867)

Rittinger considered that for the grinding of solids, the energy required should be proportional to the new surface produced and put $n = 2$.
Then

$$\frac{dE}{dx} = -\frac{K}{x^2}$$

or, integrating

$$E = K\left[\frac{1}{x_2} - \frac{1}{x_1}\right]$$

x_1 is the average initial feed size, x_2 is the average final product size. E is the energy per unit mass required for the production of this new surface and is usually measured in horsepower hour/ton. K is called Rittinger's constant and is a constant for a particular machine and material.

Rittinger's law has been found to hold better for fine grinding, where a large increase in surface results.

4.6.2. KICK'S LAW (1885)

Kick considered that the energy required for a given size reduction was proportional to the size reduction ratio, which requires that $n = 1$.
Then

$$\frac{dE}{dx} = -\frac{K}{x}$$

or

$$E = K\ln\frac{x_1}{x_2}$$

x_1/x_2 being the size reduction ratio (Section 4.1.4).

Kick's law has been found to hold more accurately for coarser crushing where most of the energy is used in causing fracture along existing fissures. It gives the energy required to deform particles within the elastic limit.

For many crushing operations the energy requirement suggested by Kick's law appears to be too low, whereas that required by Rittinger's equation appears to be excessive.

4.6.3. F. C. BOND (1952)—THIRD LAW OF COMMINUTION

In Bond's work,[13] n takes the value $3/2$ giving

$$\frac{dE}{dx} = -\frac{K}{x^{3/2}}$$

or

$$E = 2K\left[\frac{1}{(x_2)^{1/2}} - \frac{1}{(x_1)^{1/2}}\right]$$

When x_1 and x_2 are measured in micrometres and E in kWh/short ton (907·16 kg),

$$K = 5E_i$$

where E_i is the Bond Work Index—the energy required to reduce unit mass of material from an infinite particle size to a size such that 80 % passes a 100 micrometre sieve.

The Bond Work Index is obtained from laboratory crushing tests on the feed material. The third theory holds reasonably well for a variety of materials undergoing coarse, intermediate and fine grinding.

4.7. SCREENING

Screening is the unit operation in which a mixture of various sizes of solid particles is separated into two or more fractions by passing over a screen. Each fraction is more uniform in size than the original mixture. A screen is a surface containing a number of equally sized apertures. The surface may be plane (horizontal or inclined) or it may be cylindrical. Small capacity plane screens are called sieves. In general processing, screening is widely used for separating mixtures of granulated and powdered materials into size ranges. Some degree of overlap with other unit operations occurs since screens are used in filtration (Chapter 6) to separate coarse, or fibrous solid materials from a liquid phase and in the food industry for the sizing and grading of fruits and vegetables (Chapter 3). This section is concerned with the separation of solids on the basis of size.

Besides its use in the industrial separation of a feed material into two or more size ranges of particles for specific process purposes, screening, or sieving, is used in particle size analysis to determine particle sizes and size distributions of powdered materials.

4.7.1. SCREENING TERMINOLOGY

Undersize, fines or minus (−) *material*—material passing through a given screen.
Oversize, tails or plus (+) *material*—material failing to pass a given screen.
Either stream may be the desired (product) stream, or the undesired (reject) stream, depending on the particular application.
Screen aperture—the space between the individual wires of a wire mesh screen.
Woven wire sieves for laboratory particle size analysis were formerly designated by a mesh number, defined as the number of wires per lineal inch. Though this designation has now been deleted from the latest British Standard for Test Sieves (B.S. 410:1969) and from the International Sieve Specification, it is still widely encountered in industry.
Screen aperture and mesh number are not the same. For a given screen aperture, the mesh number will depend on the thickness of the wire forming the screen.
Screen interval—the relationship between successively decreasing openings in a standard screen series.
Several different screen series are in use:

(a) Tyler Standard—This is a widely used series based on a 200 mesh screen having 0·0021 in. diameter wires and a screen aperture of 0·0029 in. The ratio between apertures in consecutive screens is $(2)^{1/2}$. For closer sizing a Tyler series having a screen interval of $(2)^{1/4}$ is used.
(b) British Standards—This screen series is based on B.S. 410: 1969, 'Test Sieves'.[14] A 170 mesh screen will have a nominal aperture size of 90 μm and there is a screen interval of approximately $(2)^{1/4}$ between neighbouring screens.
(c) American Society for Testing Materials. ASTM-E 11. This series is based on an 18 mesh screen with a 1·0 mm aperture and a screen interval of $(2)^{1/4}$.

An International Standard (I.S.O.) Scale is proposed. A number of sieves on both the B.S. and the A.S.T.M. standards correspond to this proposal of the I.S.O. Committee.
Diameter of a sieve fraction—The average diameter of a fraction passing a given sieve, but retained on the next smaller in the series, is often taken as the arithmetic average of the two screen apertures.
Diameter of solid particles—The particle dimension controlling its retention on a particular sized screen is often called its diameter. Particles encountered in industry are usually irregular in shape. An

average diameter is used. This average diameter depends on the method of measurement[2] so a number of different particle diameters are in common use. This can lead to confusion.

4.7.2. INDUSTRIAL SCREENS

Industrial screens are made from metal bars, perforated plates and cylinders, or woven wire cloth and fabrics. Materials of construction for screens handling foodstuffs include stainless steel, Monel metal and nylon fabric.

4.7.2.1. Grizzlies or bar screens. These are used for screening larger particles—pieces greater than 25 mm. They consist of a set of parallel bars, spaced to the desired separation. The bars are often wedge-shaped to minimise clogging (Fig. 4.8). They may be used horizontally or inclined at angles up to 60°. Vibrating grizzlies are available, the feed material passing over the screening surface in a series of jerks.

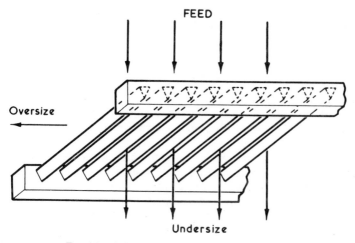

FEED

Oversize

Undersize

FIG. 4.8. A bar screen with triangular section bars.

4.7.2.2. Vibrating screens. The simplest vibrating screens consist of a frame supporting a wire mesh screen or a perforated plate. They can be shaken mechanically or electromagnetically, the motion carrying feed material across the screen surface. They are normally inclined to the horizontal and are widely used in grading fruits and vegetables, when perforated screens are used. These screens may be multi-deck units, a series of screens being mounted beneath each other, permitting separation of a given feed stock into several size ranges.

4.7.2.3. Reels or trommels. These units are revolving cylindrical screens mounted almost horizontally. Again the screening surface may consist of wire mesh or perforated sheet. Hexagonal cross-sections are also used since these lead to agitation which aids the separation of fine material. Wire mesh or fabric screens are used with powders and circular perforations for fruit and vegetable grading.

The capacity of a trommel increases with increasing speed of rotation until a critical speed is achieved. At speeds greater than this, the material does not cascade over the surface but is carried round by centrifugal force and separation is seriously impaired.

The critical speed of a trommel[1] is given by

$$N = \frac{42 \cdot 3}{(D)^{1/2}}$$

N is the number of revolutions of the trommel per minute, D is the diameter of the trommel in metres.

Specialised types of sizing equipment used in fruit and vegetable preparation are discussed in Chapter 3.

4.7.3. FACTORS AFFECTING THE EFFICIENCY OF A SCREENING OPERATION

Ideally, the object of screening is the complete separation of desired from undesired material. A number of factors can influence the degree of separation achieved.

(i) *Rate of feeding.* If the feed rate is too high, insufficient residence time on the screening surface will result. The screen becomes overloaded and material capable of passing leaves with the oversize.

The angle of inclination of the screen also influences residence time. Too steep an angle will result in insufficient residence time while too small an angle may restrict gravity flow across the screen.

(ii) *Particle size.* Even though sufficiently small, the particle will only pass the screen if its alignment, relative to the openings, is favourable. Large particles tend to impede the passage of smaller, and a preliminary separation may be required if a high proportion of bigger particles are present.

(iii) *Moisture.* The presence of moisture in the feed can cause adhesion between small and large particles. Undersize particles will be removed with the oversize materials.

(iv) *Worn or damaged screens.* Oversize particles will pass through the damaged area and the efficiency of the separation will be impaired. Damaged screens should be repaired immediately. Fine screens are very fragile and should be treated with great care.

(v) *Blinding (clogging) of screens.* Blinding or clogging of the openings is particularly likely to occur when the size of the particles is near to that of the screen aperture. Particles capable of passing are prevented from doing so and are carried over with the oversize. Blinded screens should be cleaned immediately or screening efficiency will suffer.

4.7.4. LABORATORY SIEVING

For size analysis by screening, standard laboratory sieves up to 16 mm aperture are used. The usual range of particle size measured using this method is 50–3000 μm. The size of coarser particles is usually determined by direct measurement.

Details of laboratory particle size analysis techniques for powders using fine mesh test sieves are given in B.S. 1796:1952.[15]

REFERENCES

1. Brown, G. G., and Associates, 'Unit Operations'. (John Wiley and Sons: 1950).
2. McCabe, W. L., and Smith, J., 'Unit Operations of Chemical Engineering' 2nd ed. (McGraw-Hill: 1967).
3. North, R., 'The Characteristic Properties of Material'. Trans. Inst. Chem. Eng., **3**(1), (1954).
4. Ministry of Labour (Safety, Health and Welfare), 'Dust Explosions in Factories'. New Series No. 22 (H.M.S.O.: 1963).
5. London, A. V., 'The time to think about dust explosions is now'. Journal of Flour and Animal Feed Milling, **157**(3), 28–32 (1975).
6. Kerr, R. W., 'Chemistry and Industry of Starch', 2nd ed. (Academic Press: 1960).
7. Lockwood, J. F., 'Flour Milling'. (Henry Simon Limited: 1960).
8. Williams, C. T., 'Chocolate and Confectionery', 3rd ed. (Leonard Hill: 1964).
9. Hugot, E., 'Handbook of Cane Sugar Engineering', 2nd ed. (Elsevier: 1960).
10. Simmons, N. O., 'Feed Milling', 2nd ed. (Leonard Hill: 1963).
11. Altschul, A., 'Processed Plant Protein Foodstuffs'. (Academic Press: 1958).
12. Coulson, J. M., and Richardson, J. F., 'Chemical Engineering', Volume II, 2nd ed. (Pergamon Press: 1964).
13. Bond, F. C., 'Some Recent Advances in Grinding Theory and Practice'. British Chemical Engineering, **8**(9), 631–634 (1963).
14. B.S. 410: 1969 'Test Sieves'. (British Standards Institution).
15. B.S. 1796: 1952 'Methods for the Use of B.S. Fine Mesh Test Sieves'. (British Standards Institution).
16. Podmore, H. L., 'Vibration Grinding in Close Packed Media Systems'. Chemy Ind., 1443–1450 (1967).

CHAPTER 5

MIXING AND EMULSIFICATION

5.1. MIXING

5.1.1. INTRODUCTION

Mixing may be defined as an operation in which two or more components are interspersed in space with one another. The aim is to achieve a uniform distribution of the components by means of flow. The flow is normally generated by mechanical means. The degree of uniformity attainable varies widely. With miscible liquids, or soluble solids in liquids, very intimate mixing is possible. With immiscible liquids, paste-like materials and dry powders the degree of uniformity obtainable is invariably less.

The efficiency of a mixing process depends on effective utilisation of the energy used to generate the flow of the components. The provision of adequate input energy, the design of the mechanical agency introducing the energy, the configuration of the containing vessel and the physical properties of the components are all important in the design of a mixer.

The materials fed to a mixer may vary from low viscosity liquids to highly viscous pastes or dry powders. Excluding the newer, continuous 'in-line' mixers (Section 5.1.3.6) three basic types of mixing system can be considered.

Type (1)—Stationary vessel containing a moving stirrer, agitator, paddle, *i.e.* an impeller or impeller assembly mounted on a rotating shaft (Fig. 5.2). Impellers mounted in vertical tanks are widely used for mixing low-viscosity liquids, free-flowing liquid/solid suspensions, and for the dispersion of gases in liquids.

Type (2)—Stationary vessel containing moving paddles, vanes, knives, ploughs, screws, etc. These mixers have been developed for mixing higher-consistency materials—viscous liquids, doughs, pastes, fats, etc.

Type (3)—Moving vessel containing moving and/or stationary paddles, vanes, knives, ploughs, screws, etc. Mixers in this category are

84

used for very high consistency mixes—doughs, pastes and plastic materials.

These three classes of mixer cater for low, intermediate and high consistency mixes. Types (2) and (3) also handle dry powders. The objective, common to all three types, is the promotion of flow.

5.1.2. MIXERS FOR LIQUIDS OF LOW OR MODERATE VISCOSITY

The most commonly used form of mixer for handling low or moderate viscosity liquids is the impeller agitator. This type of mixer consists of one or more impellers, fixed to a rotating shaft, which create currents within the liquid. These currents should travel throughout the mixing vessel. It is not sufficient simply to circulate the liquid; turbulent conditions must be created within the moving stream of liquid. When a moving stream of liquid comes into contact with stationary or slow-moving liquid, shear occurs at the interface and low-velocity liquid is entrained in the faster moving streams, mixing with the liquid therein. In order to achieve mixing in a reasonable time the volumetric flow rate must be such that the entire volume of the mixing vessel is swept out in a reasonable time.

The fluid velocity created by an impeller mixer in a tank has three components: (a) a radial component acting in a direction perpendicular to the shaft, (b) a longitudinal component acting parallel to the shaft and (c) a rotational component acting in a direction tangential to the circle of rotation of the shaft. Both radial and longitudinal components generally contribute to mixing but the rotational component may not. In the case of an impeller rotating on a vertical shaft mounted centrally in the mixing vessel the rotational component promotes flow in a circular path around the shaft. This flow is generally laminar and leads to the formation of layers in the liquid. Little or no longitudinal flow may occur between these layers. The net result may be that the vessel contents simply rotate with little mixing. Since the relative velocity between the impeller blade and the liquid is low, the power that can be absorbed by the liquid is limited. Further, this tangential component can lead to the formation of a vortex at the surface of the liquid. As the speed of rotation of the impeller is increased this vortex deepens. Once the vortex reaches the suction of the impeller the power imparted to the liquid is suddenly reduced and air is drawn into the liquid. The introduction of air by means of vortex formation can be used to advantage in certain circumstances, *e.g.* fermentations, but it is generally undesirable. Another disadvantage associated with rotational flow is that solid particles may separate out under the influence of centrifugal force.

Vortexing, and the other disadvantages of rotational flow, may be reduced by positioning the agitator off-centre in the mixing vessel. Alternatively, baffles may be employed to interrupt this rotational flow and thereby reduce its effects. An effective method of baffling is to fix vertical strips perpendicular to the wall of the vessel as shown in Fig. 5.1. Four such baffles are generally sufficient.[1]

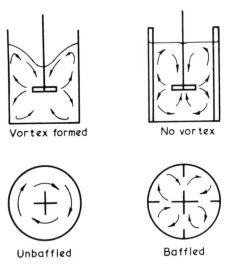

Vortex formed   No vortex

Unbaffled   Baffled

FIG. 5.1.   Flow patterns in baffled and unbaffled vessels with paddle or turbine agitators.

5.1.2.1. Paddle agitators. In its simplest form a paddle agitator consists of a flat blade fixed to a rotating shaft (Fig. 5.2a). The shaft is usually mounted centrally in the vessel and rotates at speeds in the range 20–150 rev/min. The liquid flow has a high radial component in the plane of the paddle and also a high rotational component. Little vertical flow is developed. Baffling is normally employed to reduce swirling and vortexing (Fig. 5.1). Two- or four-bladed paddles are common. Pitched blades may be used to promote vertical flow. Multivane paddles or gate agitators may be used for more viscous liquids (Fig. 5.2b). Paddles designed just to clear the vessel walls (anchor paddles) are often used to promote heat transfer and minimise deposits on jacketed vessels (Fig. 5.2c). Counter-rotating multiblade paddles may be used to develop high localised shear where required (Fig. 5.2d). Paddles generally measure $\frac{1}{2}-\frac{3}{4}$ of the vessel diameter and the width of the blade is generally $\frac{1}{10}-\frac{1}{6}$ of its length. Paddle agitators are relatively easy to fabricate and can be coated with a variety of corrosion resistant materials. Single paddle agitators have

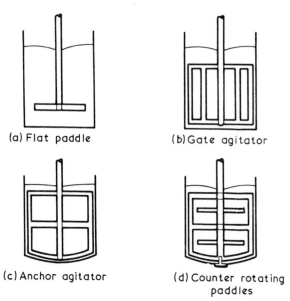

(a) Flat paddle   (b) Gate agitator

(c) Anchor agitator   (d) Counter rotating
paddles

FIG. 5.2.   Some typical paddle impellers.

a gentle mixing action often desirable when handling fragile, crystalline materials. They are useful for simple mixing duties, *e.g.* mixing of miscible liquids or preparation of solutions of solids.

5.1.2.2. Turbine agitators. A turbine agitator consists of an impeller with more than four blades mounted on the same boss and fixed to a rotating shaft (Fig. 5.3a). They are generally smaller than paddles, measuring 30–50 % of the vessel diameter, and commonly rotate at speeds in the range 30–500 rev/min. The shaft, again, is usually mounted centrally in the vessel. The simple straight bladed turbine generates strong radial and rotational currents. Baffling is normally employed to reduce swirling. Vertical flow is also set up due to deflection of the radial currents from the vessel walls (Fig. 5.1). The velocity of the liquid is relatively high and currents travel throughout the mixing vessel. High turbulence and shear are developed near the impeller itself. Impeller blades may be pitched to increase vertical flow (Fig. 5.3b). The vaned disc impeller (Fig. 5.3(d)) may be used for dispersing gases in liquids. Turbine agitators are useful for handling a wide variety of materials and are particularly effective in mixing moderately viscous liquids. The turbulence and shear developed close to the impeller make them useful for emulsion premixing (*see* Section 5.2.2.1).

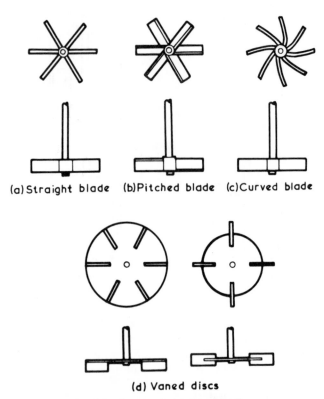

(a) Straight blade   (b) Pitched blade   (c) Curved blade

(d) Vaned discs

FIG. 5.3.   Some typical turbine impellers.

5.1.2.3. Propeller agitators. These consist of short bladed impellers (usually measuring less than $\frac{1}{4}$ of vessel diameter) rotating at high speed (500 to several thousand rev/min). The currents generated are primarily longitudinal and rotational (Fig. 5.5a) and are very persistent. Thus these comparatively small agitators are effective in quite large vessels when used with lower viscosity liquids. Because of the predominantly longitudinal nature of the flow currents, propellers are not very effective if mounted on vertical shafts located at the centre of the vessel. They are commonly mounted off centre and with the shaft at an angle to the vertical (Fig. 5.5c). In large tanks propeller shafts may be mounted through the side wall of the tank in a horizontal plane but off centre (Fig. 5.5d). Propeller agitators are most effective in mixing low viscosity liquids. Propeller blades cut and shear the material and can be used for dispersing solids and for emulsification duties. Some typical impeller designs are shown in Fig. 5.4.

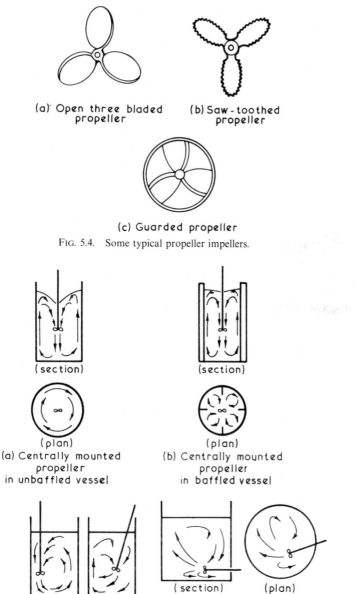

(a) Open three bladed propeller

(b) Saw-toothed propeller

(c) Guarded propeller

FIG. 5.4. Some typical propeller impellers.

(section)

(section)

(plan)

(plan)

(a) Centrally mounted propeller in unbaffled vessel

(b) Centrally mounted propeller in baffled vessel

(c) Propeller mounted off centre

(section)   (plan)

(d) Side - entering propeller

FIG. 5.5.   Flow patterns in propeller agitated systems.

5.1.2.4. Other types of impeller agitators. Other impellers employed for relatively low viscosity mixes include disc impellers, cone impellers and a wide variety of special designs for particular purposes. An example of one such special type is given in Fig. 5.6. This particular type subjects the material to high shear on being forced out through the slots and is recommended for emulsion premixing and liquid–liquid and solid–liquid dispersion.[1,2]

5.1.2.5. Mixing vessels. In practice these take various shapes, but the most commonly used design is a vertical cylindrical tank with a dished bottom. This minimises the dead spaces in corners, etc., which might occur in rectangular tanks, or cylindrical tanks with flat or conical bottoms. The filling ratio, *i.e.* ratio, liquid depth:vessel diameter, is usually 0·5–1·5 and 1·0 is recommended for most purposes. If tall vessels are used, one impeller should be installed for each vessel diameter of height. These and other recommendations for vessel and agitator designs are given by the EEUA.[3]

5.1.2.6. Power requirements for low viscosity liquid mixing systems. The power introduced into a liquid mixing system by an agitator is determined by its speed of rotation, the configuration of the mixer and the physical properties of the mixture. Using the method of dimensional analysis, Rushton *et al.*[4] related the power requirement to these various parameters. If linear dimensions such as the depth of liquid in the tank, the diameter of the tank, the number, dimensions and position of baffles are all in a definite geometrical ratio with the impeller diameter, then the power input to the agitator can be expressed as a function of the following variables:

Diameter of the impeller	D
Rotational speed of the impeller	N
Liquid density	ρ
Liquid viscosity	μ
Acceleration due to gravity	g

such that

$$P = f(N, D, \rho, \mu, g)$$

Dimensional analysis then gives

$$\frac{P}{D^5 N^3 \rho} = c \left(\frac{D^2 N \rho}{\mu} \right)^a \left(\frac{D N^2}{g} \right)^b$$

where a, b, and c depend on the system and its geometry; $P/D^5 N^3 \rho$ is the dimensionless power number, N_p; $D^2 N \rho / \mu$ is the dimensionless Reynolds number, N_{Re}; $D N^2 / g$ is the dimensionless Froude number, N_{Fr}.

A number of workers have applied this equation to liquid mixing using impeller-type agitators in vertical cylindrical tanks. The Reynolds number represents the ratio of applied forces to the viscous drag forces. The Froude number represents the ratio of applied forces to gravity forces. Vortex formation is a gravitational effect and if suppressed, consideration of the Froude number is avoided. The Froude number can be neglected: (1) with baffled systems; and (2) with Reynolds numbers less than 300.

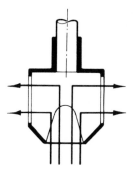

FIG. 5.6.   Dispersator impeller. (By courtesy of Premier Colloid Mills Ltd.)

For baffled systems the 'power equation' may be written as

$$\frac{P}{D^5 N^3 \rho} = c \left(\frac{D^2 N \rho}{\mu}\right)^a$$

Plots for N_p *vs.* N_{Re} on log–log coordinates, so-called 'power curves', are available in the literature for particular mixer configurations. Power curves are independent of vessel size and find use in the 'scale-up' of liquid mixers from pilot-plant studies but it must be realised that a given curve is only applicable to the geometric configuration for which it was developed.[5]

5.1.3.   MIXERS FOR HIGH VISCOSITY PASTES AND PLASTIC SOLIDS

The mixing of materials of high viscosity, a common process in the food industry, involves the use of a wide variety of equipment of different designs. The materials handled by such equipment vary widely in physical properties and in many cases changes occur in these properties during the mixing operation. A further complication arises since, in many so-called mixing operations performed in this equipment, the object may not only be the production of a uniform mix. It may also involve the subjecting of materials to a particular type

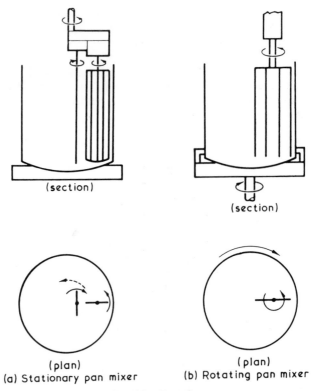

(section)

(section)

(plan)
(a) Stationary pan mixer

(plan)
(b) Rotating pan mixer

FIG. 5.7. Pan mixers.

of mechanical action so as to obtain a product with certain desirable physical characteristics (*e.g.* in dough mixing). Many mixers are designed for specific duties and few general principles apply to equipment in this category. Discussion in this section will be confined to mixers of a reasonably versatile nature having a number of applications.

One general principle which does apply to mixers for viscous and paste-like materials is that their performance depends on direct contact between the mixing elements and the materials of the mix. Thus the material must be brought to the mixing elements or the elements must travel to all parts of the mixing vessel. The local actions responsible for mixing have been described as kneading, in which the material is pressed against other adjacent material or against the vessel walls, and folding, in which fresh material is enveloped by already mixed material. The material is subjected to shear and is often stretched and torn apart by the action of the mixing elements. In general, the higher the consistency of the mixture the greater the diameter of the impeller system and the slower the speed of rotation.

5.1.3.1. Pan mixers. These are of two general types. In the stationary pan mixer (Fig. 5.7a) the mixing elements move in a planetary path, visiting all parts of the stationary mixing pan. Elements are used singly or in pairs and are usually designed to provide only a small clearance between each other and the pan walls.

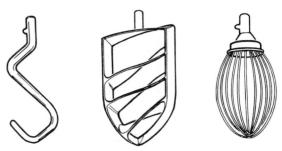

FIG. 5.8.   Some special mixing elements ('tools') used in planetary type pan mixers. (By courtesy of Wodschow & Co., Copenhagen.)

In the rotating pan type, the mixing vessel is mounted on a rotating turntable (Fig. 5.7b). The mixing elements also rotate, but in one position, and are located near the pan wall. Mixing elements vary in design depending on the duty. Simple gate type elements conforming in general shape to the contours of the pan are common. Fork-like elements also find wide use. The blades may be twisted to give the desired mixing action and induce vertical motion. Some other typical element designs are shown in Fig. 5.8. Pans are removable either by raising or tilting the elements or by lowering the pan support.

5.1.3.2. Horizontal trough mixers (kneaders, dispersers, masticators). These consist of a pair of heavy blades rotating on horizontal axes in a trough with a saddle-shaped bottom. The blades rotate towards each other at the top of their cycle and may follow tangential or interlocking paths. The material is drawn down over the point of the saddle and kneaded and sheared between the blades, the container walls and the bottom. The blades generally rotate at different speeds and may be independently driven or linked by gears. Blades vary in design but a common shape is that of the Z-blade or sigma blade element (Fig. 5.9). The vessel may be open or closed and may be evacuated. It may be jacketed for temperature control and usually tips up for emptying.

A new type of mixer,[6] the Maxta mixer, developed jointly by the UK Government's Warren Spring Laboratory and Gardners of Gloucester Ltd, has been designed to achieve short mixing times and high degrees of uniformity of components with highly viscous pastes and heavy paste-like materials. The main feature is a pair of rotors of special shape such that, when in contra-rotation, the tip of either one

'Z' blade mixing elements   Mixing vessel

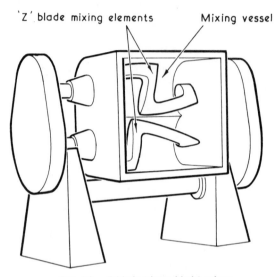

FIG. 5.9.   Z-blade (sigma-blade) mixer.

or other of the rotors is always in contact with the opposite rotor and with the walls of the mixing chamber. The mixing action is obtained by squeezing the material in the spaces between the rotors and expelling it through small clearances between them. The material to be mixed is gathered from the walls of the chamber and from the surfaces of the rotors by the rotor tips. This action also serves to clean the mixer. Intense shearing action is said to result; the flow properties of the material do not influence the mixing; dead zones cannot exist so mixing is achieved uniformly and rapidly. It is claimed that one Maxta mixer will give the same throughput as at least 4 conventional Z-blade mixers of the same capacity while in many other applications mixing time is very much reduced.

5.1.3.3. Continuous paste mixers. A wide variety of devices are used to mix and knead viscous materials continuously. A common principle is to force the material through a series of obstructions (*e.g.* perforated plates, wire meshes, grids, etc.) by means of single or twin screw conveyors. The conveyors are rotated in troughs or cylindrical barrels with only small clearances between them and the walls of the retaining vessel; sometimes stationary teeth intermesh with the screws. The material is kneaded and sheared between the screws and the walls and further acted on mechanically by being forced through the obstructions. Examples of this principle are the working devices used in butter and margarine manufacture (Section 5.2.3).

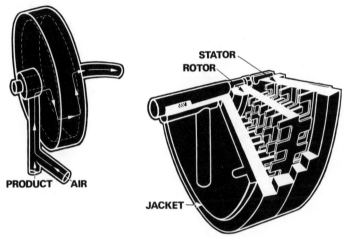

'FIG. 5.10.   Diagram of Oakes continuous mixing head as used for air injection. (By courtesy of E. T. Oakes Ltd, Macclesfield.)

A commercial mixer finding increasing use in continuous, in-line mixing and blending applications, particularly with bakery mixes, batters, etc., is the Oakes continuous mixer (Fig. 5.10). It consists of a toothed disc rotating between two toothed stators. High degrees of shear result giving high intensity mixing. A large volume, low intensity mixing machine—the Oakes continuous mixer-modifier—is also being used extensively in the UK for the continuous production of bread dough.[7]

5.1.3.4. Other devices. Many other devices are employed for mixing paste-like materials. Mixing or blending is sometimes achieved by passing the materials between rollers, or between a roller and another surface. Tumbling of the mass of material such as in butter churns (Section 5.2.3.1) is also employed. Colloid mills (Section 5.2.2.3) perform mixing operations. Other devices employ rotating knives to simultaneously reduce particle size and mix heavy materials.

5.1.3.5. Power requirements for higher viscosity liquid systems. In recent years the work of Rushton and others, on power consumption in the mixing of low viscosity liquids, has been extended to higher consistency systems. Information on power consumption for certain of the Type 2 mixers (Section 5.1.1) such as helical-ribbon agitators, helical-screw agitators and anchor agitators is becoming available but is widely scattered in the literature. This more recent work on mixing is discussed by Ho and Kwong.[8]

5.1.3.6. Static, 'in-line' mixers. A development in continuous, in-line mixing, and useful for systems having a wide range of viscosities, is the static, in-line mixer. This mixer utilises the movement of materials flowing in a pipe-line, to give effective mixing without the aid of moving parts. In one of the earliest of these units (Kenic Static Mixer) material flowing under pump pressure is split into two sections and caused to flow over specially contoured helical baffles situated along the length of the pipe. A succession of splitting and twisting movements in a series of helical elements leads to very effective mixing. The degree of mixing achieved depends only on the number of elements used. The consistency of the material is not a limiting factor. Any material that can be pumped through a pipe may be mixed in this way.[9] Several proprietary static-mixers using various geometries are now available.

5.1.4. MIXERS FOR DRY SOLIDS

In the mixing of particulate solid materials the probability of getting an orderly arrangement of particles is virtually zero.[2, 10] In practical systems the best mix attainable is that in which there is a random distribution of the ingredients. However, the degree of mixing necessary in any mixing operation will depend on the use to which the mixture is to be put and the methods of control which are applied. In the food industry it may be necessary for a mix to conform to legal requirements in regard to composition. Practical tests are often applied to the mix to ascertain whether or not it is suited to the purpose for which it was prepared, *e.g.* test baking of dry cake mixes. However, some methods of controlling the mixing operation itself may be desirable. This usually involves sampling of the batch, analysis of the samples and statistical treatment of the results. A number of 'mixing indices' based on such procedures have been suggested. Many of these are reviewed by Weidenbaum.[11]

Any form of control of mixing operations involves sampling the mixture. The method of sampling, size, number and location of samples all influence the usefulness of the control. The samples must be representative of the mixture and post-sampling handling must not alter the sample. The sample size that should be taken is related to the end use to which the product material is to be put and sample variance for a set of experimental results must be estimated at some sample size characteristic of this end use. A number of workers have used the term 'characteristic sample size' or 'scale of scrutiny' in this connection. Sampling methods and problems are discussed by Perry,[2] Weidenbaum[11] and Valentin.[12]

The dynamic behaviour of solid particles being mixed is complex. Early work in this field leant heavily on analogies with liquid mixing systems but more recent work has shown that such analogies can lead to misunderstanding.

Solids mixing is generally regarded as arising from one or more of three basic mechanisms. These are: convection, *i.e.* transfer of masses or groups of particles from one location to another; diffusion, *i.e.* the transfer of individual particles from one location to another arising from the distribution of particles over a freshly developed surface; shear, *i.e.* the setting up of slipping planes within the mass, also resulting in mixing of groups of particles. Most mixing devices employ all three mechanisms although a particular type may predominate in any single mixer. Shear mixing is sometimes considered as part of a convective mechanism.

The movement of particles during a mixing operation can also result in segregation of the particles arising from differences in their properties. Thus in any mixing operation mixing and de-mixing (or unmixing) occur concurrently and the intimacy of the resulting mix depends on the predominance of the former mechanism over the latter. The properties of the ingredients that most influence their mixing are particle size, shape and density. Other properties are also important including: surface and flow characteristics, friability, moisture content and tendency to cluster or agglomerate. The closer the ingredients are in size, shape and density, the easier the mixing operation is and the more intimate the final mix. Once the mixing and de-mixing mechanisms reach a state of equilibrium, the state of the final mix is determined and further mixing will not produce a better result.

The importance of 'segregation' on the degree of homogeneity achieved in solids mixing cannot be over-emphasised. Any tendency for segregation to occur must be recognised when selecting solids mixing equipment. Segregation in a mixture of dry solids is readily detected by use of a 'heap test'. A well-mixed sample of the solids is poured through a funnel so as to form a conical heap. Samples taken from the central core and from the outside edge of the cone should have essentially the same compositions if segregation is not to be a problem. If the two samples have significantly different compositions then segregation will occur unless the choice of mixer is carefully made. Williams[13] suggested that solids mixers can be classified into either of two groups:

(1)   Segregating mixers—having a mechanism mainly diffusive in character. Non-impeller type mixers are normally of this type.
(2)   Less-segregating mixers—having mainly convective mixing mechanisms. These are typically impeller mixers in which screws, blades, ploughs, etc., sweep groups of particles throughout the mixing zone.

It is now accepted that the efficiency of a mixing process must be related to both the flow properties of the components—the physical properties influencing 'flowability'—and to the design of the mixer.[14]

5.1.4.1. Tumbler mixers. These operate by tumbling the mass of solids inside a revolving vessel. These vessels take various forms and some typical examples are shown in Fig. 5.11. Such mixers may be

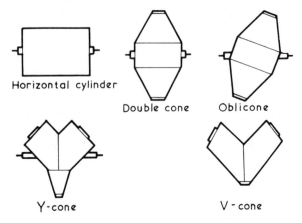

FIG. 5.11.   Some typical tumbler mixer shapes.

fitted with baffles or stays to improve their performance and some have separately driven internal rotating devices to help break up agglomerates. The shells rotate at speeds up to 100 rev/min and their working capacity is normally 50–60% of the total. They are constructed from a wide variety of materials, including stainless steel, and are fitted with ports or valves for filling and emptying. Tumbler mixers are best suited to the gentle blending of powders with similar physical characteristics. Segregation can be a problem if particles vary, particularly in size and shape.

5.1.4.2. Horizontal trough mixers. These consist of semi-cylindrical horizontal vessels in which one or more rotating devices are located. For simple operations single or twin screw conveyors are adequate and one passage through such a system may suffice. For more demanding duties a ribbon mixer (Fig. 5.12) may be used. In a

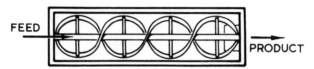

FIG. 5.12.   Schematic drawing of open ribbon mixer (plan view).

typical design of ribbon mixer, two counteracting ribbons are mounted on the same shaft. One moves the solids slowly in one direction while the other moves it quickly in the opposite direction. There is a resultant movement of solids in one direction and so the system can be used as a continuous mixer. Other types of ribbon mixers work on a batch system. Troughs may be open or closed (*e.g.* for use under pressure or vacuum or to minimise dust hazard) and may be jacketed for temperature control. Due to the small clearance between ribbon and trough wall, particle damage can occur and power consumption is high. Segregation can arise from the rolling motion but is generally not a serious problem.

The mechanism in this type of mixer is mainly convective, groups of particles being carried from one region to another by the ribbon-blades. This 'less-segregating' mixer is therefore used with materials that are likely to segregate during mixing.

5.1.4.3. Vertical screw mixers. A rotating vertical screw located in a cylindrical or cone-shaped vessel is another device used for mixing solids. The screw may be fixed centrally in the vessel (Fig. 5.13a) or it may rotate or orbit around the central axis of the vessel near the wall (Fig. 5.13b). The latter arrangement is more effective and stagnant layers near the wall are eliminated. Vertical screw mixers are quick and quite efficient and particularly useful for mixing small quantities of additives into large masses of material. Again a convective mechanism predominates so this type of unit will handle materials prone to segregation.

5.1.4.4. Fluidised-bed mixers. Fluidised beds (*see* Section 13.3.1.6 and Appendix I.2) may be used for mixing solids and are quite effective for particles with similar settling characteristics. Also, of course, the solid particles must have good fluidising characteristics. In addition to the fluidising air, high pressure jets of air causing spouting of the bed are said to improve the mixing.[10]

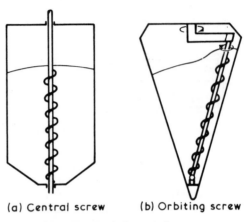

(a) Central screw   (b) Orbiting screw

FIG. 5.13.   Vertical screw mixers.

5.1.4.5. Other methods. Many other forms of mixer are used for solids blending. Heavy paddle mixers, pan mixers and Z-blade mixers have found some application in this field. Injecting additives into pneumatic lines carrying solid particles can sometimes be effective. Other devices employ centrifugal action or air jets to perform mixing operations.

5.1.5. APPLICATIONS FOR MIXING EQUIPMENT IN THE FOOD INDUSTRY

5.1.5.1. Low viscosity fluids. Examples of applications for impeller agitators include: blending of oils in the manufacture of margarine and cooking fats; diluting concentrated solutions; manufacturing fruit squashes; preparing liquid sugar mixtures for sweet manufacture; preparing brines and syrups; reconstituting dried products, *e.g.* milk powder; dissolving soluble dyes.

5.1.5.2. High viscosity liquids and pastes. Examples of applications for pan mixers, Z-blade mixers and other similar equipment include:

dough and batter mixing in bread, cake and biscuit manufacture; preparation of meat and fish pastes; manufacture of chocolate products; blending of margarines, cooking fats and butter; whipping dairy and artificial creams; preparing cheese spreads and blending cheeses.

5.1.5.3. Dry solids. Applications for tumbler, ribbon and screw mixers include: blending of grains prior to milling; blending of flours and incorporation of additives to flours; preparation of custard powders, cake mixes and other such small goods; preparation of dry soup mixes; incorporation of additives in dried products (*e.g.* baby foods).[14]

5.1.5.4. Unloading and handling of mixtures of solids. Pouring, shaking and vibrating a mixture of solid particles all encourage segregation if ingredients have significantly different particle sizes or densities. A well-mixed mixture can easily be destroyed by careless post-mixing handling. Dumping the mixture from a mixer outlet on unloading is a major cause of segregation, being in effect a large-scale heap test.

5.2. EMULSIFICATION

5.2.1. INTRODUCTION AND THEORY

Emulsification may be defined as that operation in which two normally immiscible liquids are intimately mixed, one liquid (the discontinuous, dispersed or internal phase) becoming dispersed in the form of small droplets or globules in the other (continuous, dispersing or external phase).

In most emulsions the two liquids involved are water and oil. Pure water and pure oil are seldom involved, however. The water phase may consist of solutions of salts, sugars or other organic and colloidal materials (hydrophilic materials). The oil phase may consist of oils, hydrocarbons, waxes, resins and other substances which behave like oil (hydrophobic materials). In order to form a stable emulsion a third substance, known as an emulsifying agent, needs to be included. The functions and mode of operation of this third substance will be discussed later (Section 5.2.1.2).

When oil and water are mixed, two types of emulsion are possible. The oil may become the dispersed phase, giving an oil-in-water (o/w) emulsion. Alternatively the water may become the dispersed phase, producing a water-in-oil (w/o) emulsion (Fig. 5.14). The emulsion formed tends to exhibit most of the properties of the liquid that forms the external phase. An oil-in-water emulsion may be diluted with water, coloured with water soluble dyes and exhibit electrical conductivity corresponding to that of the aqueous phase. On the other hand a water-in-oil emulsion can only be successfully diluted with oil, coloured by oil soluble dyes and has a low electrical

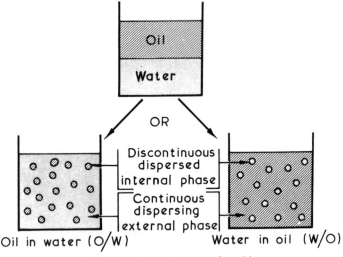

FIG. 5.14. Alternative types of emulsion.

conductivity. Thus two emulsions of similar composition can have quite different characteristics depending on whether the oil or water is the external phase. The factors which influence the type of emulsion formed when oil and water are mixed include: the type of emulsifying agent used; the relative proportions of the phases; the method of preparation of the emulsion.

5.2.1.1. Interfacial tension. The interface between two immiscible liquids is a seat of free energy arising from an imbalance in the cohesive forces of the two liquids (interfacial tension). This energy causes the interface to contract to form the smallest possible interfacial area. In an emulsion the internal phase always tends to form spherical droplets representing the smallest interfacial area per unit volume of liquid. Further these droplets tend to coalesce to form larger ones, again reducing the interfacial area. In a crude emulsion this can proceed until the phases again completely separate.

On the other hand the formation of an emulsion involves the creation of a large number of new interfaces, contrary to the tendency to contract arising from interfacial tension. The higher the interfacial tension the more difficult it is to form an emulsion and the less stable the emulsion is likely to be. It is generally necessary to reduce the interfacial tension to form a stable emulsion. One important way of achieving this is by the use of emulsifying agents.

5.2.1.2. Emulsifying agents. These perform two functions in emulsification: they reduce the interfacial tension between the liquids to be emulsified and protect the emulsion formed by preventing the coalescence of the droplets of the internal phase. The substances used as emulsifying agents are numerous and varied and include: naturally occurring materials such as proteins, phospholipids and sterols; a wide range of synthetic materials such as esters of glycerol, propylene glycol, sorbitan esters of fatty acids, cellulose ethers, carboxymethyl cellulose and many others; finely divided solids such as bentonite and carbon black.

Most emulsifying agents consist of substances with molecules containing both polar and non-polar groups. Consider the simple example of a soap such as sodium palmitate with the structural formula given in Fig. 5.15. The hydrocarbon portion of the molecule is the non-polar group and the $-COONa$ group is the polar group. For

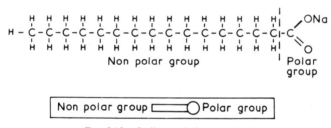

Fig. 5.15.   Sodium palmitate molecule.

convenience the non-polar group will be represented by a rectangle and the polar group by a circle. In an emulsion such an agent is positively adsorbed at the interface between the phases and thereby reduces the interfacial tension. In becoming adsorbed the molecules of the emulsifying agent orientate themselves at the interface so that the non-polar groups, which have an affinity for the oil, will point towards the oil phase, while the polar groups will point towards the aqueous phase with which they have an affinity (Fig. 5.16). Thus a layer or film of emulsifying agent is formed at the interface. This interfacial film acts as a protective coating on the droplets of the internal phase, preventing them from coalescing under the influence of interfacial tension.

The phase in which the emulsifying agent is most soluble, as a general rule, tends to become the external phase. This occurs when the polar or non-polar groups in the emulsifying agent are slightly out of balance (*i.e.* when either the hydrophilic or hydrophobic properties of the agent show a slight predominance). If the groups in the molecules of the emulsifying agent are perfectly balanced then it shows no

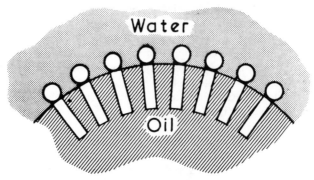

FIG. 5.16.   Orientation of emulsifying agent molecules at interface.

tendency to promote the formation of one type of emulsion more than the other. On the other hand if the polar and non-polar groups are grossly out of balance and one group dominates strongly then the substance is highly soluble in one or other of the phases. It will not remain at the interface and hence will not act as an emulsifying agent. This is a simple empirical rule and there are exceptions.[15, 16]

Finely divided solids are also adsorbed at the interface in an emulsion and can act as emulsifying agents, although not very efficiently. Here, as a general rule, solids which are most easily wetted by the water phase promote oil-in-water emulsions and *vice versa*.[15]

An emulsifying agent should, as far as possible, be specific in the type of emulsion it promotes. In the case of food emulsions, the agent should be non-toxic and many countries have regulations governing the use of emulsifying agents in foods, *e.g.* refs. 17–19. It should be relatively odourless, tasteless and colourless, and should be chemically and physically stable under the prevailing conditions of processing, handling and storage. It must be economic in price.

5.2.1.3. Methods of emulsification: general principles. In order to form an emulsion, work must be done on the system to overcome the resistance to the creation of new interfaces (arising from interfacial tension). Theoretically, this work of emulsification is equivalent to the product of the newly created surface and the interfacial tension. In addition, energy must be supplied to keep the liquids in motion and to overcome frictional resistances. As a general principle, the work is done on the liquids by subjecting them to violent agitation. The type of agitation best suited to emulsification is that which causes the large droplets of the internal phase to be subjected to shear. By this action they are deformed and broken up into smaller, more finely dispersed, droplets. Provided conditions are suitable, the protective film of emulsifying agent is adsorbed at the interface and a stable emulsion is formed.

The time required for emulsification to occur varies with the emulsion formulation and the technique employed, and must be determined by experiment.[15, 16] For each case there is an optimum time below which a relatively unstable emulsion is formed. If agitation is continued much beyond this optimum time the emulsion may again suffer as the protective film can be damaged by excessive agitation. In fact, agitation is employed for breaking emulsions (*see* Section 5.2.3.1).

5.2.1.4. Preparatory steps. The following points should be considered in formulating emulsions:

(i)   The emulsifying agent used must favour the type of emulsion required, *i.e.* o/w or w/o.

(ii) The phase volume (P/V) ratio (*i.e.* the percentage by volume of internal phase) affects the type of emulsion formed. The phase present in the larger proportion tends to become the external phase. Emulsions with P/V ratios in excess of 50 % are difficult to produce and handle.

(iii) The temperature of emulsification must be specified. Interfacial tension and viscosity fall with rise in temperature. The upper limit of temperature depends on the heat sensitiveness of the ingredients. Temperatures of up to 70 °C are common for milk products while many products containing egg yolk solids, *e.g.* mayonnaise are emulsified at much lower temperatures.

As a general rule the two phases are best prepared separately. The emulsifying agent is generally added to the external phase, but there are exceptions. Certain hydrophilic gums and colloids are best dispersed in the oil phase to minimise swelling and the formation of lumps. Where premixing of the phases is practised, the internal phase is usually added gradually to the external while the latter is being agitated. Occasionally other premixing procedures are adopted or premixing is dispensed with altogether.[15, 16]

5.2.2. EQUIPMENT: PRINCIPLES, DESIGN FEATURES AND GENERAL APPLICATIONS

5.2.2.1. Mixers. Slow speed paddle agitators (*see* Section 5.1.2.1) find only limited application for premixing or emulsification duties because of the relatively mild mixing action. Pan and Z-blade mixers (Section 5.1.3) do perform emulsification duties, *e.g.* in dough mixing as a result of shear developed in the mass of viscous material. Other types of slow speed agitators consist of rotating vessels in which the contents are tumbled, *e.g.* butter and margarine churns (Section 5.2.3.1).

High speed mixers of the turbine and propeller type are much more effective as emulsion premixers and emulsifiers, particularly for low viscosity systems. Many special types of impeller have been designed for emulsification application, *e.g.* the type shown in Fig. 5.6.

Mixers are used for premixing the ingredients in the production of salad creams, artificial creams for cake filling, etc., and margarine (*see* Section 5.2.3.2). They are also used as emulsifiers in the production of mayonnaise, processed cheeses, certain artificial creams and many other food emulsions.

5.2.2.2. Pressure homogenisers. Homogenisation is the term used to describe the operation in which the desired reduction in the size of the droplets of the internal phase is brought about by forcing the crude emulsion through a narrow opening at high velocity. A pressure homogeniser consists essentially of a homogenising valve and a high pressure pump. The valve provides an adjustable gap, of the order of a few thousandths of an inch, through which the crude emulsion is pumped at pressures up to 10 000 psi (69 MN/m^2). On entering the gap the liquids are greatly accelerated (velocities of 290 m/s are reported[23]) and the droplets of the internal phase shear against each other, are deformed and disrupted. In many valves, as the liquids leave the gap they impinge on a hard surface set normal to the direction of flow and this further promotes disruption of the unstable droplets of the internal phase. The sudden drop in pressure as the liquids leave the gap and the collapse of bubbles due to cavitation probably also contribute to the reduction in droplet size.[20].

A common type of valve design, the poppet valve, is shown in Fig. 5.17. The liquids travel between the valve and its seat causing it to lift against a strong spring. Adjustment of the tension on the spring provides the means of altering the homogenising pressure. On leaving the annular gap the liquids impinge on the breaker ring. An example of an alternative valve design is shown in Fig. 5.18. In some cases the valve is made to rotate backwards and forwards in its seat. Single service valves are also available, *e.g.* a cone of compressed wire fitting into a conical seat. The liquids are forced through the multitude of small channels in the valve body. These valves are discarded at the end of a day's run. Since the clearances between valves and seats are critical they must be carefully ground in and made of very hard materials, *e.g.* Stellite, Monel metal or stainless steels.

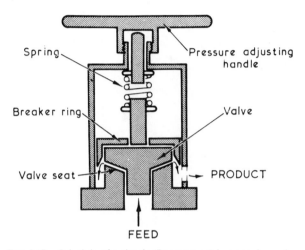

Fig. 5.17.   Principle of a simple (Poppet type) homogeniser valve.

Positive displacement pumps are necessary to supply the feed to the valve. For efficient results a steady feed rate is desirable. The most common system used is a multiple cylinder plunger pump, *e.g.* the triplex pump which has three cylinders with pistons working in sequence. In such a system the output varies up and down by about 20 %. This can be further reduced by the use of high speed short stroke plungers.

The feed is usually introduced to the homogeniser as a crude premixed emulsion. Droplet sizes of the order of $0.1–0.2\,\mu$m are common, and may be as low as $0.02\,\mu$m.

Two stage homogenisation may be necessary to obtain satisfactory dispersion in some products. In milk products, salad creams and other emulsions in which proteins act as emulsifying agents, the small droplets formed after one passage through an homogenising valve at high pressure tend to cluster and clump together. This appears to arise from a poor distribution of emulsifying agent over the newly created surfaces and the fat globules becoming entangled within solid films of the agent. To overcome this, such materials may be passed through a second homogenising valve at a lower pressure, *e.g.* 400–500 psi (2·8–3·4 MN/m²). By this means the clusters are broken up. Many modern designs of homogeniser valve are claimed to cope with such material in one stage only.

Pressure homogenisers find wide application in the food industry. These applications include the homogenisation of milk, low fat cream, evaporated milk and sterilised milk. Ice-cream mix exhibits good

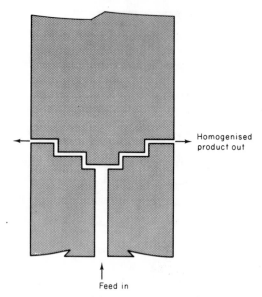

Fig. 5.18.   Homogeniser valve with stepped valve and seat.

body and texture and high over-run when homogenised. Salad creams are often subjected to high pressure homogenisation, as are artificial creams, regenerated milk and cream products, cream soups, certain sauces and many other food products.[20 – 23]

5.2.2.3. Colloid mills. In principle a colloid mill consists of a stationary surface (stator) and a rotating surface (rotor) separated by a small adjustable clearance through which the crude emulsion is passed. In passing between these surfaces the liquids are subjected to shear and turbulence resulting in the dispersion of the internal phase.

A common form of mill consists of a frustrum shaped stator and matching rotor turning on a horizontal axis. The clearance between stator and rotor is adjustable (usually within the range of 50–150 μm) by movement of the rotor horizontally. The feed is introduced under gravity at the centre of rotation, passes between rotor and stator and is

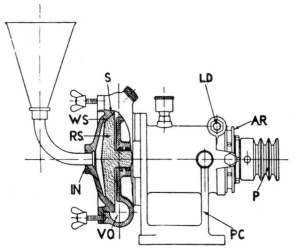

FIG 5.19. High-speed colloid mill. IN, inlet; RS, rotor; S, stator; WS, working surfaces; VO, volute (outlet); AR, adjusting ring; LD, locking device; P, pulley; PC, pedestal casting. (By courtesy of Premier Colloid Mills Ltd.)

discharged at the periphery (Fig. 5.19). Rotor speeds range from 3000 rev/min for a 15 inch (38·1 cm) rotor to 15 000 rev/min for a $3\frac{1}{2}$ inch (8·9 cm) rotor. Such mills are best suited to handling low viscosity liquids.

For more viscous materials, mills with rotors turning on vertical axes (often known as paste mills) are more generally employed (Fig. 5.20). Speeds usually range from 3000 rev/min for a 10-inch (25·4 cm) rotor to 10 000 rev/min for a $2\frac{1}{2}$-inch (6·4 cm) rotor. Such mills permit easier discharge of product and cleaning.

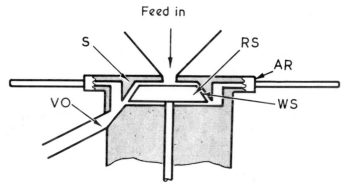

FIG. 5.20. Top-feed 'paste' colloid mill (diagrammatic). RS, rotor; S, stator; WS, working surfaces; VO, volute (outlet); AR, adjusting ring.

Stators and rotors generally have smooth stainless steel surfaces, but carborundum surfaces are also used. The latter are designed primarily for grinding solid materials but in some cases they give improved emulsification. Mills may be jacketed for temperature control. Such mills can produce fairly fine emulsions with internal phase droplet diameters of the order of 1–2 μm. One disadvantage is the incorporation of air into the product. This can result in poor performance of the mill and troublesome foaming.

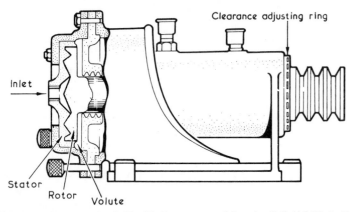

FIG. 5.21.   Corrugated colloid mill. (By courtesy of Premier Colloid Mills Ltd.)

Some mills are designed with corrugated rotors and stators (Fig. 5.21). By correct design of such corrugations a progressive emulsification is obtained—the product may be discharged under pressure, up to 100 psi (690 kN/m²), and aeration of the products is minimised.

Many other designs of mill are available incorporating different shaped rotors and stators. In some designs an impeller at the feed inlet induces flow of liquid countercurrent to the direction of the centrifugal effect of the rotor. This can have advantages for low viscosity liquids.

Colloid mills are generally more effective than pressure homogenisers for handling high viscosity products (greater than 1·0 N s/m²). Homogenisers are more effective for very low viscosity materials (less than 0·2 N s/m²). In the intermediate range of viscosities both systems are useful but the homogeniser generally tends to produce a smaller droplet size.[16, 23]

Colloid mills are used in the production of salad creams, mayonnaise, artificial creams and many other food emulsions. Paste mills are also applied to a wide variety of size reduction duties in the food industry including the production of meat and fish pastes and fruit purees.

5.2.2.4. Ultrasonic emulsification devices.

The use of ultrasonic waves, *i.e.* sound waves having frequencies higher than those the human ear can detect (about 16 kHz) provides another means of dispersing one immiscible liquid in another to form an emulsion. In a liquid irradiated with high energy ultrasonic waves each small region is alternately under tension and compression. During the negative half of the pressure cycle, when the liquid is under tension, any bubbles present in the liquid will expand. During the positive half of the cycle they will contract. Where the pressure amplitude is high and the bubbles are small the bubbles collapse violently during compression. This phenomenon is known as cavitation and it can result in the release of a relatively substantial amount of energy. Cavitation can also occur in gas-free liquids, but the presence of dissolved gases and/or gas bubbles facilitates this phenomenon. The threshold intensity to produce cavitation increases with frequency (above about 10 kHz for water). Low frequency ultrasonic waves are best suited to duties where cavitation is desirable.

In a system consisting of two immiscible liquids, if cavitation occurs at the interface between the liquids, one phase will become dispersed in the other. Thus if the internal phase is added to the external phase while the latter is subjected to ultrasonic irradiation an emulsion can be formed.

There are three commonly applied methods of generating ultrasonic waves, namely: mechanical systems; systems employing magnetostrictive oscillators and piezoelectric crystal oscillators. The latter two methods are not generally applied to emulsification duties, except in cleaning where emulsification plays a part. Mechanical

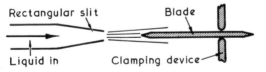

FIG. 5.22.   Principle of mechanical (wedge resonator) ultrasonic generator.

generators are finding increasing use in the food industry for emulsification applications.

The most common form of mechanical ultrasonic generator used for food emulsification is the wedge resonator. The principle of this type of generator is shown in Fig. 5.22. A blade with wedge shaped edges is positioned in front of a nozzle. Liquid is pumped through the nozzle and the jet emerging therefrom impinges on the leading edge of the blade and sets it vibrating. The blade is normally clamped at one or more nodal points and resonates at its natural frequency, imparting waves of ultrasonic frequency to the liquid. The intensity is not very great but is sufficient, in the proximity of the blade, to produce cavitation in the liquids and thus bring about emulsification.

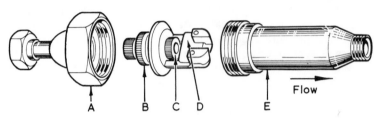

FIG. 5.23.   Ultrasonic homogeniser element. A, base; B, adjustable jet body; C, jet insert; D, vibrating blade; E, resonant bell. (By courtesy of Ultrasonics Ltd.)

Liquids are normally supplied to the nozzles by means of gear pumps at pressures of the order of 50–200 psi (345–1379 kN/m^2). The frequency of vibration is usually in the range 18–30 kHz and the disperse phase droplet size of the order of 1 to 2 μm. A typical industrial ultrasonic homogeniser element is shown in Fig. 5.23.

The many applications for ultrasonic homogenisers in the food industry include: the manufacture of salad creams, ice-cream mixes, cream soups, essential oil emulsions, peanut butters, couverture chocolate, artificial creams and baby foods. Units are also available for dispersing solids, *e.g.* reconstituting dried milk powder, and other duties include producing homogeneous fruit and vegetable purees, tomato juices and many other similar tasks.[16, 24, 25]

5.2.3. APPLICATIONS OF EMULSIFICATION IN THE FOOD INDUSTRY

5.2.3.1. Buttermaking. This is a unique example of emulsion technology. The raw material is milk, an oil-in-water emulsion. The final product, butter, is usually classed as a water-in-oil emulsion. Thus an inversion of the phases occurs during buttermaking. The changes in the emulsion structure during buttermaking are summarised in Fig. 5.24.

Batch churning methods are still very widely used. In a typical batch buttermaking operation, using fresh cream, the pasteurised milk is separated by centrifugation (Chapter 7) to produce cream containing 35–40% fat. This cream is rapidly chilled and held at a low

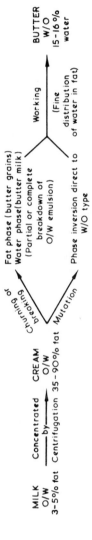

Fig. 5.24. Changes in emulsion structure during buttermaking.

temperature for a predetermined time (ageing). Chilling and ageing are important steps in controlling the solid: liquid fat ratio and hence the texture of the final product. Following ageing, the cream is subjected to churning and working. These two operations are essential steps in buttermaking. Churning involves agitation of the cream to bring about a partial breakdown of the oil-in-water emulsion. During agitation in a churn, air is incorporated and a foam produced. The fat globules in the cream accumulate at the air–plasma interface where they release a certain proportion of their liquid fat in non-globular form. Some of this free fat acts as a cement causing globules of fat which come into contact to bind together. As the foam bubbles form, burst and reform, more and more globules come together producing clusters or clumps of increasing size. Churning is continued until these clumps reach a predetermined size, clearly visible through inspection windows in the churn. After churning, the aqueous phase (buttermilk) is removed and the butter grains may be washed free of buttermilk with chilled water. Salt is added as required and the working of the butter commenced. This involves slow speed agitation of the mass of butter grains subjecting them to a kneading and folding action. The purposes of working are (a) to rupture more fat globules and produce more free fat, (b) to disperse the remaining water through the bulk of the fat in the form of fine uniform droplets and (c) to disperse the salt. Following working the butter is chilled and held in cool or frozen storage as required.[26]

The final product appears as a homogeneous mass but its detailed structure is anything but uniform. Basically it consists of a continuous phase of free fat in liquid form containing crystals of free fat, globular fat which survived the churning and working, curd granules, gas bubbles and water droplets.[27] A complete phase reversal does not occur, but the product is generally regarded as a water-in-oil emulsion. It is not a theoretically ideal model of an emulsion and its stability is due mainly to the semi-solid nature of the fat phase rather than any absorbed layer of emulsifying agent.

Most modern churns are equipped to perform both churning and working operations. Many churns of wooden construction are still used. A typical wooden churn consists of a cylindrical barrel rotating about an horizontal axis (Fig. 5.25). Flights or baffles may be fitted internally to improve agitation. The barrel is rotated at a range of speeds, the higher speeds being used for churning and the lower speeds for working. Some churns are fitted with ribbed rollers through which the butter grains pass during working. Metal churns, usually constructed of stainless steel, are also widely used. They are usually of the rollerless type and some typical shapes are shown in Fig. 5.26. In modern metal churns working may be carried out under vacuum.

'*Continuous*' *buttermaking techniques* are conveniently classified into groups as follows:

(a) Methods in which cream containing 35–40 % fat is subjected to high speed churning and continuous working. Churning is normally achieved by high speed beaters and working by means of screws which knead the mass of butter grains and force them through perforated

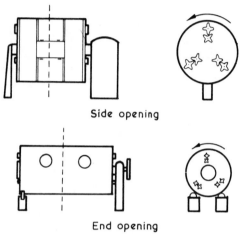

Side opening

End opening

FIG. 5.25: Typical wooden churn shapes.

plates to produce a continuous ribbon of butter. The general principles of one such machine are shown in Fig. 5.27.

(b) Methods in which a concentrated cream (o/w emulsion), containing about 80 % fat is prepared by reseparation and then subjected to cooling and mechanical treatment which results in an inversion of the phases to produce butter continuously. The phase inversion is carried out in a variety of equipment all of which involve agitating the concentrated cream in a jacketed system to bring about simultaneous cooling and phase inversion.

(c) Methods in which a highly concentrated cream is produced (o/w emulsion), the emulsion structure broken either before and during, or after, reseparation and a w/o emulsion formed from the separated phases. The emulsion is broken either in the separator or by passing the concentrated cream through an homogenising valve. Formation of the final w/o emulsion is achieved in some form of scraped surface heat exchanger which provides agitation and cooling simultaneously.[20, 22, 28]

5.2.3.2. Margarine. This is basically a w/o emulsion made up of a blend of fats and oils in milk or water with emulsifying agents and other additives.

In the batch methods of manufacture emulsification is usually brought about in churns either of the butter type (Fig. 5.25) or consisting of paddle agitators in a jacketed vessel. After churning, the margarine is chilled, tempered and then worked in a variety of devices

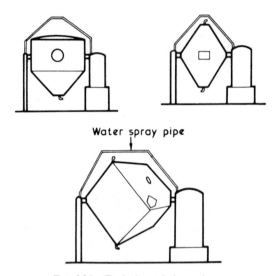

Water spray pipe

FIG. 5.26. Typical metal churn shapes.

designed to knead and fold the viscous emulsion to the desired consistency.

In the votator process for the manufacture of margarine on a continuous basis, the premixed ingredients are pumped through a series of scraped surface heat exchangers (Fig. 9.9) where simultaneous emulsification and cooling occurs. It then passes through a holding unit where the desired final texture is obtained.[29]

5.2.3.3. Milk and its products. These provide further examples of emulsion technology. Milk is an oil-in-water emulsion containing 3–5 % fat in the form of globules ranging in size from $< 1\,\mu$m to $> 18\,\mu$m (diameters). Unhomogenised milk, on standing, develops a cream layer due to reversible instability in the emulsion. This can be prevented by two-stage, pressure homogenisation which reduces the fat globule size to the order of 1–$2\,\mu$m. Homogenised milk is also said to be more digestible and have a smoother appearance than unhomogenised milk. Milk, evaporated milk and cream, which is to be sterilised, is also homogenised to improve stability and texture. Ice cream mix is an oil-in-water emulsion usually containing 10–12 % fat. The pasteurised mix is subjected to two-stage homogenisation before freezing. This influences the texture of the product and prevents

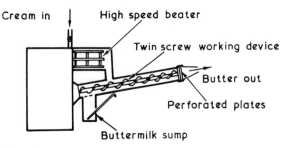

FIG. 5.27. General principle of accelerated churning and working device (Fritz principle).

separation during freezing and storage. As alternatives to pressure homogenisation, colloid mills and ultrasonic whistles have also been used to increase the stability of milk and milk products.[22, 30, 31]

5.2.3.4. Salad cream and mayonnaise.
These are both oil-in-water emulsions. The former usually contains 30–40 % oil and the emulsion is effected by pressure homogenisation. Mayonnaise usually contains more than 70 % oil and, because of the unstable nature of a system with such a high P/V ratio, it is usually prepared by careful mixing at low temperature.[30, 31]

5.2.3.5. Sausage meats and meat pastes.
These are examples of meat products in which emulsification of the fat is important both to the texture of the product and its behaviour on cooking. Satisfactory emulsification is achieved by the correct use of mincers, bowl choppers and other specialised equipment.[30, 32]

5.2.3.6. Cake and bread products.
These are also influenced by the degree of emulsification of the fat in their formulation. Inadequate emulsification can result in a poor crumb structure and cakes and loaves of unsatisfactory shape and volume. Specialised mixing equipment is used to attain the desired degree of emulsification.[30, 33]

REFERENCES

1. McCabe, W. L., and Smith, J. C., 'Unit Operations of Chemical Engineering', 2nd ed. (McGraw-Hill: 1967).
2. Perry, J. H. (Ed.), 'Chemical Engineers Handbook', 5th ed. (McGraw-Hill: 1973).
3. Engineering Equipment Users Association, 'Agitator Selection and Design'. Handbook No. 9 (Revised). (Constable & Co., Ltd: 1963.)
4. Rushton, J. H., Costich, E. W., and Everett, H. J., Chem. Eng. Progr., **46,** 395 (1950) and **46,** 467 (1950).
5. Holland, F. A., and Chapman, F. S., 'Liquid Mixing and Processing in Stirred Tanks'. (Reinhold: 1966.)
6. Cheng, D. C. H., and Schofield, C., 'A Scale-Up Procedure for a New Mixer for Paste-Like Materials'. Trans. Instn Chem. Engrs, **50**(1), 6–11 (1972).
7. Reid, J. G., 'Developments in Continuous Mixing and Blending in Bakeries'. Fd Mf., **45**(2), 36 (1970).
8. Ho, F. C., and Kwong, A., 'A Guide to Designing Special Agitators'. Chem. Engng, **80**(14), 95–104 (1973).
9. Westmore, L. E., 'Mixer With No Moving Parts'. Process Engng, 89–90, September 11th (1970).
10. Skidmore, J. A. H., 'Modern Practice in Dry Solids Mixing in Industry'. Fd Technol. Aust., **18**(10), 20–25 (1966).
11. Weidenbaum, S. S., 'Mixing of Solids', *in* Advances in Chemical Engineering, Vol. II, 211–324 (Academic Press: 1968).
12. Valentin, F. H. H., 'The Mixing of Powders and Pastes: Some Basic Concepts'. The Chemical Engineer, **208**(5), 99–104 (1967).
13. Williams, J. C., 'The Mixing of Dry Powders'. Powder Tech., **2**(1), 13–20 (1968).
14. Miles, J. E. P., and Schofield, C., 'Some Suggestions for the Selection of Solid–Solid Mixers'. Process Engng, 77–78, September (1968).
15. Sutheim, G. M., 'Introduction to Emulsions'. (Chapman and Hall: 1947), 2nd printing.
16. Sumner, C. G., 'Clayton's—The Theory of Emulsions and their Technical Treatment'. 5th ed. (J. & A. Churchill: 1954).
17. The Emulsifiers and Stabilisers in Food Regulations, 1962. No. 720 (HM Stationery Office: 1962).
18. The Milk and Dairies (Emulsifiers and Stabilisers) Regulations, 1962, No. 721 (HM Stationery Office: 1962).
19. Food Standards Committee Report on Emulsifying and Stabilising Agents (HM Stationery Office: 1956).
20. Farrall, A. W., 'Engineering for Dairy and Food Products'. (John Wiley & Sons Inc.: 1963.)
21. Clarke, R. J., 'Process Engineering in the Food Industries'. (Heywood & Co.: 1957.)
22. Davis, J. G., 'A Dictionary of Dairying', 2nd ed. (Leonard Hill: 1955).
23. Rees, L. H., 'What to Know about Homogenizers'. Fd Engng, **39**(8), 69–71 (1967).
24. Blitz, J., 'Fundamentals of Ultrasonics'. (Butterworths: 1963.)
25. Smith, J. S., 'Ultrasonics in Food Manufacture'. Fd Mf., **33**(9), 358–361, 378 (1958).
26. King, N., 'The Theory of Churning'. Dairy Sci. Abstr., **15**(8), 590–606 (1953).
27. King, N., 'The Physical Structure of Butter', Dairy Sci. Abstr., **26**(4), 151–162 (1964).
28. King, N., 'Scientific Aspects of Continuous Buttermaking'. Dairy Sci. Abstr., **14**(4), 225–246 (1952).

29. Andersen, A. J. C., and Williams, P. N., 'Margarine', 2nd ed. (Pergamon Press: 1965).
30. Brennan, J. G., 'Emulsions in Food Technology'. Process Biochem., **5**(7), 33–37 (1970).
31. Brennan, J. G., 'Emulsification, Mechanical Procedures', *in* Johnson, A. H. and Peterson, M. S. (Eds), Encyclopedia of Food Technology (AVI: 1974).
32. Saffle, R. L., 'Meat Emulsions', in Advances in Food Research, Vol. 16 (Academic Press: 1968).
33. Knightly, W. H., 'The Use of Emulsifiers in Bakery Foods'. Proc. 45th Ann. Meeting Am. Soc. Bakery Engrs (1969).

CHAPTER 6

FILTRATION AND MEMBRANE SEPARATION

6.1. FILTRATION THEORY

6.1.1. INTRODUCTION

Solid–liquid filtration, hereinafter called filtration, may be defined as that unit operation in which the insoluble solid component of a solid–liquid suspension is separated from the liquid component by passing the latter through a porous membrane or septum which retains the solid particles on its upstream surface, or within its structure, or both. The solid–liquid suspension is known as the feed slurry or prefilt, the liquid component that passes through the membrane is called the filtrate and the membrane itself is referred to as the filter medium. The separated solids are known as the filter cake, once they form a detectable layer covering the upstream surface of the medium. In practice, in order to obtain adequate recovery of the filtrate and/or a cake of adequate purity, the cake needs to be washed or blown free of filtrate once filtration ceases. In some operations air drying of the cake is also desirable. The equipment in which filtration, washing and drying is carried out, known as the filter, must provide a support for the filter medium, a space for the accumulation of the solids, channels for the introduction of the feed slurry, wash liquid, steam and/or air and for the removal of the filtrate, washings and exhaust air or steam. In addition to the filter itself, tanks must be provided for the feed slurry, filtrate and washings. A means of inducing the flow of filtrate through the filter and medium must also be provided.

The flow of filtrate may be brought about by means of gravity alone, by the application of a pressure greater than atmospheric upstream of the medium (pressure filtration), by applying a vacuum downstream of the medium (vacuum filtration) or by means of centrifugal force (centrifugal filtration). Filtration under the influence of gravity alone is limited in application to slurries containing very free-draining solids or with very low solids contents. It has very limited use in the food industry but is applied to water and sewage treatment. Such applications are treated in Chapter 18. Centrifugal filtration is dealt with in Chapter 7. Discussion in this chapter will be confined to pressure and vacuum filtration.

The applications for filtration in the food industry may be considered to fall into three categories. Category one embraces all those applications wherein slurries containing appreciable amounts of insoluble solids, *i.e.* more than one or two percent by weight, are separated into their solid and liquid components. Either the liquid or solid component, or both, may be valuable. In such operations a cake is formed on the upstream surface of the medium and the process is known as cake filtration. The second category is termed clarification and involves removing small quantities of insoluble solid from a valuable liquid. Here the object usually is to produce a clear liquid and the solids are generally unwanted. In such filtrations a cake may build up on the medium or alternatively, where the amount of solids is very small, they may become enmeshed within the structure of the medium. The third category, often referred to as microfiltration, involves the removal of very fine particles, of the order of 1 μm or less, and is generally directed at removing microorganisms from liquid foods.

6.1.2. GENERAL THEORY

The following brief treatment of the theory of filtration is applicable only to those cases where cake build-up occurs. Some of the more fundamental treatments of filtration theory are reviewed by Dickey.[1]

In the initial stages of filtration the first particles of solid to encounter the filter medium become enmeshed in it, reducing its open surface area and increasing the resistance it offers to the flow of filtrate. As filtration proceeds a layer of solids builds up on the upstream face of the medium and this layer, or cake, increases in thickness with time. Once formed, this cake in fact becomes the primary filtering medium. Filtrate passing through a filter encounters three types of resistance, namely (a) that offered by the channels and ports of the filter itself, (b) that offered by the filter medium, and (c) that offered by the filter cake. The total pressure drop across the filter is equivalent to the sum of the pressure drops resulting from these three resistances. Usually the pressure drop through the channels and ports of the filter itself is neglected in calculations.

If $-\Delta p$ is the total pressure drop across the filter and $-\Delta p_c$ and $-\Delta p_m$ the pressure drops across the cake and medium respectively then

$$-\Delta p = -\Delta p_c - \Delta p_m \qquad (6.1)$$

6.1.3. FILTER CAKE RESISTANCE

The pressure drop across the filter cake may be related to the flow rate of filtrate by the expression[2]

$$-\Delta p_c = \frac{\alpha \eta w V}{A^2}\left(\frac{\mathrm{d}V}{\mathrm{d}t}\right) \tag{6.2}$$

where $-\Delta p_c$ = pressure drop across the cake, η = viscosity of filtrate, w = mass of solids deposited on the medium per unit volume of filtrate, V = volume of filtrate delivered in time t, A = filter area normal to the direction of flow of filtrate, α = specific resistance of the cake.

α physically represents the pressure drop necessary to give unit superficial velocity (*see* Appendix I.1) of filtrate of unit viscosity through a cake containing unit mass of solid per unit filter area. α is related to the properties of the cake by

$$\alpha = \frac{k(1 - X)S_0^2}{X^3 \rho_s} \tag{6.3}$$

where X = porosity of the cake, *i.e.* the fraction of the total volume that is void; S_0 = specific surface area of the solid particles in the cake; ρ_s = density of the solids; k = constant (5 for random packed particles of definite size and shape).

In a cake composed of rigid non-deformable solid particles α is independent of $-\Delta p_c$ and does not vary throughout the depth of the cake. Such a cake is known as *incompressible*.

Many slurries contain non-rigid, deformable solid particles or agglomerates of particles. The resistance to flow in cakes, formed from such solids, depends on the pressure drop and also varies throughout the depth of the cake, being highest near the filter medium. Such cakes are called *compressible*. Since α varies throughout the depth of a compressible cake, an average value for specific resistance for the entire cake must be used in equation (6.2). This average specific resistance must be measured experimentally for each slurry. To apply equation (6.2) at different pressures the relationship between the average specific resistance and $-\Delta p_c$ must be determined experimentally.

6.1.4. FILTER MEDIUM RESISTANCE

By analogy with equation (6.2) the filter medium resistance may be defined by the equation

$$-\Delta p_m = \frac{R_m \eta}{A}\left(\frac{\mathrm{d}V}{\mathrm{d}t}\right) \tag{6.4}$$

where $-\Delta p_m$ = pressure drop across the medium; R_m = filter medium resistance.

It is usual to assume that R_m is constant during any filtration cycle and to determine its value by experiment. When treated thus, R_m also includes the resistance to filtrate flow offered by the filter channels. From equations (6.1), (6.2) and (6.4)

$$-\Delta p = -\Delta p_c - \Delta p_m = \frac{\eta}{A}\left(\frac{\mathrm{d}V}{\mathrm{d}t}\right)\left(\frac{\alpha w V}{A} + R_m\right)$$

or

$$\frac{\mathrm{d}V}{\mathrm{d}t} = \frac{A(-\Delta p)}{\eta\left(\dfrac{\alpha w V}{A} + R_m\right)} \tag{6.5}$$

Equation (6.5) is a general expression for the rate of flow of filtrate.

6.1.5. CONSTANT PRESSURE FILTRATION

When $-\Delta p$ is maintained constant, equation (6.5) may be integrated thus:

$$\int_0^t \mathrm{d}t = \frac{\eta}{A(-\Delta p)}\left(\frac{\alpha w}{A}\int_0^V V\,\mathrm{d}V + R_m\int_0^V \mathrm{d}V\right)$$

i.e.

$$t = \frac{\eta}{(-\Delta p)}\left[\frac{\alpha w}{2}\left(\frac{V}{A}\right)^2 + R_m\left(\frac{V}{A}\right)\right] \tag{6.6}$$

Equation (6.6) is a general expression for the filtration time during constant pressure filtration.

To use equation (6.6), values of α and R_m must be determined experimentally.

Equation (6.5) may be written in the form:

$$\frac{\mathrm{d}t}{\mathrm{d}V} = KV + B \tag{6.7}$$

where

$$K = \frac{\alpha w \eta}{A^2(-\Delta p)} \tag{6.8}$$

and

$$B = \frac{R_m \eta}{A(-\Delta p)} \tag{6.9}$$

Equation (6.7) represents a straight line if $\mathrm{d}t/\mathrm{d}V$ is plotted against V.

Thus if a constant pressure filtration is carried out and values of V for various values of t recorded, a graph of dt/dV vs. V can be constructed as shown in Fig. 6.1. The slope of this line is K and the intercept on the ordinate when $V = 0$ is B. Thus values of α and R_m can be determined from equations (6.8) and (6.9).

For incompressible cakes equation (6.6) can be used directly at different pressures. For compressible cakes however the relationship between α and $-\Delta p$ needs to be determined experimentally by carrying

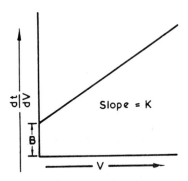

FIG. 6.1.   Plot of results from constant pressure filtration run.

out filtration runs at at least two different constant pressures. Empirical equations may be fitted to the results obtained. Two such equations have been suggested.[2]

$$\alpha = \alpha_0(-\Delta p)^s \tag{6.10}$$

and

$$\alpha = \alpha_0'[1 - \beta(-\Delta p)^{s'}] \tag{6.11}$$

where $\alpha_0, \alpha_0', s, s'$ and β are empirical constants. Equation (6.10) is used more commonly than (6.11) but the latter is applicable over a wider range of pressure drops. The average specific resistance is more correctly a function of $-\Delta p_c$ than $-\Delta p$. However, during most of a filtration cycle $-\Delta p_c$ is large compared with $-\Delta p_m$ and so little error arises in relating α to $-\Delta p$. s in equation (6.10), known as the compressibility coefficient, is zero for incompressible cakes and rises towards $1 \cdot 0$ as compressibility increases. Having determined values for α_0 and s then equations (6.10) and hence (6.6) can be used for constant pressure filtration calculations at different pressures.

6.1.6. CONSTANT RATE FILTRATION

If filtration is carried out at constant rate then

$$\frac{dV}{dt} = \text{constant} = \frac{V}{t} \tag{6.12}$$

Equation (6.5) may be written:

$$-\Delta p = \left(\frac{\eta \alpha w V}{A^2 t}\right) V + \left(\frac{\eta V R_m}{At}\right) \tag{6.13}$$

or

$$-\Delta p = K'V + B' \tag{6.14}$$

Equation (6.14) represents a straight line if $-\Delta p$ is plotted against V. The slope of the line is K' and the intercept to the $-\Delta p$ axis when $V = 0$ is B'. Thus for incompressible cakes α and R_m can again be determined by experiment and equation (6.13) used for cycle calculations.[5]

For compressible cakes the relationship between α and $-\Delta p_c$ must again be determined by experiment. If a relationship of the form shown in equation (6.10) is assumed to apply, equation (6.2) may be modified to:

$$(-\Delta p_c)^{1-s} = [-(\Delta p - \Delta p_m)]^{1-s} = \frac{\eta \alpha_0 w V}{A^2} \frac{V}{t} \tag{6.15}$$

which may be written:

$$[-(\Delta p - \Delta p_m)]^{1-s} = K''t \tag{6.16}$$

where

$$K'' = \frac{\eta \alpha_0 w}{A^2}\left(\frac{V}{t}\right)^2 \tag{6.17}$$

If it is assumed that $-\Delta p_m$ is constant throughout a constant-rate filtration then by plotting $-\Delta p$ vs. t, passing a smooth curve through the points and extrapolating the curve to the $-\Delta p$ axis, an approximate value for $-\Delta p_m$ can be obtained. If $\log t$ is then plotted against $\log[-(\Delta p - \Delta p_m)]$ and a straight line obtained, the slope of this line is $1 - s$. K'' can also be obtained from the above log–log plot or calculated from equation (6.16). α_0 may be calculated from equation (6.17). If at the first attempt the log–log plot is not a straight line then further approximations for $-\Delta p_m$ need to be made.[2]

6.1.7. WASHING THE CAKE

In most filters, cake washing is carried out by substituting wash liquid for the feed slurry when filtration is complete. Thus the wash liquid follows the same paths through the cake as the filtrate. In such an operation if the physical properties of the wash liquid, notably viscosity, are the same as the filtrate, the rate of washing will be approximately equal to the final rate of flow of filtrate. Since washing is usually carried out at constant pressure the rate of washing will remain approximately constant. This behaviour is only approximate since 'channelling' which can occur in the cake may alter flow rates.

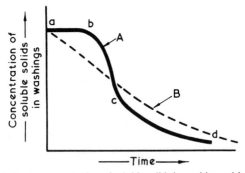

FIG. 6.2.   Variation in concentration of soluble solids in washings with time. Curve A: Displacement washing (applicable to most filters). Curve B: Thorough washing (applicable to plate-and-frame presses fitted with wash plates).

The concentration of filtrate solids in the wash liquid generally varies with time to the general pattern shown in Fig. 6.2, curve A. Under optimum conditions up to 90 % of the solubles in the cake may be removed in the initial stage a–b. Washing is continued until the soluble solids content of the washings reaches an economic limit.

In the plate-and-frame press (Section 6.2.1) fitted with wash plates, the wash liquid follows a different path to that of the filtrate. It travels through twice the cake thickness and has only half the filtering area available as compared with the filtrate. Thus the rate of flow of wash liquid is approximately a quarter of the final filtration rate. The change in soluble solids concentration in the washings is then more gradual and uniform as in Fig. 6.2, curve B.

6.1.8. APPLICATION OF THEORY

The general expressions for rate of filtration at constant pressure and rate may be used for interpreting the effects of changes in operating conditions on throughput, downtime, etc., and scaling up plant. They should always be regarded as approximate guides, however, and should be supported by practical trials where at all possible. The filtering characteristics of slurries are very sensitive to methods of preparation and handling, and where small-scale tests are used to obtain data to apply to larger-scale operations it is important to use slurries as nearly as possible identical to those which are to be filtered on the industrial equipment and to use methods of preparation and handling similar to the full-scale methods. Such precautions are particularly important when compressible cakes are encountered. Compressible cakes are common in food filtration.

6.1.9. FILTER MEDIA

The main functions of the filter medium are to promote the formation of a cake of solids and to support it once formed. The medium should offer the minimum resistance to flow consistent with the rapid formation of a filter cake. It must be strong enough to support the cake and retain its strength under the extreme conditions occurring during the operation. Its surface characteristics should be such as to facilitate cake removal. The medium must be non-toxic and chemically compatible with the material being filtered. It must not be too expensive.

Filter media may be rigid or flexible. Rigid media may be loose, such as sand and/or gravel, diatomaceous earths, or charcoal. Such loose media are seldom used alone in food applications. Fixed rigid media are also used. These include porous carbon, porcelain, fused alumina, perforated metal plates, rigid wire meshes or edge media (*see* Section 6.2.1.5). Such rigid media are available in the form of plates, discs, tubes and other shapes.

Flexible media may consist of woven fabrics of cotton, silk, wool, and jute. Many synthetic materials are finding applications, including nylon, polypropylene, polythene, polyvinylchloride and co-polymers and terylene. Glass fibre and flexible metal meshes are also used as media. Non-woven materials are also used, including cotton and wool fibres, and paper pulp. These are available in preformed pads of various shapes.

All the types of media mentioned above can be obtained with specified pore sizes to suit particular filtration applications. The only reliable method of selecting a medium for a particular duty is by practical trials. Further details of filter media are given by Dickey[1] and Perry.[3]

6.1.10. FILTER AIDS

When the solids to be filtered off are very finely divided or are of a slimy, highly compressible character the filter medium tends to block quickly and only short runs are possible. In such circumstances materials known as filter aids are often used. These usually consist of comparatively large, inert, non-compressible solid particles of different shapes. They may be applied by mixing with the feed slurry or they may be suspended in a clear liquid, often some filtrate from a previous run, which is then passed through the filter so that a precoating of the filter aid builds up on the medium. The filter aid forms a rigid lattice structure on the medium and provides numerous channels through which the filtrate can flow, thus slowing up the plugging of the medium and prolonging the filtration cycle. Sometimes a combination of precoating and premixing is used. Kieselguhr, or diatomaceous earth, is commonly used as a filter aid. Paper pulp, carbon, fuller's earth and many other materials are also used as filter aids. As with filter media, filter aids are available in a wide range of grades to suit particular applications.[1, 3]

6.2. FILTRATION EQUIPMENT—PRINCIPLES, DESIGN FEATURES AND GENERAL APPLICATIONS

6.2.1. PRESSURE FILTERS

In pressure filters a superatmospheric pressure is maintained upstream of the medium to induce the flow of filtrate through the system. This upstream pressure is achieved by pumping the feed slurry into the filter. Pressure filters may be operated at constant pressure throughout filtration or the pressure may be gradually increased so as to maintain a constant flow rate of filtrate. Various combinations of these two basic methods may also be used. Since centrifugal pumps are commonly employed, constant rate followed by constant pressure filtration is a common combination as this corresponds to the feed-discharge characteristics of such pumps. In particular, when handling compressible solids, a low initial pressure is desirable to minimise plugging of the medium. The maximum pressure used in pressure filters is usually of the order of 25–75 psig (276–621 kN/m²) but some filters operate at much higher pressures.

6.2.1.1. Vertical plate pressure filters (filter presses). A vertical drainage plate supporting a filter medium is the basic filtering element in a vertical plate press. A commonly used design is the *Plate-and-frame press*. In this type of filter grooved plates, covered on both sides with filter medium, alternate with frames in a rack (Fig. 6.3). The assembly of plates and frames can be squeezed tightly together by a screw, hydraulic or pneumatic mechanism to form a liquid-tight unit. The filter medium also acts as a gasket, preventing leakage between the plates and frames. Both plates and frames are provided with

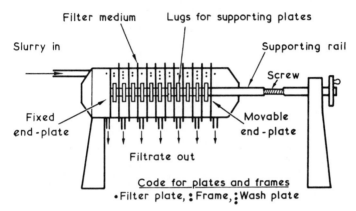

FIG. 6.3.   Schematic drawing of assembled plate-and-frame filter press.

openings at one corner and when the press is closed these openings form a channel through which the feed slurry is introduced. In addition, the hollow centre of each frame is connected by an auxiliary channel to this feed channel (Fig. 6.4). The feed slurry enters the frames and the cake builds up in the hollow centre of the frames. The filtrate passes through the medium and on to the grooved surfaces of the filter plates from where it is removed *via* an outlet channel in each plate. Filtration is continued until the flow of filtrate drops below a practical level or the pressure reaches an unacceptably high level, due to the cake packing tightly in the frames. After filtration, washing of the cake may be carried out by replacing the flow of feed slurry with wash liquid. However, more effective washing is obtained by the use of special wash plates (Fig. 6.4). These are arranged in the press so that every second plate is a wash plate. During filtration these wash plates act as filter plates. During washing the outlets from the wash plates are closed and the wash liquid introduced on to their surfaces through a special inlet channel. The flow path for both filtration and washing when wash plates are used is shown in Fig. 6.5. The cake is removed manually after opening the press.

Another common design of filter press is known as the *recessed-plate press*. In this filter the cake accumulates within recesses in the plates and no frames are used. The feed is usually introduced centrally and removed *via* an outlet on the corners of each plate (Fig. 6.6). For washing, the feed slurry is replaced by wash liquid entering through the same inlets. Many other types of vertical plate filters are available.[3] Larger presses have facilities for lifting or moving plates

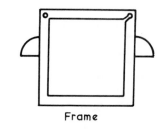

Frame

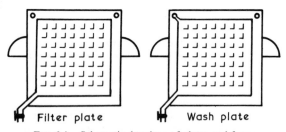

Filter plate   Wash plate

FIG. 6.4.   Schematic drawings of plates and frame.

and frames mechanically. Presses may be jacketed for temperature control.

The vertical plate filter has found very wide application in industry. It is simple in design and operation, compact, flexible and can be used to handle a wide variety of types of slurry. It is relatively cheap initially. On the other hand labour costs and filter cloth consumption are high and washing of the cake is not always efficient.

6.2.1.2. Horizontal plate filters. This type of filter consists of a number of horizontal plates, suitably designed to allow free drainage of the liquid, assembled in a vertical stack in a cylindrical pressure vessel. The filter medium covers the top surface of the plates. The feed slurry is introduced through a central duct (as in Fig. 6.7) or through a hollow annular inlet. The cake builds up on the upper surfaces of the medium and the filtrate passes through the medium on to the drainage plates and out through an annular or central outlet. After filtration,

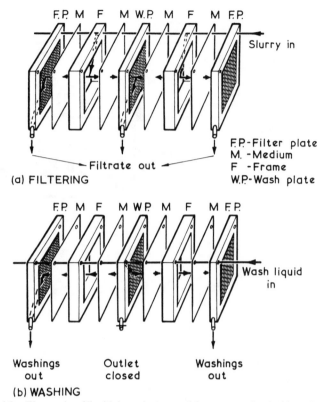

F.P. M F M W.P. M F M F.P.

Slurry in

F.P.-Filter plate
M. -Medium
F -Frame
W.P.-Wash plate

◄— Filtrate out ◄—

(a) FILTERING

F.P. M F M W.P. M F M F.P.

Wash liquid
in

Washings
out

Outlet
closed

Washings
out

(b) **WASHING**

FIG. 6.5. Flow paths of liquid through plate-and-frame press, fitted with wash plates, during (a) filtering and (b) washing.

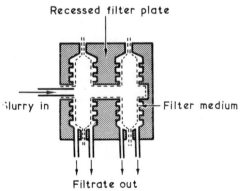

Recessed filter plate

Slurry in

Filter medium

Filtrate out

FIG. 6.6. Schematic drawing (sectional view) of a recessed-plate press.

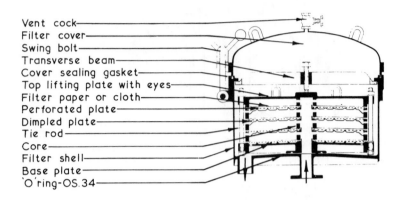

Vent cock
Filter cover
Swing bolt
Transverse beam
Cover sealing gasket
Top lifting plate with eyes
Filter paper or cloth
Perforated plate
Dimpled plate
Tie rod
Core
Filter shell
Base plate
O'ring-OS.34

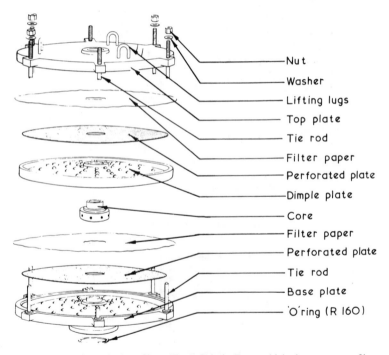

Nut
Washer
Lifting lugs
Top plate
Tie rod
Filter paper
Perforated plate
Dimple plate
Core
Filter paper
Perforated plate
Tie rod
Base plate
O'ring (R 160)

FIG. 6.7. Horizontal plate filter. (Top) Calmic E type high duty pressure filter. (Bottom) Calmic filter element assembly sequence. (By courtesy of Calmic Engineering Co. Ltd.)

the feed is replaced by wash liquid and washing carried out by displacement. Blowing of the cake with steam or air is carried out where required. For cake removal, the plates are usually lifted vertically out of the shell and the solids removed manually. Some units have mechanical devices to aid cake removal.

The horizontal plate filter is compact. The horizontal plates promote uniform cake build up. The units are readily cleaned or sterilised if required, and cake washing is effective. Simple units have relatively high labour requirements and are normally available only in relatively small sizes, *e.g.* up to 30 in (76·2 cm) diameter and up to 24 plates per unit. They are most useful for removing small quantities of solids (*e.g.* as polishing filters) or for short cycles, particularly where very clean conditions are important.

6.2.1.3. Shell-and-leaf pressure filters. These filters have a filter leaf as the basic filter element. A filter leaf consists of a wire mesh screen or grooved drainage plate over which the filter medium is stretched. The leaf may be suspended from the top or supported from the bottom or centre. The supporting member is usually hollow and forms an outlet channel for the filtrate (Fig. 6.8).

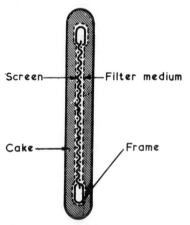

Screen — Filter medium

Cake — Frame

FIG. 6.8.   Schematic drawing of filter leaf (sectional view).

In horizontal shell-and-leaf filters the filter leaves are mounted vertically in a horizontal pressure-tight vessel. The feed slurry is introduced under pressure into the shell and the cake builds up on the outer surfaces of the leaves. The filtrate passes through the medium and drains from the inner structure of the leaves into the outlet channel provided. Leaves may be rectangular or circular in shape and

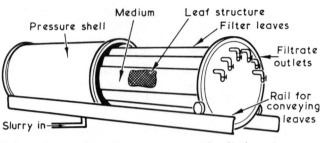

(a) Stationary leaf filter, open for cake discharge

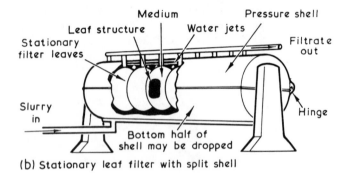

(b) Stationary leaf filter with split shell

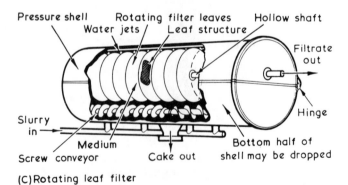

(C) Rotating leaf filter

FIG. 6.9. Schematic drawings of some common horizontal shell-and-leaf pressure filters.

may be stationary as shown in Fig. 6.9(a), (b), or rotating slowly about a horizontal axis as in Fig. 6.9(c). The rotation of the leaves at 1–2 rev/min promotes uniform cake build up. Filtration is continued until the cake thickness reaches a predetermined value, and then washing is carried out either by replacing the slurry with wash liquid or alternatively by sluicing down the cake using water jets, reslurrying, and refiltering it. Cake removal is achieved either by withdrawing the

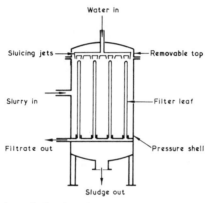

FIG. 6.10.   Schematic drawing of vertical shell-and-leaf pressure filter.

leaves from the shell and cleaning them manually (Fig. 6.9a) or by sluicing down the cake with the bottom half of the shell open (Fig. 6.9b). Some such filters can discharge dry cake continuously from the shell by means of screw conveyors (Fig. 6.9c), if the cake can be satisfactorily removed from the leaves by 'blowing back' with compressed air. Compressed air may also be employed for loosening the cake prior to sluicing down. In vertical shell-and-leaf pressure filters, rectangular leaves are mounted vertically in a vertical cylindrical pressure vessel (Fig. 6.10).

Shell-and-leaf filters are flexible and can be economic in the use of labour, especially where cake discharge from the closed shell is possible. On the other hand the cake formed is not usually as dry as in presses. Classification of solids and uneven cake build up can occur. They have a higher capital cost than plate filters. Pressures used do not normally exceed about 60 psig ($0·52$ MN/m^2), but some units can work at 250 psig ($1·85$ MN/m^2). They are best suited to long filtration runs with slurries of unchanging characteristics.

6.2.1.4. Shell-and-tube pressure filters. These filters incorporate a cylindrical tube, instead of a leaf, as the basic filter element. The tubes are usually suspended vertically from the filtrate take-aways in vertical pressure vessels. Tubes may be made of perforated metal, wire mesh, plastics or porous stone. Their features are similar to shell-and-leaf filters but they usually have smaller capacities and are almost always used with a precoating of filter aid.

6.2.1.5. Edge (pressure) filters. A stack of closely spaced rings or discs, often known as a filter pile, forms the basic feature of an edge

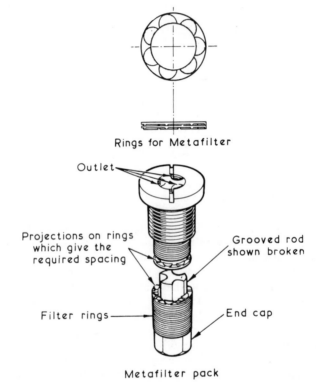

Rings for Metafilter

Outlet

Projections on rings which give the required spacing

Grooved rod shown broken

Filter rings

End cap

Metafilter pack

FIG. 6.11.   Filter pile. (Diagram reproduced by courtesy of Stella-Meta Filters Ltd.)

filter. The discs are mounted one above the other on a fluted rod and held in position between a boss and nut (Fig. 6.11). The edges of the discs are separated by gaps of the order of 0·001–0·01 in (25·4–254 μm) by means of projections on the rings. The required number of these filter piles may be fixed in a header plate and enclosed in a pressure vessel (Fig. 6.12).

In operation, a precoat of filter aid is built up at the edges of the discs. The feed is introduced under pressure into the shell and the cake builds up over the precoat. Filtrate passes through the precoat, through the spaces between the discs and out *via* the grooves in the supporting rod. Premixing of filter aid with the slurry is usually practised in addition to precoating. Cake is removed when filtration and washing are complete by back blowing and/or back flushing

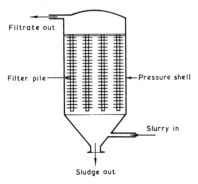

Fig. 6.12. Schematic drawing of assembled edge filter.

through the filtrate outlet and removing the sludge formed through a bottom outlet.

Edge filters are usually constructed of metal (commonly stainless steel). They are economical in labour requirements and use no filter cloth. They are most suited to the removal of small quantities of finely divided solids to produce very clear liquids.

6.2.1.6. Continuous pressure filters. Rotary drum and disc filters can be operated as continuous pressure filters. However, they are far more commonly used as continuous vacuum filters and so will be described in detail in Section 6.2.2. Cake discharge is the biggest problem. Some units employ a self-sealing screw conveyor to continuously remove the cake from the shell. Others use pressure receivers operated singly or in pairs. The latter arrangement permits intermittent discharge of the cake. They are best suited to handling large throughputs of standard slurry where pressures greater than atmospheric are advantageous (*e.g.* for volatile or hot filtrates).

6.2.2. VACUUM FILTERS

In vacuum filters a subatmospheric pressure is maintained downstream of the medium and atmospheric pressure upstream.

Because the pressure drop across the filter is limited to one atmosphere, they are not suited to batch operation. Some types of leaf filter, tube filters and edge filters are operated under vacuum but continuous vacuum filters are far more common. Because the upstream pressure is atmospheric, cake discharge, and hence continuous operation, is facilitated. Most vacuum filters are operated at constant pressure drop, except during the initial stages when the system is being evacuated.

6.2.2.1. Continuous rotary drum vacuum filters. As its name implies, this type of filter consists of a cylindrical drum rotating about a horizontal axis. In one very common design, the surface of the drum consists of a number of shallow compartments formed between dividing strips running the length of the drum (Fig. 6.13). Each compartment is connected, by one or more pipelines, to an automatic rotary valve situated centrally at one end of the drum. The drum is partly submerged in an open tank of slurry. Filter medium covers the

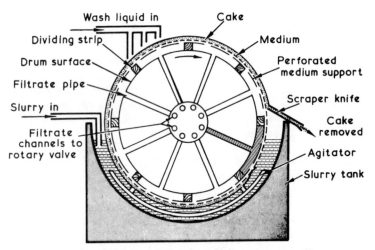

FIG. 6.13.   Schematic drawing of rotary drum vacuum filter.

entire drum surface and is supported by perforated plates, grids or wire meshes to provide drainage space between the medium and the floor of each shallow compartment. The drum rotates at speeds of the order of 0·1–2 rev/min. Consider one compartment on the drum surface, *e.g.* the shaded one shown in Fig. 6.13. As the drum rotates and this compartment becomes submerged in the slurry, a vacuum is drawn on it by means of the automatic rotary valve. Filtrate flows through the medium and out through the drain pipe from the compartment and is directed to the filtrate receiver by means of the valve. A layer of cake builds up on the outer surface of the medium. As the compartment emerges from the slurry the cake is sucked free of filtrate. As it proceeds further on its cycle the drainings from the compartment are diverted to another receiver by means of the rotary valve and wash liquid is applied to the cake by means of sprays. As the compartment passes from beneath the sprays the cake is sucked free of washings. Further on its cycle the compartment is disconnected from its vacuum source and compressed air is introduced beneath the filter medium for a short period, loosening the cake from the surface of the medium. This is again controlled by the automatic rotary valve. The cake is removed by means of a scraper knife. Then, as the compartment becomes submerged in the slurry again, vacuum is re-applied and a new cycle commences. Thus each compartment behaves as an individual filter operating in a sequence which results in the continuous delivery of filtrate and discharge of cake.

Many alternative designs of drum filter are available. Feed is normally applied by rotating the drum partly submerged in a slurry tank. As an alternative, for quick-settling solids, top-feeding may be used. In this system the slurry is fed to a distributor trough on top of the drum, whence it flows on to the medium surface. An alternative system of cake removal employs an endless belt which passes around the drum and upon which the cake builds up. At the point of discharge of the cake the belt passes over rollers to effect cake removal. In other designs, closely spaced strings (string-discharge) or coiled springs (coil filter) are used instead of a belt. In the precoat drum filter a layer of precoat material up to 3 in (7·62 cm) thick is applied to the drum before use. As the drum rotates, a thin layer of this precoat, together with the thin cake formed thereon, is removed by an advancing knife edge. The precoat filter is mainly applicable to slurries with low solids contents and where thin, highly deformable cakes are formed.

The advantages of rotary drum vacuum filters are low labour costs, large capacity for the space occupied and flexibility in cake thickness. On the other hand they are limited in use to fairly permeable cakes which discharge readily. Dry cakes are difficult to obtain and the capital cost of the equipment, including vacuum equipment, is relatively high. As with all vacuum filters they are not suited to handling very hot filtrates or volatile materials. Their best field of application is in handling large volumes of slurry of standard characteristics with reasonably free draining properties.

6.2.2.2. Rotary vacuum disc filters. Such a filter (Fig. 6.14) consists of a number of circular filter leaves mounted on a horizontal axis about which they rotate. Each disc is fitted with a cake removal device and is divided into sectors, each of which has an individual outlet to the central shaft. These outlets form a continuous channel through which the filtrate and wash flow from all sectors at the same angle. These channels terminate in a rotary valve similar to that used on drum filters. In operation each disc behaves as a drum filter, the cycle being controlled by the rotary valve.

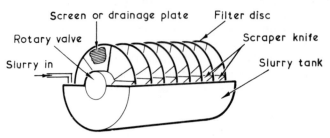

FIG. 6.14. Schematic drawing of rotary vacuum disc filter.

6.2.2.3. Other types of continuous vacuum filters. These incorporate rotating tables, endless moving belts and other forms of support for the filter medium and cake. Scroll conveyors, rollers, pulleys and devices for lifting or inverting the filter medium support are employed for discharging the cake.[1-4]

6.3. APPLICATIONS FOR FILTRATION EQUIPMENT IN THE FOOD INDUSTRY

6.3.1. GENERAL SOLID/LIQUID SEPARATION

In the extraction of sugar from sugar cane the mill juice contains much solid impurity. This is mostly removed by sedimentation but the liquid remaining is still far from pure and is then filtered. Due to the compressible nature of the solids, special steps are taken to promote flocculation of the solids prior to filtering. Rotary vacuum drum filters find wide application for this duty. At one stage in the purification of sugar extracted from beet the juice is also filtered free of solid impurities after preliminary treatment to promote sedimentation. Here again rotary drum filters, also stationary and rotating shell-and-leaf pressure filters and plate-and-frame presses, are used.

Rotary vacuum filters, often employing string discharge, are used for dewatering starch and for the filtration of gluten suspensions.

In the extraction and refining of edible oils, plate-and-frame presses, recessed plate and shell-and-leaf pressure filters have found application both for filtering the crude oil free of fragments of seeds, cell tissue, etc., and for filtering off bleaching earths after decolorising of the oils. Another application here is for removing the precipitate formed on controlled cooling of the oil, *i.e.* winterisation. Plate-and-frame presses are used in breweries for filtering mash and recovering yeast after fermentation.

6.3.2. CLARIFICATION BY FILTRATION

Vertical and horizontal plate filters, tubular filters and edge filters have all found application for clarifying food liquids including: beer, wines, vinegar, fruit juices, yeast and meat extracts, salad and table oils, brines, sugar syrups and jellies. Solids from the products are usually very fine and/or of a colloidal or slimy nature. Filter aids are almost always used in the form of precoats and/or mixed with the feed to the filter. Precoat rotary vacuum filters have also been used for fruit juice clarification.

6.3.3. REMOVAL OF MICRO-ORGANISMS BY FILTRATION

Horizontal and vertical plate filters and tubular filters are used to reduce the number of micro-organisms (yeasts and some bacteria) in wines, beers, fruit juices and yeast extracts. The success of this application depends mainly on the use of appropriate filter media and aids. Such systems can be used as a substitute for, or a supplement to, heat treatment in reducing the numbers of micro-organisms present in such products.[6-9]

6.4. MEMBRANE SEPARATION—ULTRAFILTRATION AND REVERSE OSMOSIS

6.4.1. INTRODUCTION

A number of novel methods for the separation of various solutes from solutions of liquid food-stuffs have been proposed in recent years. Of these methods, which include electrodialysis, enzyme-extraction, gel-filtration, ion-exchange, reverse osmosis and ultrafiltration, several are based on the use of membranes. At least two of these membrane separation methods—ultrafiltration and reverse osmosis—now have important commercial applications.

Ultrafiltration and reverse osmosis are both pressure-activated membrane separation techniques in which solutes of different molecular weights are separated from solution. The major difference between ultrafiltration and reverse osmosis is in the pressure required to effect separation and, in consequence, in equipment and pumping costs.

6.4.1.1. Ultrafiltration (UF). As commonly defined (Section 6.1.1), filtration is a unit operation used to separate solid particles from a fluid by passage through a porous membrane. The membrane retains the particles but permits fluid to pass. The pore size required decreases as the size of particles being separated decreases. Filters of a variety of types are available and for separating very small particles (as small as 0·1 μm) so-called 'micro filters' are used. At the sub-micron level the membrane pore size is approaching a size capable of preventing the passage of larger molecules in solution. Membranes capable of selectively preventing the passage of larger solute molecules in solution by means of filtration through micropores in a membrane structure are known as *ultrafiltration membranes*. In operation, ultrafiltration is concerned with the separation of high molecular weight large molecules from low molecular weight small molecules.

6.4.1.2. Reverse osmosis (RO). When solute molecules or ions in solution are comparable in size to those of solvent molecules, if the separation mechanism is simply one of filtration in the micropores, then similar sized species might be expected to be transported across the membrane without separation. This is not the case with certain membranes.

In an attempt to find new methods for the desalination of sea-water, Reid and Breton[10] found that solute ions did not necessarily flow across some membranes even though similar sized solvent molecules did. These workers noticed that homogeneous thin films of commercial cellulose acetates of varying degrees of acetylation were, under pressures of 5–10 MN/m^2 (50–100 atm), permeable to water molecules though, to a large extent, preventing the passage of sodium ions and chloride ions. In this early work, salt rejections of up to 99 % were obtained. Though desalination was shown to be possible, resulting water permeation rates were much too low to permit exploitation as a commercial desalination process. By preparing films of cellulose acetate from specific mixed solvents containing swelling agents, Loeb and Sourirajan[11] obtained high salt rejection rates from sodium chloride solutions but at much higher rates of permeation than those achieved by Reid and Breton. Since this development in the 1950s membranes suitable for a variety of different separation purposes have been developed.[12] In membrane separation processes

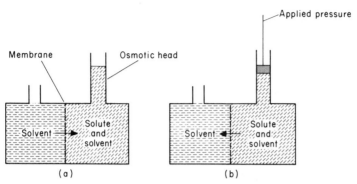

FIG. 6.15. Principle of reverse osmosis. (a) Natural osmosis. (b) Reverse osmosis.

reverse osmosis (Fig. 6.15) is concerned with the separation of different molecules of low molecular weight of a size comparable to those of water molecules.

6.4.2. ADVANTAGES OF MEMBRANE SEPARATION

Membrane separation processes take place without phase change so energy requirements are less than those of conventional concentration operations. The energy requirement for the evaporation of water, for example, is about $25\,kW/m^3$, whereas with RO the requirement is only about one tenth of this amount. Other advantages over evaporation are to be had. The risk of heat damage is avoided since no heating is needed, aroma losses due to the stripping of volatile substances on vaporisation are eliminated and large volumes of cooling water (an increasingly more expensive commodity) are no longer required. These advantages, if attainable on an industrial scale, would appear to be overwhelming.

6.4.3. OSMOTIC EFFECT IN MEMBRANE SEPARATION

When liquid flows through the tortuous micropores in a membrane, energy is expended in overcoming the resistance to flow. This energy loss manifests itself as a drop in pressure exactly as in flow through pipelines. Pressure must be applied to the liquid on the upstream side of the membrane if flow is to occur. With smaller pore sizes (tighter membranes) higher applied pressures will be required to maintain a particular flow rate. For a particular membrane, increasing the applied pressure, at least initially, results in larger *flux* values. In the case of permeable membranes a second pressure component, not experienced in conventional filtration, arises. This is osmotic pressure.

It is well known that when an ideal, semi-permeable membrane separates a solution from its pure solvent, then solvent molecules pass spontaneously across the membrane from the solvent to the solution. In general, solvent molecules pass from a region of lower concentration to a region of higher concentration. The driving force for the flow of solvent molecules is the difference in chemical potential on the two sides of the membrane. This phenomenon is called osmosis. The flow of solvent across the membrane continues until the fluid pressure developed in the concentrated solution is sufficiently high to prevent the passage of further solvent molecules (Fig. 6.15). At equilibrium this pressure is called the osmotic pressure of the solution. The osmotic pressure of a solution is a characteristic for a particular solvent–solute system and is proportional to concentration and to absolute temperature. This spontaneous flow of solvent molecules across a permeable membrane by osmosis is in the opposite direction to that required in membrane separations. In these separations the object is to promote the flow of solvent molecules from the more concentrated solution to the less concentrated thereby leaving the solution still more concentrated. Since osmotic pressure opposes the desired flow, pressures sufficient to nullify the osmotic pressure and overcome the resistance to flow in the pores of the membrane at the desired flux-rate must be applied to the upstream side. So ultrafiltration and reverse osmosis both require the application of pressure. With larger molecules in solution, *e.g.* solutes with molecular weights greater than about 500, the osmotic pressure developed is small. Separation of molecules of this molecular weight range is the province of ultrafiltration. In UF then, pressures as low as $0.1–1.0 \, MN/m^2$ (1–10 atm) are capable of maintaining acceptable permeate (liquid passing the membrane) flows. Summarising—in ultrafiltration applications 'loose' membranes are used to separate large molecules: proteins, micro-organisms, etc.; osmotic pressures are small so low pressure operation is sufficient to achieve acceptable flow rates.

With low molecular weight solutes such as simple electrolytes, in aqueous solution, where the molecular dimensions of both solute and solvent are comparable, the osmotic pressures developed are very much higher. In addition the 'tighter' membranes necessary to effect separation also offer a much greater resistance to flow. Not surprisingly then, in reverse osmosis application of considerably higher pressures of some $5–7.5 \, MN/m^2$ (50–75 atm) are required to effect separations. It must be stressed that the distinction between RO and UF is not clear-cut. It is now possible to tailor the transport properties of membranes from very tight reverse osmosis membranes to loose ultrafiltration membranes so the dividing line between the two separation techniques is not sharp.

6.4.4. MEMBRANES

Not surprisingly, the characteristics of the membrane play a key part in any particular application of RO or UF.

6.4.4.1. General operational requirements for membranes. Important requirements for a membrane suitable for food processing purposes include:

(1)   The membrane must be capable of giving the degree of separation required, at high rates of flow and over extended periods of operation.

(2)   Membranes must be capable of withstanding effective cleaning and disinfection to the requirements necessary for satisfactory hygienic operation.

(3)   Membranes should have a long 'in-place' life under the operating conditions experienced.

Satisfying these requirements can be difficult in particular applications.

In dairy operations, for example, deposits of proteinaceous matter which tend to build up on membrane surfaces can quickly lead to an unacceptable fall in permeation rates. For this reason cleaning programmes assume major importance in membrane separations other than for the avoidance of microbiological contamination.

Some membranes are rapidly destroyed by certain detergents and sterilants. Other membranes cannot withstand elevated temperatures and other than limited pH ranges. The choice of 'cleansing agents' (Section 17.3) must be made with great care and extensive trials may be required to establish suitable cleaning procedures.[13]

Earlier membranes often did not possess long 'in-place' lives and for this reason were suspect. In many industrial applications a life of up to two years is not now uncommon and newer materials are likely to improve on this. It is apparent that a given membrane may well be limited in its range of application and that membranes must be 'tailored' to particular requirements. An understanding of how these important requirements might be satisfied can best be got by looking at the principles underlying membrane separation.

6.4.4.2. Membrane flow. It should be realised that although ultrafiltration and reverse osmosis are frequently regarded as extensions of filtration to molecular size ranges, any analogy to flow through conventional filter beds must be regarded with caution. This simple approach does not adequately describe the flow across either UF or RO membranes.

Though important in ultrafiltration, investigation suggests that micropores are not responsible, to any great extent, for flow across reverse osmosis membranes. This means that a mechanism other than 'Poiseuille flow' in capillaries must play a part in flow across these membranes.

Two models for membrane transport are usually considered.[14]

(a) *Capillary flow model.* In this simple model, solute is rejected by a filtering or sieving action as liquid flows through a microporous structure which prevents the passage of larger molecules. The model considers flow to occur through pores in an otherwise impermeable layer. A laminar flow regime is established so the Hagan–Poiseuille equation can be applied to determine the 'flux' (volumetric flow rate per unit area of membrane surface) across the membrane.

(b) *Solution–diffusion model.* A second model for the transport of material across a membrane postulates the dissolution of the molecular species being transported, in the material of the membrane, followed by molecular diffusion across the barrier. Since both the solubilities and the rates of diffusion of the various molecular species present will be different for different components, the solution–diffusion model appears to explain the selectivity of a reverse osmosis membrane to various components in solution. Both mechanisms probably occur in membrane transport, the solution–diffusion mechanism predominating in reverse osmosis and that of capillary flow in ultrafiltration. The so-called 'preferential, sorption–capillary flow' mechanism takes into account both mechanisms and is discussed by Sourirajan.[15] Certainly, as might be expected if these models are valid, the chemical nature or molecular structure of the membrane appears to be of less importance in determining solute rejection or solvent flux rates in ultrafiltration than is the case with reverse osmosis membranes.

6.4.4.3. Structure of membranes. Studies of the commonly used Loeb and Sourirajan cellulose acetate membranes show them to be both asymmetric and ultramicroporous. They consist of an ultrathin skin of dense polymer some $0.5–1.5 \mu m$ thick, supported on a relatively thick but microporous polymer substructure. Some workers suggest that the dense polymer layer itself is also microporous. The laminate of dense film and porous support is made in a single casting process and has a total thickness of 0·1–0·2 mm. For industrial use the laminate is supported on a rigid, but porous, backing structure.

6.4.4.4. Membrane materials. As mentioned previously the performance of UF membranes with respect to transport properties, depends mainly on their physical structure and not to any great extent on chemical properties. A wider range of materials is available for these applications than is the case with RO membranes.

Cellulose esters were the first polymers to be successfully employed in low-pressure membrane separation processes and they can be constructed with various porosities according to need. However, they suffer from a number of disadvantages. Cellulose acetates are subject to hydrolysis in both strongly acidic and mildly alkaline conditions. Hydrolysis is a minimum in the pH range 4·5–5·0. They are unable to withstand elevated temperatures, upper limits being in the range 40–60 °C according to the type of material. Cellulose acetate membranes are also subject to microbial and enzymatic attack. The permeability of these membranes to water also tends to decrease during normal use due to creep consolidation. Notwithstanding these drawbacks cellulose acetate membranes find extensive use in food processing applications. Pepper[16] lists a number of membranes and gives typical applications. For ultrafiltration other materials can be used. These include polyvinyl chloride, polyacrylonitrile and nylons. Some newer materials—aromatic polyamides and polyimides—are able to withstand elevated temperatures under corrosive conditions. They have high resistance to collapse or consolidation under applied pressures, resistance to change in properties at higher temperatures, possess good mechanical strengths and abrasion resistance and withstand acidic, alkaline and oxidative conditions.[12]

Only two materials have found extensive use in commercial reverse osmosis applications—cellulose acetate and polyamide, a modified form of nylon.

6.4.4.5. Membrane configurations. Several different membrane geometries are in use, including flat sheets, spirally wound sheets and tubular constructions.

(*a*) *Flat sheet membranes.* These are used in assemblies similar in construction to plate and frame filter presses, the membrane being stretched across a series of perforated baffles supported on a grooved plate. The liquid flows at low velocity (0·5 m/s) through narrow channels (0·3–0·5 mm) and is only in contact with the membrane for a distance of about 150 mm. The laminar flow–short pass system is claimed to have advantages when working with more viscous liquids.[17] This type of construction is being used in the dairy field, *e.g.* whey concentration.[18]

(*b*) *Tubular membranes.* Here the membrane is cast onto the inside of a porous support tube and they are widely used. A complete module consists of the tubular membrane carried inside an outer jacket (rather like a simple pipe heat-exchanger). The liquid being treated is pumped through the inner porous tube, in a number of designs, at a velocity sufficiently high to promote turbulent flow. After passing through the membrane *permeate* is collected in the outer jacket. The *concentrate* is collected separately or, alternatively, recycled back to the membrane for further concentration.

(*c*) *Spiral-wound flat sheet membranes.* This is a variation of the flat sheet membrane and is frequently used in reverse osmosis where, as seen, higher pressures are required. Two flat sheets of membrane sandwiching a porous support medium are wrapped, with a plastic spacer, around a central tube. The tube connects with the porous material along one edge of the sandwich. The spiral-wound roll is contained inside a cylindrical, metal tube. Liquid, under pressure in the pipe, flows into the space created by the plastic spacer and across the membrane surfaces. Permeate, after passing the membrane, is removed from the system *via* the porous support and the central tube. This design enables a large membrane area to be contained in a relatively small pressure containment space, thus reducing the capital cost of the system. This type of module, using cellulose acetate membranes, was one of the first reverse osmosis systems to receive wide acceptance in commercial water treatment.

(*d*) *Hollow-fibre membranes.* One of the most widely used membrane systems in reverse osmosis applications is that based on the use of hollow-fibre membranes of an asymmetric polyamide marketed by Du Pont.[19] The use of very narrow bore hollow fibres (the bore is about 40 μm and overall diameter 80 μm) allows a very large membrane surface to be packed into a small volume. The fibres are wrapped around a porous feed tube so as to fill the annular space between this tube and an outer cylinder. Permeate (usually water) flows from the feed tube, through the outer wall of the fibres, to leave *via* the hollow centre of the fibres which themselves connect to a common outlet. Concentrate, containing the rejected dissolved solids, having failed to pass the membrane flows to a common concentrate outlet. Not surprisingly hollow-fibre systems, though most compact and least expensive,[20] are the most easily fouled of the available systems. Regular cleaning is essential. They are more suitable for the treatment of waters low in suspended solids.

Other types of membrane module, *e.g.* 'Spaghetti' module,[20] are commercially available and more will doubtless appear as membrane technology advances.

6.4.5. ULTRAFILTRATION AND REVERSE OSMOSIS SYSTEMS

6.4.5.1. Basic features. Though at first sight a variety of systems appear to find use in UF and RO processes, basically they are very similar. Dilute feed from a storage vessel is fed under pump pressure, *via* a manifold, to the appropriate number of membrane modules necessary to give the surface area for separation at the required rate. Permeate passing through the membrane is taken off. In food processing applications the desired stream is usually the enriched concentrate (retentate) stream. 'Once-through' systems (Fig. 6.16a) or

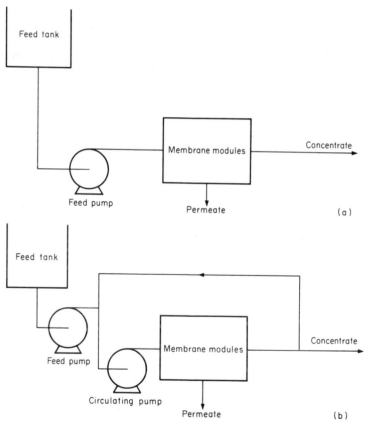

FIG. 6.16. (a) Once-through system. (b) Recirculating system.

'recirculating systems' (Fig. 6.16b) may be used. In the latter, concentrate is recycled for further concentration. A heat exchanger is often included in the system to permit any desired temperature control, *e.g.* to avoid temperatures at which microbiological growth is rapid.[18] For RO applications, high pressure pumps are needed. These can be positive displacement (often piston type) pumps or multistage centrifugal pumps. Hygienic design principles and facilities for 'inplace cleaning' must be included in the design of the overall system (Chapter 17).

In the operation of these units the aim is to achieve the desired degree of separation ('rejection' of undesired components) at the required production level. Maximum flux-rates at the working pressure—thus minimising the area of membrane surface required—are highly desirable. In practice, the degree of separation likely to be achieved is difficult to predict at the design stage for any particular membrane and comparison of membrane performances is impossible in the absence of 'performance standards'.[21] On-stream rates of permeation are also difficult to predict so pilot-scale trials are usually carried out. Permeation rates, in practice, often fail to reach those predicted and a common cause of the discrepancy is a combination of membrane fouling and concentration polarisation.

6.4.5.2. Concentration polarisation.

It might be expected that the permeabilities (hence 'flux') for 'looser' ultrafiltration membranes would be considerably greater than those of 'tighter' reverse osmosis membranes. Though attainable with pure water, in practice these high fluxes are rarely achieved. As in all fluid flow systems, when liquid flows over the membrane surfaces a boundary layer develops. Since the membrane surface is rejecting solute from solution the concentration of solute at the interface—that is in the laminar region of the boundary layer—is high. The accumulation of solute at the interface rapidly results in the formation of a viscous layer which resists the flow of fluid across the membrane. This phenomenon is called concentration polarisation and it leads to a rapid reduction in flux. Concentration polarisation arises in both RO and UF separations but the higher solute concentrations normally encountered make the problem more acute with ultrafiltration.

Various designs of membrane modules have attempted to counter the drop in flux resulting from concentration polarisation. They include:

(a) Increasing the liquid flow rate.
(b) Decreasing the module tube diameter or plate separation (Section 6.4.4.5).

(c) Using short flow paths—use of shorter tubes, channels, etc.
(d) Increasing the temperature of the liquid to decrease viscosity and increase the rate of diffusion of solute away from the membrane.

In food processing applications elevation of temperature is of limited applicability. Protein denaturation is very likely in many applications if temperatures rise too high. Apart from the resulting heat damage a gelatinous layer of deposited solute tends to arise only too quickly. Any further deposition must be avoided. The importance of regular cleaning procedures becomes obvious.

A common fallacy in membrane separation operation is to assume that an increase in applied pressure will necessarily lead to an increase in permeate flux. Though an increase in pressure may bring about an initial improvement the boundary layer rapidly becomes thicker and any deposited solids tend to become compressed. The net result for the increased pumping costs (always assuming the system capable of withstanding the higher pressure) might well be a reduction in flux-rate.

6.4.6. APPLICATIONS OF ULTRAFILTRATION AND REVERSE OSMOSIS

We have seen that the demarcation between UF and RO is not always clear-cut. In general, because of the smaller osmotic effect, considerably lower pressures are required to effect separation by ultrafiltration than is the case with reverse osmosis. The chemical nature of the membrane would appear to play a more significant role in RO, but similar membranes can be found performing in both categories of separation.

It is in the application of the methods that the differences do become more apparent. Reverse osmosis is more concerned with the separation of pure water as permeate, *e.g.* from ground waters and surface waters (Section 18.2.2) having low concentrations of dissolved solids; in desalination; in the treatment of brackish waters, etc. It is finding use for the concentration of low molecular weight organic materials in dilute aqueous solution. In the food industry several commercial plants for the recovery of lactose from whey are in operation.[22] The feed liquor is the permeate from ultrafiltration of whey for whey protein recovery. As well as lactose, the permeate from the protein concentration stage contains mineral salts. The reverse osmosis membrane can be selected so as to permit varying degrees of demineralisation of the lactose concentrate.

Sugar recovery from confectionery waste water containing about

3 % sugar, at a rate of about 38 m^3/day (10 000 US gallons/day), has been reported in the USA. The 'retentate' has a final concentration of 23–30 %.

It is in the recovery of lower molecular weight organic materials from food processing waste streams that the major potential for reverse osmosis may lie, as far as the food industry is concerned. In these applications, the recovery of an economically useful product from a waste stream will also lower the 'Biochemical Oxygen Demand' (Section 18.4.2). A number of these applications have been suggested in the literature.[18, 23]

Large industrial-scale cheese whey ultrafiltration plants are now in operation in New Zealand, the USA and France.[22] Whey protein is potentially valuable, although to dispose of all the whey protein capable of being recovered will necessitate developments in the utilisation of the material. In this ultrafiltration process the 'concentrate', after separation from the lactose and mineral salts, contains some 12-fold (or even greater) protein content and is suitable for spray-drying. Another major commercial application of UF is the production of a protein rich concentrate from skim milk. This concentrate is being used in the manufacture of soft cheese.[18]

Though in the last decade the use of membrane separations (both UF and RO) for separating and concentrating a variety of other food materials has been investigated—egg-white, maple syrup, apple juice, blood protein, etc., some to commercial scale—much development work remains to be done if these methods are to achieve their predicted potential.

Note: Grateful acknowledgement is hereby made for information received from Messrs Dorr-Oliver Co. Ltd, Johnson-Progress Ltd, Calmic Engineering Co. Ltd and Stockdale Engineering Ltd.

REFERENCES

1. Dickey, G. D., 'Filtration'. (Reinhold: 1961.)
2. McCabe, W. L., and Smith, J. C., 'Unit Operations of Chemical Engineering', 2nd ed. (McGraw-Hill: 1967).
3. Perry, R. H., and Chilton, C. H. (Eds), 'Chemical Engineers' Handbook', 5th ed. (McGraw-Hill: 1973).
4. Coulson, J. M., and Richardson, J. F., 'Chemical Engineering', Vol. 2, 2nd ed. (Pergamon Press: 1968).
5. Foust, A. S., Wenzel, L. A., Clump, C. W., Maus, L., and Bryce Anderson, L., 'Principles of Unit Operations'. (John Wiley: 1960.)
6. Clarke, R. J., 'Process Engineering in the Food Industries'. (Heywood: 1957.)
7. Tressler, D. K., and Joslyn, M. A., 'Fruit and Vegetable Juice Processing Technology'. (AVI, USA: 1961.)

8. Anderson, A. J. C., 'Refining of Oil and Fats for Edible Purposes'. (Pergamon Press: 1953.)
9. Lawler, F. K., 'Filter Replaces Pasteurizer'. Fd Engng, **35**(12), 45–47 (1963).
10. Reid, C. E., and Breton, E. J., J. Appl. Polymer Sci., **1**, 133 (1959).
11. Loeb, S., and Sourirajan, S., Adv. Chem. Ser., **38**, 117 (1962).
12. Michaels, A. S., 'Tailored Membranes', *in* Spicer, A. (Ed.) 'Advances in Preconcentration and Dehydration of Foods'. 213–250 (Applied Science Publishers: 1974).
13. McDonough, F. E., and Hargrove, R. E., 'Sanitation of Reverse Osmosis/Ultrafiltration Equipment'. J. Milk Fd. Technol., **35**(2), 102–106 (1972).
14. Evans, E. W., and Glover, F. A., 'Basic Principles of Reverse Osmosis and Ultrafiltration'. J. Soc. Dairy Technol., **27**(3), 111–120 (1974).
15. Sourirajan, S., 'Reverse Osmosis'. (Logos Press: 1970).
16. Pepper, D., 'Reverse Osmosis and Ultrafiltration Techniques'. Effl. Wat. Treat. J., **13**(12) (1973).
17. Madsen, R. F., 'Membrane Concentration', *in* Spicer, A. (Ed.) 'Advances in Preconcentration and Dehydration of Foods'. 251–301 (Applied Science Publishers: 1974).
18. Coton, S. G., 'Ultrafiltration–Fractionation Applications'. J. Soc. Dairy Technol., **27**(3), 121–127 (1974).
19. Anon., 'Why Hollow-Fibre Reverse Osmosis Won the Top CE Prize for Dupont'. Chemical Engineering, November 29th (1971).
20. Anon., 'Reverse Osmosis Today'. Process Biochem., **11**(1/2) 32–34 (1976).
21. Murkes, J., 'Semi-Permeable Membranes—a Need For Performance Standards'. Chemical Processing, January (1974).
22. Horton, B. S., 'Industrial Scale Ultrafiltration and Reverse Osmosis Plants in the Food Industries', *in* Spicer, A. (Ed.) 'Advances in Preconcentration and Dehydration of Foods'. 309–314 (Applied Science Publishers: 1974).
23. Donelly, J. K., O'Sullivan, A. C., and Delaney, R. A. M., 'Reverse Osmosis-Concentration Applications'. J. Soc. Dairy Technol., **27**(3), 128–140 (1974).

CHAPTER 7

CENTRIFUGATION

7.1. INTRODUCTION AND THEORY

Centrifugation may be defined as a unit operation involving the separation of materials by the application of centrifugal force. The applications of centrifugation are discussed under four headings, *viz.*: separation of immiscible liquids; centrifugal clarification; desludging; centrifugal filtration. Other applications for centrifugal equipment are mentioned elsewhere in this text, for example: separation of gas–solid systems (cyclone separator, Chapter 13); separation of vapour–liquid systems (entrainment separators, Chapter 12).

7.1.1. SEPARATION OF IMMISCIBLE LIQUIDS

The centrifugal force, F_c, acting on an object of mass m, rotating in a circular path of radius R, at an angular velocity of ω is:

$$F_c = mR\omega^2 \tag{7.1}$$

and

$$\omega = \frac{\pi N}{30} \tag{7.2}$$

where N = rotational speed in revs/min and ω is in radians/s.

Thus the magnitude of the centrifugal force depends on the radius of rotation, the speed of rotation and the mass of the body or, for a unit volume of material, the density of the material. If two immiscible liquids A and B with densities ρ_A and ρ_B respectively are placed in a cylindrical bowl which is rotated about a central axis, the more dense liquid A will tend to move towards the wall of the bowl and form an annular ring near its inner surface as shown in Fig. 7.1. The less dense liquid B will be displaced towards the centre of rotation and form an inner annular ring again as in Fig. 7.1. If provision is made for introducing the liquid feed continuously to the bowl and for tapping off from the two liquid layers separately, separation of the liquids can be achieved. The feed is usually introduced to the bottom of the bowl by a centrally located pipe and the liquids removed from each layer by a weir system such as that illustrated in Fig. 7.2. The cylindrical interface, of radius R_i, separating the two phases is known as the neutral zone. In practical systems this interface is not as clearly

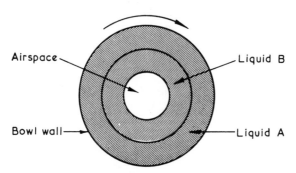

FIG. 7.1.   Separation of immiscible liquids in a cylindrical bowl (plan view).

defined as Fig. 7.2 suggests. The dense liquid flows out over a circular weir of radius R_A and the lighter liquid over one of radius R_B. If we assume that the liquid rotates at bowl speed, that is, that slippage and friction are negligible, then the drop in pressure, arising from centrifugal force, between R_i and R_A must equal the pressure drop between R_i and R_B. If this was not so the interface would not be stable at radius R_i.

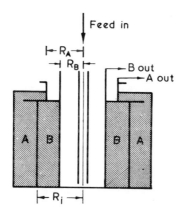

FIG. 7.2.   Separation of immiscible liquids in a cylindrical bowl with submerged weir (sectional view).

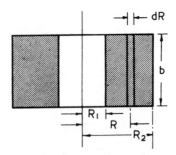

FIG. 7.3. Annular ring of liquid in cylindrical centrifuge bowl.

Consider an annular ring of liquid of thickness $(R_2 - R_1)$ as shown in Fig. 7.3. The centrifugal force, dF, acting on the volume element dR thick and of mass dm at radius R is:

$$dF = \omega^2 R \, dm \qquad (7.3)$$

but

$$dm = 2\pi\rho b R \, dR \qquad (7.4)$$

where ρ = density of the liquid; b = height of the liquid layer in the centrifuge. Therefore

$$dF = 2\pi\rho b \omega^2 R^2 \, dR \qquad (7.5)$$

The pressure drop over the element is dP and

$$dP = \frac{\text{Force}}{\text{Area}} = \frac{2\pi\rho b\omega^2 R^2 \, dR}{2\pi b R} = \rho\omega^2 R \, dR \qquad (7.6)$$

The pressure drop over ring of liquid $(R_2 - R_1)$ thick is

$$\Delta P_{(R_2 - R_1)} = \omega^2\rho \int_{R_1}^{R_2} R \, dR = \frac{\omega^2\rho(R_2^2 - R_1^2)}{2} \qquad (7.7)$$

Returning to the system shown in Fig. 7.2 and using equation (7.7) the pressure drops over the two liquid layers are:

$$\Delta P_{(R_i - R_A)} = \frac{\omega^2\rho_A(R_i^2 - R_A^2)}{2} \qquad (7.8)$$

$$\Delta P_{(R_i - R_B)} = \frac{\omega^2\rho_B(R_i^2 - R_B^2)}{2} \qquad (7.9)$$

If the neutral zone is to remain stable then

$$\frac{\omega^2\rho_A(R_i^2 - R_A^2)}{2} = \frac{\omega^2\rho_B(R_i^2 - R_B^2)}{2} \qquad (7.10)$$

or

$$R_i = \left(\frac{R_A^2 - (\rho_B/\rho_A)R_B^2}{1 - \rho_B/\rho_A} \right)^{1/2} \qquad (7.11)$$

(*Note*: In deriving the above expression it is assumed that the inner liquid radius is that of the outlet in each case. Cresting of the liquids, particularly at high throughputs, may render this assumption invalid and adjustments need to be made to the equations above.[8])

Thus the radius of the neutral zone depends theoretically on the radii of the two phase outlets and the liquid densities. For example, for two liquids of known densities, if R_B is fixed then as R_A is increased so R_i increases. This affords a means of controlling R_i, that is controlling the relative size of zone A to zone B in the centrifuge. In zone A light liquid is effectively stripped from a mass of dense liquid, while in zone B dense liquid is more effectively removed from a mass of light liquid. If, therefore, the duty to which the centrifuge is put involves stripping a mass of dense liquid free of light liquid, that is a pure dense phase is required, then the dwell time in zone A should exceed that in zone B. In such a case R_A would be reduced, thus reducing R_i and increasing the relative size of zone A to zone B. An example of such a duty is the separation of cream from milk where the object is to minimise the fat (light phase) content of the separated milk (dense phase). If the requirements were reversed, *e.g.* if the operation involved stripping small amounts of water from an edible oil, then R_A would be increased, increasing the size of zone B. In practice it is common to control R_i by varying R_A with R_B fixed.[2, 4]

Equation 7.11 also shows that R_i depends on the relative densities of the two phases. If the difference in density is very small the neutral zone becomes unstable. The difference between ρ_A and ρ_B should not be less than about 3 %.[1] It has also been found that the best separation is achieved if the feed is introduced to the bowl at a point near the neutral zone.

7.1.2. CENTRIFUGAL CLARIFICATION

This is the term used here to describe the removal of small quantities, a few per cent or less, of insoluble solids from a liquid by centrifugal means. If a liquid containing solids with a greater density than the liquid is fed to a rotating cylindrical bowl, the solids will move towards the bowl wall. If an outlet is provided for the liquid near the centre of rotation, *e.g.* if the outer exit (radius R_A) in the bowl shown in Fig. 7.2 is closed off, then those particles of solid which reach the bowl wall will remain in the bowl. Those particles which do not reach the bowl wall will be carried out in the liquid. The fraction remaining in the bowl and the fraction passing out in the liquid will be controlled by the rate of feed, *i.e.* the dwell time in the bowl.

Consider a solid particle of diameter D_p in the liquid in the bowl shown in Fig. 7.3. If it is assumed that this particle moves radially at its terminal velocity under laminar flow conditions, the radial velocity of the particle is:

$$v_t = \frac{\omega^2(\rho_s - \rho_l)D_p^2 R}{18\eta} \tag{7.12}$$

where v_t = terminal velocity of particle; ρ_s and ρ_l = densities of solid and liquid respectively; D_p = diameter of particle; R = distance of the particle from centre of rotation; η = viscosity of liquid.

Since the gravitational effect is very small compared with the centrifugal effect and since we are interested mainly in the movement of the smallest particles, these assumptions seem reasonable.[3, 4]

The time required for a particle to travel an elemental radial distance dR is

$$dt = \frac{dR}{v_t} = \frac{18\eta}{\omega^2(\rho_s - \rho_l)D_p^2}\frac{dR}{R} \tag{7.13}$$

Assume that half of all those particles present in the feed with a particular diameter, D_{pc}, are removed during their passage through the bowl. Most particles with diameters greater than D_{pc} will be removed from the liquid while most particles of a smaller size will remain in the liquid. D_{pc}, as here defined, is known as the 'cut-point' or

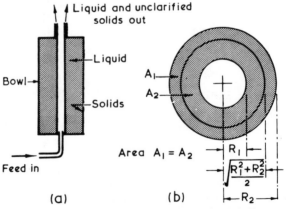

FIG. 7.4.   Principle of simple cylindrical centrifugal clarifier.

'critical' diameter. Assume that clarification is being carried out in a simple cylindrical centrifuge as shown in Fig. 7.4a, and that all particles are distributed uniformly over the cross section of the annular ring of liquid at the base of the bowl and flow upwards to the discharge point with equal velocity. All particles of diameter D_{pc} contained in the outer half of the cross sectional area of the ring of liquid will reach the bowl wall and be removed from the liquid. The maximum distance a particle in this zone has to travel to reach the bowl wall is

$$\left[R_2 - \left(\frac{R_1^2 + R_2^2}{2} \right)^{1/2} \right]$$

see Fig. 7.4b. The time required for a particle of diameter D_{pc} to travel this distance is

$$t = \frac{18\eta}{\omega^2(\rho_s - \rho_l)D_{pc}^2} \int_{\left(\frac{R_1^2 + R_2^2}{2}\right)^{1/2}}^{R_2} \frac{dR}{R}$$

$$= \frac{18\eta \ln\left(\frac{R_2}{[(R_1^2 + R_2^2)/2]^{1/2}} \right)}{\omega^2(\rho_s - \rho_l)D_{pc}^2} \qquad (7.14)$$

The minimum residence time for a particle in the bowl is V/q, where V is the volume of liquid held in the bowl at any time, and q is the volumetric flow rate of liquid through the bowl.

Thus for a particle of diameter D_{pc} to be separated out

$$\frac{V}{q} = \frac{18\eta \ln\left(\frac{R_2}{[(R_1^2 + R_2^2)/2]^{1/2}} \right)}{\omega^2(\rho_s - \rho_l)D_{pc}^2} \qquad (7.15)$$

Equation 7.15 may be written in the form

$$q = 2 \left[\frac{g(\rho_s - \rho_l)D_{pc}^2}{18\eta} \right] \left[\frac{\omega^2 V}{2g \ln\left(\frac{R_2}{[(R_1^2 + R_2^2)/2]^{1/2}} \right)} \right] \qquad (7.16)$$

$$= 2 \cdot v_g \cdot \Sigma \qquad (7.17)$$

where g = acceleration due to gravity; v_g = sedimentation velocity of a particle of diameter D_{pc} in a gravitational field; Σ = characteristic of the centrifuge, equivalent to the area of a gravity settling tank with similar settling characteristics to the centrifuge (*i.e.* one which will remove half of all particles of diameter D_{pc}).

Now

$$\frac{1}{2\ln\left(\dfrac{R_2}{[(R_1^2 + R_2^2)/2]^{1/2}}\right)} \simeq \frac{(3R_2^2 + R_1^2)}{2(R_2^2 - R_1^2)} \tag{7.18}$$

Therefore

$$\Sigma \simeq \frac{\omega^2 V(3R_2^2 + R_1^2)}{2g(R_2^2 - R_1^2)} \tag{7.19}$$

For a simple cylindrical bowl such as that shown in Fig. 7.4a

$$V = \pi(R_2^2 - R_1^2)b$$

where b = height of the bowl.
  Therefore

$$\Sigma \simeq \frac{\pi\omega^2 b(3R_2^2 + R_1^2)}{2g} \tag{7.20}$$

Alternative values of Σ are given in the literature for different types of bowl, *e.g.* for a disc-bowl centrifuge (*see* Section 7.2.1.2)

$$\Sigma = \frac{2\pi\omega^2(S - 1)(R_x^3 - R_y^3)}{3g\tan\Omega} \tag{7.21}$$

where S = number of discs in stack; R_x and R_y = outer and inner radius of stack; Ω = conical half angle of discs.[7, 8]
  For centrifuges of the same type but of different sizes to have the same performance, that is, to clarify out particles of a particular diameter and above, the quantity q/Σ should be the same. This provides a useful guide for scaling up calculations. These expressions apply best to simple cylindrical bowls at low or moderate feed rates. The more complex the centrifuge the more difficult it is to apply simple analyses such as these. Extrapolation on the basis of constant value of q/Σ cannot be made between different types of centrifuge, *e.g.* tubular-bowl and disc types, without special correction factors being introduced.[7, 8]

7.1.3. DESLUDGING

  This term is used here to describe the removal of solids from a liquid by centrifugal means when the quantity of solids present exceeds that which can be handled by a simple clarifier (that is, when solids content is greater than 5 % or 6 % by weight of feed). In such systems provision is made for removal of the solids from the centrifuge bowl during its operation. The general theory discussed in 7.1.2 is applicable, but errors occur due to the solids movement system altering the conditions on which the formulae are based and more complex expressions need to be used.[8]

7.1.4. CENTRIFUGAL FILTRATION

This term describes the separation of solids from a liquid by filtration when the flow of filtrate is induced by centrifugal means. The general principle of the centrifugal filter is shown in Fig. 7.5. The slurry is fed into a rotating bowl with a perforated wall, which is lined with a suitable filter medium. The solids are thrown to the bowl wall and form a filter cake through which the filtrate passes, under the influence of centrifugal force, then through the filter medium and perforated basket wall.

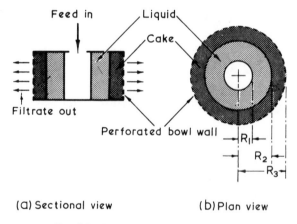

(a) Sectional view   (b) Plan view

FIG. 7.5.   Principle of simple centrifugal filter.

Direct comparison of pressure filtration and centrifugal filtration reveals certain differences. In the latter both the centrifugal force and the filtering area increase with increase in radius. Centrifugal force acts on the filtrate passing through the cake and on the cake itself supplementing the hydraulic pressure head. For a comparatively simple system (such as that shown in Fig. 7.5) assuming an incompressible cake and neglecting kinetic energy changes in the filtrate, the rate of flow of filtrate through a centrifugal filter may be expressed as:

$$q = \frac{\rho\omega^2(R_3^2 - R_1^2)}{2\eta\left(\dfrac{\alpha M_c}{[2\pi b(R_3 + R_2)/2][2\pi b(R_3 - R_2)/\ln(R_3/R_2)]} + \dfrac{R_m}{2\pi b R_3}\right)}$$

$$= \frac{\rho\omega^2(R_3^2 - R_1^2)}{2\eta\left(\dfrac{\alpha M_c}{A_a A_l} + \dfrac{R_m}{A_m}\right)} \tag{7.22}$$

where q = volumetric flowrate of filtrate; ρ = filtrate density; ω = angular velocity; η = filtrate viscosity; α = specific cake resistance; M_c = mass of solid cake in basket; R_1 = radius of inner surface of the liquid ring; R_2 = radius of the inner surface of the cake; R_3 = radius of inner surface of bowl; A_a = arithmetic mean cake area; A_l = logarithmic mean cake area; A_m = area of filter medium; R_m = resistance of filter medium; b = height of basket. (*See* Chapter 6, Sections 6.1.3 and 6.1.4 for definitions of α and R_m.)

Such an equation applies only to cakes of uniform thickness. In most practical cases cakes are thicker near the base than the top. Such systems give a filtration rate 5–20 % greater than a cake of constant thickness of similar volume and permeability.[3, 9]

7.2. EQUIPMENT—PRINCIPLES, DESIGN FEATURES AND GENERAL APPLICATIONS

7.2.1. LIQUID–LIQUID CENTRIFUGAL SEPARATORS

As equation (7.1) shows, the centrifugal force is proportional to the radius of rotation. The self stress developed in a bowl wall is proportional to the square of the radius of the bowl.[3] The latter factor usually determines the upper speed limit of a bowl. Centrifugal separators are available in two general classes, small diameter high speed machines and large diameter lower speed machines. The centrifugal force developed in the former class is generally greater than in the larger machines.

7.2.1.1. Tubular-bowl centrifuge. This type of centrifuge consists of a long, narrow, cylindrical bowl rotating at high speed in an outer stationary casing. The bowl is usually suspended from the top with a guide provided for the base. The feed is introduced through a stationary pipe to the bottom of the bowl and quickly accelerated to bowl speed by means of vanes or baffles. The two liquids are removed from the annular layers formed through a circular weir system as shown in Fig. 7.6 and discharge into stationary covers. Control over the neutral zone radius, as discussed in Section 7.1.1, is achieved by fitting rings with different internal diameters to the dense phase outlet. Such rings are often known as 'gravity discs' or ring dams. Bowl dimensions range from 3 to 6 in (7·6–15·2 cm) diameter and up to 5 ft (1·5 m) high. A typical unit 4 in diameter and 30 in high would rotate at 15 000 rev/min. Smaller laboratory models rotate at speeds up to 50 000 rev/min.

7.2.1.2. Disc-bowl centrifuge.

In this type of centrifuge a relatively shallow, wide cylindrical bowl rotates at moderate speed in a stationary casing. The bowl is usually bottom driven. The feed is normally introduced to the bottom of the bowl through a centrally located feed pipe from above. The bowl contains a number of closely spaced metal cones, called discs, which rotate with the bowl and are located one above the other with a fixed clearance between them, Fig. 7.7a. The discs have one or more sets of matching holes which form channels through which the feed material flows, Fig. 7.7b. Under the influence of centrifugal force the dense phase, travelling towards the bowl wall, streams down the undersides of the discs while the light phase, displaced towards the centre, flows over the upper faces of the discs, Fig. 7.7c. The liquids are thus divided into thin layers and the distance any drop of one liquid must travel to get caught up in, and removed in, the appropriate outgoing stream is very small. Also considerable shearing is said to take place at the liquid–liquid interface between the countercurrent streams of liquid which can help to break up certain types of emulsions and improve separation.[1, 6] The separation efficiency of a disc-bowl centrifuge is much better than that of a cylindrical bowl of the same dimensions without discs, rotating at a similar speed. The separated liquids are removed by means of a weir system, and again different gravity discs on the dense phase outlet may be used to control the neutral zone position. In some machines provision is made for introducing the feed near the neutral zone by substituting different discs at the bottom of the stack with holes at the appropriate radius. Bowl diameters range from 8 to 40 in (20–102 cm) and the spacing between the discs is of the order of 0·02–0·05 in (0·5–1·3 mm). A typical 12-in diameter bowl rotating at 6400 rev/min develops a force equivalent to 7000 times that of gravity. Special 'hermetic' bowls are available which permit operation at pressures up to 100 psi (690 kN/m^2) above atmospheric. Such units are useful where foaming is a problem and for handling carbonated beverages.

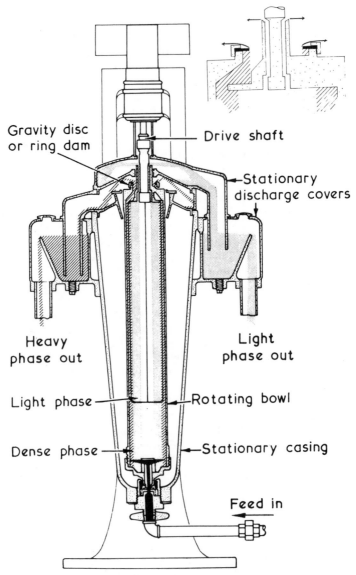

Gravity disc
or ring dam

Drive shaft

Stationary
discharge covers

Heavy
phase out

Light
phase out

Light phase

Rotating bowl

Dense phase

Stationary casing

Feed in

FIG. 7.6. Tubular bowl centrifuge (Sharples Super Centrifuge). (By courtesy of Pennsalt Ltd.) The insert shows how the heavy phase discharges over the gravity disc (solid black) while the light phase discharges through channels in the drive shaft.

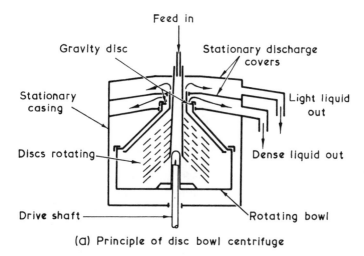

Feed in

Gravity disc

Stationary discharge covers

Stationary casing

Light liquid out

Discs rotating

Dense liquid out

Drive shaft

Rotating bowl

(a) Principle of disc bowl centrifuge

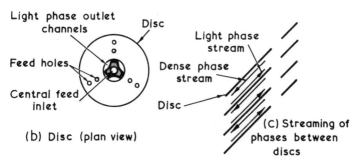

Light phase outlet channels

Disc

Light phase stream

Feed holes

Dense phase stream

Central feed inlet

Disc

(C) Streaming of phases between discs

(b) Disc (plan view)

FIG. 7.7. Principle of disc-bowl centrifuge.

7.2.2. CENTRIFUGAL CLARIFIERS

Both tubular and disc-bowl centrifuges may be used for clarifying small quantities of solids from liquids. If the dense phase outlets are closed off and the liquid is removed through the central outlet, then most of the solid particles with diameters greater than the 'cut-point' diameter as defined in Section 7.1.2 will remain as a deposit on the bowl wall. This is a batch operation and, when the solids build up on the bowl wall results in contamination of the outgoing liquid, the operation must be stopped, the bowl dismantled and cleaned out. As the amount of solids in the feed increases so does the frequency of cleaning and the cost of the operation.

The solids capacity of tubular bowl machines is seldom more than

2–4·5 kg and for economical operation the solids content of the feed should normally not exceed about 1 % by weight. Disc-bowl machines have solids capacities in the range 2–20 kg and are usually only suited to clarifying feeds with less than a few per cent by weight of solids. Both types are useful for removing small traces of solids to produce clear liquids, especially if the solids are gelatinous in nature and unsuited to filtration. Also both clarification and liquid–liquid separations can be carried out simultaneously.

7.2.2.1. Solid-bowl clarifier. Where large volumes of liquid containing small quantities of solids (1–2%) with good settling characteristics need to be clarified, simple large diameter, 24–42 in (60–108 cm) cylindrical bowls, without discs, may be used (Fig. 7.8). These are operated on a batch principle and, when a cake of solids of the maximum thickness is formed, the feed is cut off, excess liquid removed with a skimmer pipe and the solids cut out with a knife or plough and dropped through an opening in the bowl floor.

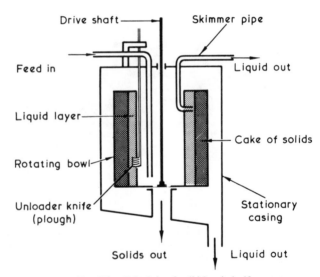

FIG. 7.8.   Principle of solid-bowl clarifier.

7.2.2.2. Cylinder-bowl (multichamber) centrifuge. This machine is shown in Fig. 7.9. The bowl is divided into a number of annular chambers and the liquid follows a circuitous path to the bowl wall and exit port. The coarsest particles are removed in the inner chamber and the finest in the outer. Again the centrifuge is operated on a batch

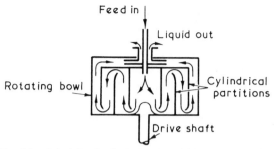

FIG. 7.9. Principle of cylinder-bowl (multichamber) centrifuge.

principle and is suitable for handling feed with about 1 % or less of solids. Some classification of solids in terms of size is possible.

7.2.2.3. Nozzle-discharge (self-cleaning) centrifuge. This centrifuge is of the disc-bowl type but the bowl, Fig. 7.10, is biconical in shape. A number of holes of the order of $\frac{1}{8}$-in (3–4 mm) diameter, are spaced around the bowl at its largest diameter. The solids removed from the liquid are continuously discharged, in the form of a thick slurry, into an outer casing. Feeds containing up to 25 % solids can be handled in this type of clarifier. Recirculation of part of the rejected slurry is possible to reduce loss of liquid, and displacement washing of the solids is also possible.

7.2.2.4. Valve-discharge and self-opening centrifuge. This centrifuge is similar in principle to the one described in Section 7.2.2.3

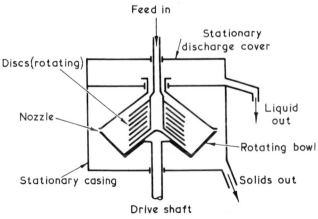

FIG. 7.10. Principle of nozzle-discharge centrifuge.

above, but valves are fitted in the solids discharge ports in the bowl. These valves can be opened at desired intervals to discharge the solids. They may be controlled by timers or alternatively be automatically opened by hydrostatic control. In an alternative system shown in Fig. 7.11 the lower section of the bowl moves vertically and is actuated by hydraulic pressure which, when high, keeps the discharge ports closed.

CLARIFYING – BOWL CLOSED   BOWL CLEANING WITH TOTAL DISCHARGE

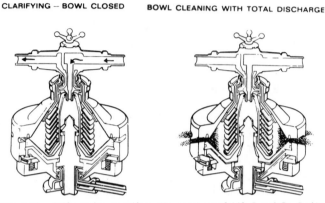

FIG. 7.11.   Self-opening centrifuge. (By courtesy of Alfa-Laval Co. Ltd.)

When the pressure is released the lower part of the bowl descends, opening discharge ports for the solids. The action is swift, taking only a fraction of a second, and is controlled by timers. In such machines feeds with solids contents of up to about 6 % can be clarified, and the solids released are drier than those obtained in the nozzle-discharge machine.

7.2.3. DESLUDGING CENTRIFUGES

Both the nozzle and valve discharge centrifuges can be said to perform desludging operations when handling feeds containing more than a few percent of solids. Where the solids content exceeds this amount alternative systems are available, such as the conveyor-bowl centrifuge. The principle of this type of centrifuge is shown in Fig. 7.12. Both the solid bowl and the helical conveyor rotate in the same direction, the former at one or two revolutions per minute faster than the latter. The solids are carried to one end of the bowl by the conveyor and discharged while the liquid leaves through adjustable ports at the other end. Such machines can handle feeds with up to 50 % solids and a wide range of particle sizes. Provision can be made

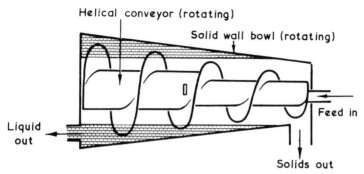

FIG. 7.12. Principle of conveyor-bowl centrifuge.

for washing the solids. They are not especially good clarifiers but do produce quite dry solids.

7.2.4. FILTERING CENTRIFUGALS (BASKET CENTRIFUGES OR DEWATERING CENTRIFUGES)

This type of equipment is used for handling slurries which lend themselves to separation by filtration, that is suspensions of fairly large particulate solids or crystalline materials which form suitably porous cakes.

7.2.4.1. Batch filtering centrifugal. Such a unit is shown in Fig. 7.13. The cylindrical metal basket with a perforated wall is suspended

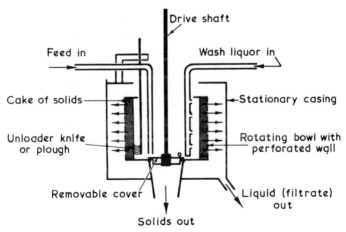

FIG. 7.13. Batch filtering centrifugal.

from the end of a vertical shaft. A filter medium lines the inside of the basket wall. In a typical cycle, the feed is introduced with the basket rotating at moderate speed. The bowl is then accelerated and filtration occurs through the cake of solids formed on the bowl wall. Wash liquid may be sprayed on to the cake and the cake spun dry at high speed. The basket is then slowed down, the cake cut out with an unloader knife or plough and removed through an opening in the basket floor. The filter medium is rinsed and the cycle repeated. Automatic systems can be used to control the complete cycle. Bowls are usually 30–48 in (76–122 cm) in diameter, 18–30 in (46–76 cm) deep and rotate at speeds up to about 2000 rev/min. Cycle times vary from 3 to 30 min.

7.2.4.2. Automatic batch centrifugal. This type of centrifugal is similar in principle to the one just described, but it rotates at constant speed throughout the whole cycle of operation. Feed and wash liquid are introduced automatically and the cake cut out with a knife or plough while the basket rotates at fairly high speed. Baskets may rotate about vertical or horizontal axes. They are suited to handling solids with good draining characteristics, have short cycle times, 0·5–1·5 min, and may give rise to mechanical damage in delicate crystals due to the vigorous action of the plough.

7.2.4.3. Reciprocating conveyor (push-type) centrifuge. One such machine is shown in Fig. 7.14. The feed enters the rotating basket

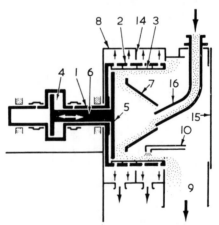

FIG. 7.14.   Schematic drawing of single-stage push-type centrifuge. 1, Hollow shaft; 2, basket; 3, sieve of basket; 4, hydraulic drive for pusher; 5, pusher member; 6, pusher shaft; 7, inlet funnel; 8, casing; 9, catcher; 10, washing device; 14, separating wall; 15, door; 16, feed pipe. (By courtesy of Escher Wyss (UK) Ltd.)

through a rotating funnel which accelerates it gently to bowl speed. A layer of solids 1–3 in (2·5–7·6 cm) thick forms on the bowl wall and this layer is moved towards the open end of the basket by a reciprocating pusher, a few inches at a time. On each return stroke of the pusher the feed funnel, which reciprocates also, delivers feed to the freshly exposed basket wall. The cake may be washed as shown and is finally spun off the open lip of the basket into the stationary casing.

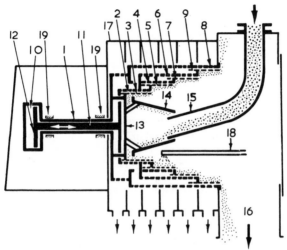

FIG. 7.15. Schematic drawing of multi-stage push-type centrifuge. 1, Hollow shaft; 2, first stage; 3, sieve covering; 4, second stage; 5, sieve covering; 6, third stage; 7, sieve covering; 8, fourth stage; 9, sieve covering; 10, pressure cylinder; 11, piston rod; 12, piston; 13, pusher member; 14, inlet funnel; 15, inlet pipe; 16, catcher; 17, casing; 18, washer pipe; 19, bearing. (By courtesy of Escher Wyss (UK) Ltd.)

Basket diameters are of the order of 1–4 ft (0·3–1·2 m). Crystal damage is reduced by the gentle acceleration and deceleration of the feed and discharged solids respectively.

A multistage push-type centrifuge is shown in Fig. 7.15. The stages are arranged in a telescopic fashion and alternate baskets reciprocate in an axial direction while the remainder are stationary axially. Thus each basket acts as a pusher for the following one. In such a machine the total distance the cake has to be pushed in each basket is less than in the single stage unit for a given total centrifuging time. Thus problems associated with buckling of the cake layer are minimised. The loosening of the cake occurring on transfer from one stage to the next is said to improve filtration and washing, and also the power consumption is more uniform and lower than in large single stage units.

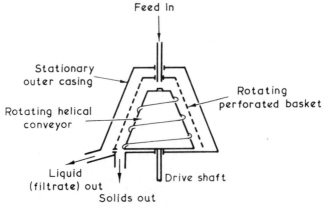

FIG. 7.16. Principle of vertical screen-conveyor system.

7.2.4.4. Screen-conveyor centrifuge. This type of machine is similar in principle to that shown in Fig. 7.12 but a perforated bowl is used through which the filtrate escapes. Other types employ baskets rotating about a vertical axis as shown in Fig. 7.16.

7.2.4.5. Constant angle bowl. This type of centrifuge is similar to that in Fig. 7.16 without the screw conveyor. The bowl angle is set to discharge the solids from the lip continuously.

7.2.4.6. Vibrating or oscillating screen centrifuge. As shown in Fig. 7.17, the basket is oscillating in a vertical direction while rotating, thus causing the solids to move to the top for discharge.

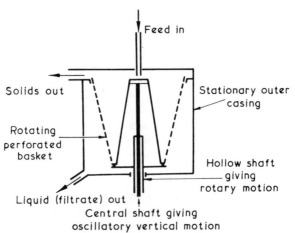

FIG. 7.17. Principle of vibrating screen centrifuge.

7.3. APPLICATIONS FOR CENTRIFUGAL EQUIPMENT IN THE FOOD INDUSTRY

The following are some examples of the numerous applications for centrifugal equipment in food processing.

Tubular-bowl machines have found application in dewatering animal fats and vegetable and fish oils; in the clarification of fruit juices, cider and sugar syrup for clear sweet manufacture.

Disc-bowl separators have been applied widely in the dairy industry for separating cream from milk; in the refining of animal fats and vegetable and fish oils, for drying and clarifying; in the clarification of fruit juices and citrus oils.

The various types of *clarifying* and *desludging centrifuges* have found very many applications including: treatment of animal fats, and vegetable or fish oils; fruit juice clarification; clarification of beer and wort; dewatering of corn, wheat and rice starches; recovery of yeasts. The type of bowl and solids discharge system used depends on the nature of the product handled and the required characteristics of both liquid and solid components.

Conveyor-bowl centrifuges are used in recovering animal and vegetable protein; separating cocoa, coffee and tea slurries; desludging fish oils and in preparing fish meal, etc.

Filtering centrifugals of various types are used extensively in sugar refining for recovering, washing and drying sugar crystals. They have also been applied to fruit and vegetable juice extraction; to the recovery of vegetable proteins, in freeze concentration operations and in many other fields.[5]

Note: Grateful acknowledgement is hereby made for information received from Messrs Alfa-Laval Ltd and Pennsalt Ltd.

REFERENCES

1. McCabe, W. L., and Smith, J. C., 'Unit Operations of Chemical Engineering', 2nd ed. (McGraw-Hill: 1967).
2. Brown, G. G. (Ed.), 'Unit Operations'. (Wiley: 1955.)
3. Perry, R. H., and Chilton, C. H. (Eds), 'Chemical Engineers Handbook', 5th ed. (McGraw-Hill: 1973).
4. Foust, A. S., Wenzel, L. A., Clump, C. W., Maus, L., and Anderson, L. B., 'Principles of Unit Operations'. (Wiley: 1960.)
5. Clarke, R. J., 'Process Engineering in the Food Industries'. (Heywood: 1957.)
6. Coulson, J. M., and Richardson, J. F., 'Chemical Engineering', Vol. 2, 2nd ed. (Pergamon Press: 1968).

7. Ambler, C. M., 'The Evaluation of Centrifuge Performance'. Chem. Engng Prog., **48**(3), 150–158 (1952).
8. Trowbridge, M. E. O'K., 'Problems in the Scaling-up of Centrifugal Separation Equipment'. Chem. Engr., **40**(162), 73–86 (1962).
9. Grace, H. P., 'Resistance and Compressibility of Filter Cakes'. Chem. Engng Prog., **49**(8), 303–318, 367–377, 427–436 (1953).

CHAPTER 8

SOLID–LIQUID EXTRACTION AND EXPRESSION

8.1. SOLID–LIQUID EXTRACTION (LEACHING, WASHING)

In the food and biochemical industries the transfer of mass between phases is often of interest. The phases may be solid, liquid or gaseous and two or more phases may be involved in any one transfer operation. Often when a phase contains more than one component the individual components differ in their tendencies to transfer to another phase or phases. For example, one of the components in a liquid may be more volatile than the others and so transfer more readily to a gaseous phase. This is the basis of distillation operations. Alternatively one component may be more soluble in another phase and so transfer between phases more readily than the other components in the system. This is the basis of solvent extraction operations. Where such differences exist between the components in a phase and that phase is placed in intimate contact with another phase or phases then mass transfer may occur between the phases and result in the redistribution of the components among them. Thus the composition of all the phases may change. In this way a separation of the components of a phase may be brought about.

Solid–liquid extraction is an example of such a separation operation in which a desired component, the *solute*, in a solid phase is separated by contacting the solid with a liquid, the *solvent*, in which the desired component is soluble.

Separation operations of this kind are carried out in single or multiple steps or *stages*. A stage is a unit of equipment in which two or more phases are brought into contact, maintained in contact for a predetermined period and then separated mechanically from each other. During the period of contact mass transfer of components between the phases takes place and they approach a state of equilibrium. An *equilibrium* (*ideal* or *theoretical*) stage is one in which the phases are intimately mixed and retained in contact for a time sufficient to allow thermodynamic equilibrium to be achieved between the phases before they are separated. In an *actual* (*real*) stage a true

175

state of equilibrium is not reached and so the change in composition is less than that theoretically possible. *Stage efficiency* may be defined as the ratio of the compositional change brought about in an actual stage to that which would have occurred in an equilibrium stage under the same operating conditions.

In a solid–liquid extraction stage the solvent is brought into intimate contact with the solid, solid and solvent are held in contact for the required time and then the mixture is separated into two streams: a 'clear' liquid stream or *overflow* stream consisting of a solution of the solute in the solvent and a 'residue' stream or *underflow* stream consisting of the insoluble solid component with some solution adhering to it. In this context an equilibrium stage may be defined as a stage in which the solution adhering to the solid in the underflow stream has the same composition as the clear liquid constituting the overflow stream. In an actual stage the concentration of the solute in the overflow stream would be less than in the solution adhering to the solid in the underflow stream.

8.1.1. SINGLE STAGE CALCULATIONS

Consider an equilibrium stage as shown diagrammatically in Fig. 8.1, where L_2 and L_1 represent the total mass (or mols) of the overflow streams entering and leaving the stage, S_0 and S_1 represent the total

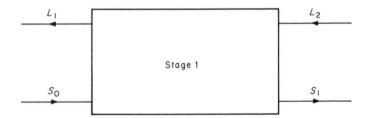

FIG. 8.1. An equilibrium stage.

mass (or mols) of the underflow streams entering and leaving, Y is the mass (or mol) fraction of a component in the L stream, X is the mass (or mol) fraction of a component in the S stream. If the two streams are thoroughly mixed in the stage then a mixture of mass ε results. Let Z represent the mass (or mol) fraction of a component in this mixture. Mass balances may be carried out on the stage as follows.

Total mass balance:

$$S_0 + L_2 = \varepsilon \qquad (8.1)$$

Mass balance for component '*a*'

$$S_0 X_{a0} + L_2 Y_{a2} = \varepsilon Z_{a1} \tag{8.2}$$

Mass balance for component '*b*'

$$S_0 X_{b0} + L_2 Y_{b2} = \varepsilon Z_{b1} \tag{8.3}$$

In a three component system (a ternary system) a mass balance for the third component '*c*', similar in form to equations (8.2) and (8.3) may be written. However, this may not be necessary as the mass fraction of '*c*' in the streams may be obtained by difference since

$$X_a + X_b + X_c = 1 \tag{8.4}$$

and

$$Y_a + Y_b + Y_c = 1 \tag{8.5}$$

Considering component '*a*', from equations (8.1) and (8.2) the relationship

$$S_0 X_{a0} + L_2 Y_{a2} = (S_0 + L_2) Z_{a1} \tag{8.6}$$

may be written. Rearranging (8.6)

$$\frac{S_0}{L_2} = \frac{Y_{a2} - Z_{a1}}{Z_{a1} - X_{a0}} \tag{8.7}$$

A similar expression may be written for component '*b*' thus

$$\frac{S_0}{L_2} = \frac{Y_{b2} - Z_{b1}}{Z_{b1} - X_{b0}} \tag{8.8}$$

Thus the composition of the mixture in the stage can be obtained from a knowledge of the masses and compositions of the streams entering. If the compositions of the incoming streams are represented graphically as shown in Fig. 8.2 then the composition of the mixture can be shown to lie on a straight line between the points representing the compositions of streams S_0 and L_2, and its position on that line will be such that the ratio S_0/L_2 is equal to the distance from L_2 to ε divided by the distance from ε to S_0. This is known as the *inverse lever-arm rule*. If these lengths are expressed in terms of distances on the axes rather than the line $S_0 L_2$ itself, then

$$\frac{S_0}{L_2} = \frac{Y_{a2} - Z_{a1}}{Z_{a1} - X_{a0}} = \frac{Y_{b2} - Z_{b1}}{Z_{b1} - X_{b0}}$$

i.e. equations (8.7) and (8.8).

Subtraction of streams may also be carried out graphically. If Δ

represents the mass (or mols) difference between the S and L streams then a total mass balance is

$$\Delta = S - L \tag{8.9}$$

and a component balance is

$$\Delta X_\Delta = SX - LY \tag{8.10}$$

where X_Δ is the composition of the Δ stream. If such a subtraction is represented graphically the composition of the stream will lie on a straight line drawn through the points representing the compositions of the S and L streams but beyond S from L. In Fig. 8.3 graphical addition and subtraction are represented diagrammatically.

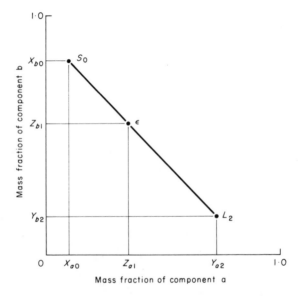

FIG. 8.2. Graphical representation of the composition of incoming streams and mixture in an equilibrium stage.

When equilibrium conditions have been established in the stage and if the mixture still consists of two phases then the composition of the phases will depend on the equilibrium relationship between them. This relationship will be specific to each system and will also depend on the operating conditions. When subsequently the two phases are separated the masses of the outgoing streams will be related to their

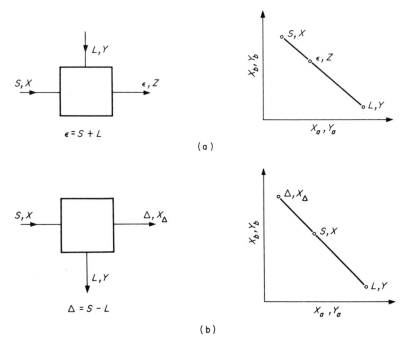

FIG. 8.3. Graphical addition and subtraction of streams. (a) Graphical addition; (b) graphical subtraction.

compositions by mass balances similar to those applicable to the incoming streams thus

$$\varepsilon = S_1 + L_1 \tag{8.11}$$

$$\varepsilon Z_{a1} = S_1 X_{a1} + L_1 Y_{a1} \tag{8.12}$$

$$\varepsilon Z_{b1} = S_1 X_{b1} + L_1 Y_{b1} \tag{8.13}$$

8.1.2. MULTISTAGE CALCULATIONS

Since the two phases leaving an equilibrium stage are by definition in equilibrium those equilibrium conditions represent the maximum degree of separation of the components that can be obtained in a single stage. Further changes in composition may be achieved by contacting one of these phases with a fresh quantity of the other phase. For example in a solid–liquid extraction operation the underflow stream from an equilibrium stage may be contacted with fresh solvent to bring about further extraction of the solute. This application of fresh solvent to the underflow from each stage may be continued until the concentration of solute in the underflow reaches a satisfactorily low level. However, this technique requires large quantities of solvent and the solution obtained when all the overflow streams are bulked will be relatively weak in solute. Thus the costs of recovery of the solute will be relatively high.

An alternative procedure for obtaining maximum separation of components is to use a multistage countercurrent system such as that shown in Fig. 8.4. The two phases enter at opposite ends of a series of

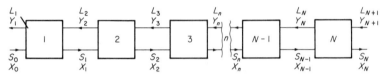

FIG. 8.4.   Multistage, countercurrent mass transfer system. N refers to last stage in the system; n refers to any stage.

stages and flow countercurrent to each other through the series. In a solid–liquid extraction system of the countercurrent type the underflow from stage 1 enters stage 2 where it is contacted with overflow from stage 3. The concentration of solute in the overflow from stage 3 will be less than that in the solution adhering to the solid in the underflow from stage 1. The two streams entering stage 2 will not be in equilibrium and will tend to move towards that state. Thus a change in composition of the two streams will occur. A similar change, not necessarily of the same magnitude, will occur in each stage of the series and result in a relatively large change in the composition of the streams after they have passed through the complete series.

For some purposes it is convenient to consider a mass balance on a complete countercurrent series, treating it very much like one equilibrium stage, as follows.

Total mass balance:

$$S_0 + L_{N+1} = S_N + L_1 = \varepsilon \tag{8.14}$$

where ε is the total mass of the mixture in the system.

Component mass balance:

$$S_0 X_0 + L_{N+1} Y_{N+1} = S_N X_N + L_1 Y_1 = \varepsilon Z_\varepsilon \tag{8.15}$$

where Z_ε is the average composition (mass fraction) of a component in the mixture in the series.

Also

$$Z_\varepsilon = \frac{S_0 X_0 + L_{N+1} Y_{N+1}}{S_0 + L_{N+1}} = \frac{S_N X_N + L_1 Y_1}{S_N + L_1} \tag{8.16}$$

Thus the value of Z_ε may be obtained graphically by the application of the inverse lever-arm rule from a knowledge of the masses and compositions of the streams entering or leaving the system.

8.1.2.1. Net flow concept. Between each pair of stages of a countercurrent system two streams pass one another (*see* Fig. 8.4). The net flow is the difference in mass flow rate between these two streams. The net flow concept may apply to the total mass flow or to the flow of one or more components in the counterflowing streams. Since there is no accumulation of total mass or components in the system the net flow is constant throughout the system. It is of course a fictitious quantity since the streams are not actually subtracted one from the other.

The total net flow Δ is given by:

$$\Delta = S_0 - L_1 = S_n - L_{n+1} = S_N - L_{N+1} \tag{8.17}$$

The net flow of a component is given by:

$$\Delta X_\Delta = S_0 X_0 - L_1 Y_1 = S_n X_n - L_{n+1} Y_{n+1} = S_N X_N - L_{N+1} Y_{N+1} \tag{8.18}$$

where X_Δ is the mass fraction of the component in the fictitious net flow stream. Also

$$X_\Delta = \frac{\Delta X_\Delta}{\Delta} = \frac{S_0 X_0 - L_1 Y_1}{S_0 - L_1} = \frac{S_n X_n - L_{n+1} Y_{n+1}}{S_n - L_{n+1}}$$
$$= \frac{S_N X_N - L_{N+1} Y_{N+1}}{S_N - L_{N+1}} = \frac{\text{net flow of component}}{\text{total net flow}} \tag{8.19}$$

It is possible to locate Δ on a composition diagram by graphical subtraction. The point representing the composition of $\Delta(X_\Delta)$ must be on a straight line through the points representing the compositions of the streams S_0 and L_1 (*i.e.* X_0 and Y_1 respectively) and also on a straight line through the points representing the compositions of streams S_N and L_{N+1} (*i.e.* X_N and Y_{N+1} respectively). It can thus be located as shown in Fig. 8.5. Since the total mass and component net flow rates are constant from stage to stage X_Δ must also lie on a straight line through X_1, Y_2; X_2, Y_3; X_3, Y_4; etc. This common point, the delta point, provides a means of relating the compositions of streams leaving adjacent stages.[1, 2]

8.1.3. STAGE-TO-STAGE CALCULATIONS

Frequently it is necessary to estimate the number of equilibrium stages required to bring about a specified degree of extraction.

Alternatively information may be required on the performance of a system with a specified number of stages. Such information may be obtained by stage-to-stage calculations. These may be started at either end of the series of stages. For example, if Y_1, the composition of the solution stream leaving the system, is known then X_1 can be obtained from a knowledge of the equilibrium relationships between the streams. In order to obtain a value for Y_2 some relationship between

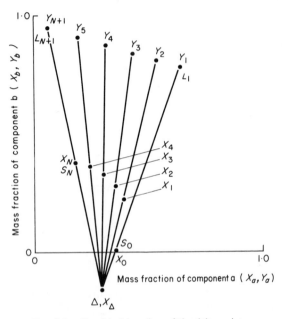

FIG. 8.5.   Graphical location of the delta point.

the streams S_1 and L_2 needs to be established. The delta point, derived from a consideration of the net flow of material between stages, may provide this stage-to-stage link. Thus with alternate use of equilibrium data and the delta point it is possible to progress from stage to stage until the specified end value of X_N is reached. In this way the number of equilibrium stages can be estimated. If the number of stages is known then this same technique may be used to obtain a value for X_N (or Y_1, if the calculation is started from the other end of the series, stage N).

The composition of each stream in a countercurrent extraction system may be represented graphically on a triangular diagram as shown in Fig. 8.6. In this diagram the right angle vertex represents pure insoluble solids. The abscissa (where $X_s = 0$) represents mixtures of insoluble solids and solute. The vertical coordinate (where $X_a = 0$) represents mixtures of insoluble solids and solvent. The hypotenuse represents mixtures of solute and solvent ($X_c = 0$). Some such triangular diagrams may be divided into saturated and unsaturated regions or two-phase regions. However, in most practical applications for solid–liquid extraction a single unsaturated solution is formed and subdivision of the triangle is unnecessary. If the quantity of solution

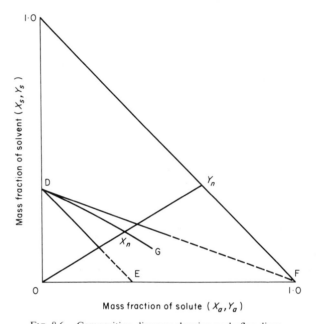

FIG. 8.6. Composition diagram showing underflow lines.

(or solvent) adhering to unit mass of insoluble solids in the underflow from each stage is known, the composition of the underflow may be represented by a line on this diagram. If the mass of solution (or solvent) retained per unit mass of insoluble solids is the same from each stage the system is said to operate under *constant underflow* conditions. If the mass of *solution* per unit mass of insoluble solids is constant for all stages the composition of the underflow may be represented by a line such as DE in Fig. 8.6. The equation to this line is:

$$X_s = \frac{k}{(k + 1)} - X_a \qquad (8.20)$$

where X_s = mass fraction of solvent in the underflow, X_a = mass fraction of solute in the underflow, k = mass of solution retained per unit mass of insoluble solids.

This line may be drawn by locating points D

$$\left(X_a = 0, X_s = \frac{k}{(k+1)} \right)$$

and E

$$\left(X_s = 0, X_a{}^\cdot = \frac{k}{(k+1)} \right)$$

on the vertical and horizontal axes respectively.

If the mass of *solvent* per unit mass of insoluble solids in the underflow from all stages is the same then the underflow composition may be represented by a line such as DF in Fig. 8.6. The equation to this line is:

$$X_s = \frac{K}{(K+1)} - \frac{K}{(K+1)} X_a \qquad (8.21)$$

where K = the mass of solvent retained per unit mass of insoluble solids. Line DF may be drawn by locating points D ($X_a = 0$, $X_s = K/(K+1)$) and F ($X_s = 0$, $X_a = 1$). If neither the mass of solution or solvent retained per unit mass of insoluble solids remains constant from stage to stage then the values obtained experimentally from each stage may be plotted on the triangular diagram to give a curved line such as line DG in Fig. 8.6.

Any straight line connecting the right angle vertex 0 ($X_s = 0$, $X_a = 0$) with the hypotenuse ($X_c = 0$) will intersect the underflow line at a point representing the composition of the underflow in equilibrium with the clear solution whose composition is represented by the point of intersection of the first line with the hypotenuse. Thus in Fig. 8.6 underflow whose composition is represented by point X_n is in equilibrium with clear solution of composition Y_n. In this example it is assumed that line DG is the underflow line. By definition, in an equilibrium stage, this means that the mass fraction of solute in the solution retained by the insoluble solids in the underflow leaving stage n is the same as that in the clear solution represented by point Y_n. Further, since the right angle vertex represents insoluble solids and point Y_n clear solution the ratio 'clear solution/insoluble solids' in the underflow, represented by point X_n, may be obtained by the application of the inverse lever-arm rule and is equivalent to the ratio of the distances $0X_n/X_nY_n$. Note that for line DE, for constant 'solution' underflow, this ratio is constant.

The delta point (*see* Section 8.1.2), may be located on the triangular composition diagram by extending straight lines through Y_{N+1}, X_N

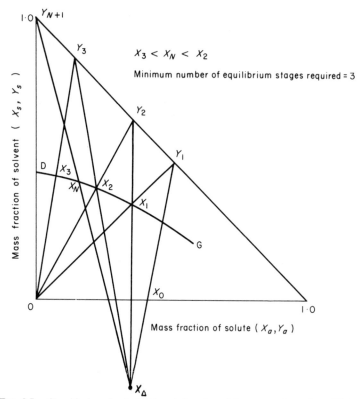

FIG. 8.7. Graphical method of determining the minimum number of equilibrium stages.

and Y_1, X_0 until they intersect as shown in Fig. 8.7. By connecting the right angle vertex 0 and point Y_1 with a straight line, X_1 may be located where this straight line intersects the underflow line DG. By extending a straight line through X_Δ and X_1 to intersect the hypotenuse, Y_2 may be located. By connecting Y_2 to 0, X_2 may be located and following that Y_3, as shown in Fig. 8.7. This procedure may be followed until the value of X_n obtained is equal to or less than the specified final value X_N. The number of straight lines connecting 0 with the hypotenuse represents the minimum number of equilibrium stages required to reduce the mass fraction of solute in the underflow to X_N. In the example shown in Fig. 8.7 the minimum number of stages required is 3. If the number of stages is specified, then provided sufficient data is available to locate the delta point, the same procedure may be used to calculate X_N (or Y_1 if the procedure is started at stage N).[1–3]

The number of actual stages required to obtain a specified degree of extraction will be greater than the estimated number of equilibrium stages. If the stage efficiency is determined and found to be independent of concentration then the number of actual stages is equal to the number of equilibrium stages divided by the stage efficiency. If the efficiency varies from stage to stage then it must be taken into account at each stage when using the graphical method for

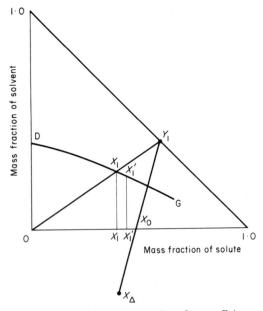

Fig. 8.8. Graphical representation of stage efficiency.

estimating the number of actual stages required. For example in the case shown in Fig. 8.8 the underflow composition, X_1, in equilibrium with the overflow composition, Y_1, is shown. If the actual composition of the underflow leaving stage 1 is found to be X'_1 then this is the value that should be used to obtain Y_2 graphically. Stage 1 efficiency in this case is $(X_0 - X'_1)/(X_0 - X_1)$.[2]

8.1.4. RATE OF EXTRACTION

The extraction of solute from a solid particle is usually considered to take place in three stages. The solute first dissolves in the solvent. The solute in solution diffuses to the surface of the solid particle.

Finally the solute moves from the surface of the solid particle, where it is assumed to be in the form of a saturated solution, into the bulk of the solution. Any one of these three steps could limit the rate of extraction. It is usually assumed that, when a correct choice of solvent has been made, the solution of the solute takes place rapidly and does not greatly influence the overall rate of extraction. It is difficult to quantify the rate of movement within the solid particle due to the complex structure of most solids. The rate of movement of solute from the saturated layer at the surface of the particle to the bulk of the solution may be described by the expression:

$$\frac{dw}{dt} = KA(C_s - C) \tag{8.22}$$

where dw/dt = rate of mass transfer of solute, A = area of solid–liquid interface, C_s and C = concentrations of solute at the surface of the solid and in the bulk of the solution respectively, K = mass transfer coefficient.

In a single stage extraction unit where V is the total volume of the solution and is constant, then

$$dw = V\,dc$$

and so

$$\frac{dc}{dt} = \frac{KA(C_s - C)}{V} \tag{8.23}$$

Integrating this expression within the limits $-t = 0$, $C = C_0$ to $t = t$, $C = C$,

$$\int_{c_0}^{c} \frac{dc}{C_s - C} = \int_{0}^{t} \frac{KA}{V}\,dt$$

gives

$$\ln\left(\frac{C_s - C_0}{C_s - C}\right) = \frac{KA}{V}t \tag{8.24}$$

If pure solvent is used initially, *i.e.* $C_0 = 0$

$$\ln\left(\frac{C_s}{C_s - C}\right) = \frac{KA}{V}t \tag{8.25}$$

Thus the solution approaches saturation at an exponential rate.[2,4]
Factors which influence the rate of extraction include:

(a) *The area of the solid–liquid interface.* According to equation (8.22) the rate of mass transfer from the surface of the solid is directly proportional to this area. Thus a reduction in particle size should result in a greater rate of extraction, due to the increased area and a reduction in the distance the solute has to move within the solid to get to the surface. However, there are limits to the degree of comminution desirable to obtain the best results in many practical cases. Too fine a solid may impede the flow of solution through the bed of solid in an extractor and in some cases cause undesirable substances to be released into the solution (*see* Section 8.1.6).

(*b*) *Concentration gradient.* The concentration gradient between that at the surface of the solid and that in the bulk of the solution is also important. The solvent must be selective with respect to the solute to be extracted. It must also have a low enough viscosity to permit

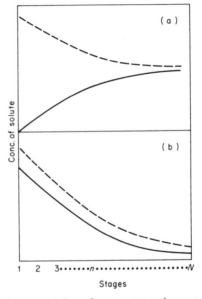

FIG. 8.9.   Graphical representation of concurrent and countercurrent extraction systems. (a) Concurrent system; (b) countercurrent system. - - - - - - - - - solid; ———————— solution.

good circulation through the bed of solid. Countercurrent systems of extraction enable control to be exercised over the concentration gradient so that extraction can continue even when the concentration of solute in the solid is low. This facilitates more complete recovery of solute as compared with that attainable in single stage or multistage concurrent systems (*see* Fig. 8.9).

(*c*) *Temperature.* Elevation of temperature usually increases both rate of solution of solute in solvent and rate of diffusion of solute through the solution. It usually, therefore, leads to an increased rate of extraction. Limits on temperature for some materials may need to be imposed, to avoid undesirable physical and/or chemical changes which could impair product quality (*see* Section 8.1.6).

(*d*) *Rate of flow of solvent.* In general the higher the velocity and the more turbulent the flow of solvent over the surface of the solid, the higher the rate of extraction. When fine solids are being extracted mechanical agitation is often employed. In the case of most food applications the solvent is made to flow, under the influence of gravity or with the aid of a pump, through a static bed of the solid. Excessive agitation of the solid can sometimes lead to undesirable disintegration of the solid particles.

8.1.5. EXTRACTION EQUIPMENT—PRINCIPLES, DESIGN FEATURES AND GENERAL APPLICATIONS

In the food industry solid–liquid extraction is mainly applied to relatively coarse, particulate materials, usually greater than 200 mesh in size. In many cases the solid has a cellular structure. The equipment used includes single and multistage static tanks and continuous moving-bed extractors. Vigorous movement of the solid is seldom desirable.

8.1.5.1. Single stage extractors. The simplest form of extractor consists of an open tank, fitted with a false bottom which supports a bed of the solid to be extracted. The solvent is distributed over the surface of the bed of solid, percolates down through it and the solution is removed through a drain beneath the false bottom. In food applications extraction is often carried out at high temperatures and pressures. In the case of oil extraction the solvent is relatively volatile. For these reasons and also for hygienic considerations, vessels are usually totally enclosed and capable of withstanding the required pressure. A simple single stage extraction unit is shown diagrammatically in Fig. 8.10. Provision may be made for recirculating the overflow. A heater may be incorporated in the feed line and/or recirculation line to enable the temperature of the solution to be maintained at the desired value. Some units are jacketed for this purpose. Such cells may be filled manually or with the aid of a conveyor or some other mechanical device. The solid residue is removed manually or dumped through an outlet in the base of the cell.

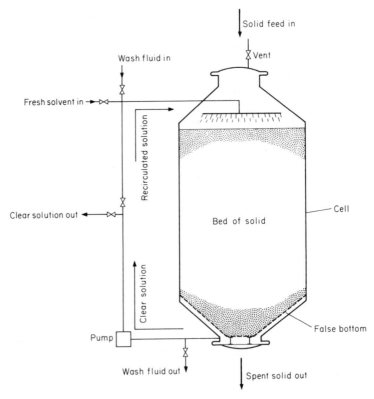

FIG. 8.10.   Single-stage, enclosed extraction cell.

Where volatile solvents are being used, it is possible to incorporate a solvent recovery and recycling system in such units. This enables a relatively concentrated overflow to be obtained (*see* Fig. 8.11). Large cells may need to be fitted with perforated shelves, chains or some other internal structures to support the bed of solid and minimise consolidation which would impair the flow of solution through the bed. Single stage units are used for pilot plant and small scale commercial operations for the extraction of oil from seeds, beans, and nuts, coffee solubles from ground, roasted beans and tea from dried leaves. Unless a solvent recovery system is included the bulked overflow from such operations will be relatively dilute, necessitating expensive solute recovery procedures.

8.1.5.2. Multistage static-bed systems. In order to carry out countercurrent extraction a number of cells may be arranged in series

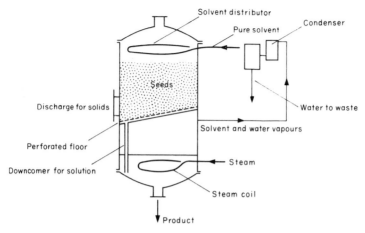

FIG. 8.11. Single-stage extractor with solvent recycle. (Reproduced from *Chemical Engineering*[2] by courtesy of Pergamon Press.)

as shown in Fig. 8.12. Each cell in the circuit contains a charge of solid and the solution from the adjacent cell is introduced into the top of the cell, percolates through the bed of solid, leaves *via* an outlet beneath the false bottom and passes on to the next cell in the series. Heaters may be interposed between cells as required. Two header pipes are usually used, one to carry solution when a cell is being bypassed, the other to carry solvent or wash liquid. The solid is not physically moved from one cell to the next, countercurrent to the direction of flow of the solution. However, a countercurrent effect is obtained as follows: at any particular time one or more of the cells is isolated from the circuit. In Fig. 8.13 three cells are shown to be thus isolated. At the time depicted in this diagram, cells numbered 10, 11 and 12 are being filled, washed and emptied respectively. The fresh solvent is being introduced into cell 13 and clear solution removed

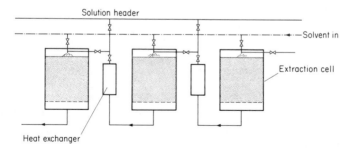

FIG. 8.12. Multistage, countercurrent, static-bed extraction system.

from cell 9. When the solid in cell 13 is fully extracted, this cell will be isolated from the circuit and cell 10 introduced in its place. The fresh solvent will then enter into cell 14 and clear solution leave from cell 10. By proceeding in this way, isolating cells in turn around the circuit, the benefits of countercurrent extraction may be obtained.

The number of cells in a countercurrent system can vary from 3 to 14 and the capacity of individual cells may be as high as 10 tons of

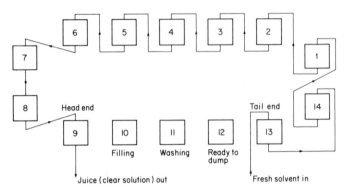

Fig. 8.13.   Multistage, countercurrent extraction battery showing flow of solution at one particular point in time.

solid. Such systems are used for the extraction of coffee, tea, oil and sugar from beet.

8.1.5.3. Continuous, moving-bed extractors. Very many designs of moving-bed extractors are available. Most operate on a counter-current principle, but some employ a combination of concurrent and countercurrent flow of solid and solution. The following are some examples of moving-bed extractors used for food applications.

Bollmann (*Hansa-Mühle*) *extractor* (*Fig.* 8.14). This is basically a bucket elevator, contained within a vapour-tight vessel. The buckets are perforated to permit throughflow of solution. Each bucket has a capacity of up to 40 kg of solid and takes about 1 h to complete a cycle. Fresh solvent is introduced near the top of the left hand leg of the unit as shown in Fig. 8.14. The solvent flows down through the buckets, countercurrent to the direction of movement of the solid, and into a sump at the base. This solution is pumped to the top of the right hand leg and flows concurrently through the downward moving solid. The final concentrated solution collects in another sump at the base from where it is pumped to filters and on to the next stage of the process.

The fresh solid is fed from a charge hopper into the buckets at the top of the right hand leg. As each bucket reaches the top of the left hand leg, having completed a cycle, it is inverted and the spent solid is discharged into a hopper from which it is removed by a conveyor. Such extractors are mainly used for the extraction of oil from bean flakes and seeds.

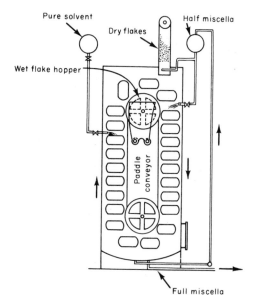

FIG. 8.14. Bollmann extractor (being used for oil extraction; miscella is solution of oil in solvent). (Reproduced from *Unit Operations of Chemical Engineering*[6] by courtesy of McGraw-Hill.)

Hildebrandt extractor (or diffuser) (Fig. 8.15). This extractor consists of two vertical, cylindrical towers, connected at the bottom by a short, horizontal cylinder. Each cylinder contains a screw conveyor, with perforated blades. These conveyors move the solid from the top of the short tower down to its base, across to the base of the second, taller tower and up to the discharge port at the top of this tower. Fresh solvent is introduced near the top of the taller tower, below the level of the spent solid discharge port. The solvent flows, under gravity, countercurrent to the direction of movement of the solid. It passes through screens and out *via* a port near the top of the short tower, below the inlet for fresh solid. The screws turn at about 1 rev/min and the capacities of such units may be as high as 40 ton/h. They are used for the extraction of oil from bean flakes and sugar from beet.

Bonotto extractor (Fig. 8.16). This unit consists of a single, vertical tower, divided into sections by horizontal plates. Each plate has an opening through which the solid can pass downwards and these openings are positioned 180° from each other on successive plates. The solid is fed onto the top plate. A rotating wiper blade moves the solid to the opening in this top plate through which it falls onto the

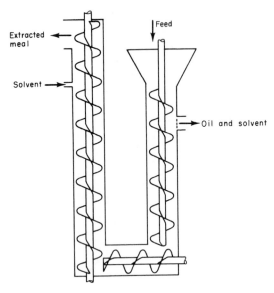

Fig. 8.15.   Hildebrandt extractor. (Reproduced from *Unit Operations of Chemical Engineering*[6] by courtesy of McGraw-Hill.)

plate below. Each plate is fitted with a wiper blade and the solid follows a spiral path down through the tower, and is discharged at the base. Fresh solvent enters at the base and is pumped upwards, countercurrent to the direction of flow of solid, to a discharge port at the top of the tower. This unit is mainly used for oil extraction from nuts and seeds.

Rotocel extractor (Fig. 8.17). In this extractor a cylindrical tank, divided into a number of sector-shaped cells, rotates slowly over a compartmented, stationary tank, covered with a wire mesh screen or perforated disc. Solid is fed into each cell as it passes beneath a conveyor feeder. After completing a cycle, spent solid is discharged through an opening in the perforated floor and removed by a screw

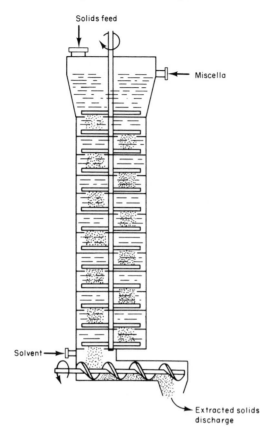

FIG. 8.16. Bonotto extractor.

conveyor. Fresh solvent is sprayed onto the solid just before it is discharged. The solvent percolates through the solid in the cell and into one of the compartments in the stationary tank beneath. From there it is pumped up and sprayed onto the solid in the preceding cell in the sequence. This occurs in each cell and so a countercurrent effect is obtained. Rich solution is removed from the compartment beneath the cell which has just been charged with fresh solid. Such units have been applied to sugar beet and oil extraction.

Many other designs of extractor are available, some for specialised applications such as coffee or sugar beet. Desludging centrifugal separators (*see* Sections 7.2.2 and 7.2.3) are also used for countercurrent extraction or washing, for example in the preparation of yeast extract and the recovery of protein isolates.[1–3, 5, 6]

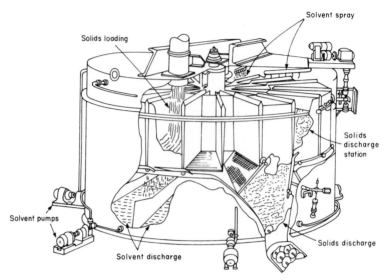

Fig. 8.17. Rotocel extractor. (By courtesy of Dravo Corporation, Chemical Plants Division.)

8.1.5.4. Complete extraction plants. The units described in the preceding section are where the actual mass transfer of solute from solid to solvent occurs. However, in a complete extraction process many other operations may need to be carried out to obtain products of the desired character and quality. The solid feed material usually has to be prepared for the extraction operation. This may involve cleaning, trimming, peeling, size reduction and heat treatment. The spent solid from the extractor may have to be stripped of solvent, dried and milled or otherwise modified for its end use. The rich solution from the extractor has to be separated into solvent and solute. This usually involves filtration, concentration and separation, by settling, centrifugation or crystallisation. The solute may need to be further treated for its end use. If the solvent is to be recycled it may need to be further purified by steam stripping, filtration and separation. An example of a complete extraction plant is shown in Fig. 8.18.

8.1.6. APPLICATIONS FOR SOLID–LIQUID EXTRACTION IN THE FOOD INDUSTRY

8.1.6.1. Extraction of sugar from sugar beet. Sugar is extracted from sliced beets using water as the solvent. Multistage,

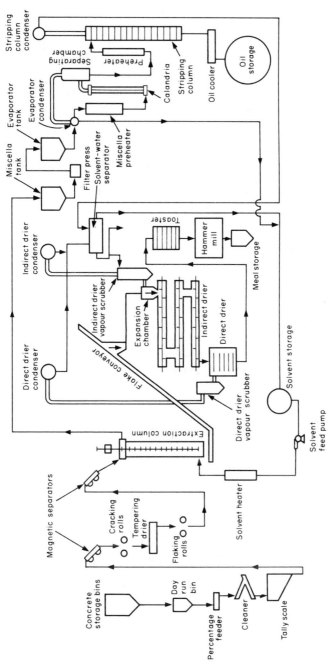

FIG. 8.18. Flow diagram for solvent extraction of soybeans. (Reproduced from *Unit Operations*[3] by courtesy of John Wiley and Sons.)

countercurrent, static-bed systems, such as that shown in Fig. 8.12, are commonly used. Some moving-bed extractors also find application in this field, particularly those shown in Figs. 8.15 and 8.16. The beet is sliced to provide an increased surface area for extraction while at the same time limiting the amount of cell damage. Excessive cell damage can result in undesirable non-sugar compounds being released into the solution. Temperature control is important. Too high a temperature can lead to peptisation of the beet cells and contamination of the solution with non-sugar compounds. The final solution, produced by extraction, usually contains about 15% dissolved solids. This is purified by settling and filtration and concentrated by vacuum evaporation. Crystallisation of the sugar from the concentrated solution is brought about as indicated in Section 9.5.2. The crystals are separated from the syrup by centrifugation and air dried.[6, 7]

8.1.6.2. Extraction of edible oil. Solvent extraction is often used as an alternative to or in combination with expression for the recovery of oil from beans, nuts and seeds. It usually results in more complete recovery of oil, as compared with that attainable by expression, with less than 1 % of oil remaining in the spent solid. Extraction is also used to a limited extent for the recovery of oil from fish products, such as livers, and meat byproducts, such as crackling. The solvents used in oil extraction are usually light petroleum fractions of the hexane (BP 63·5–69 °C) or heptane (BP 90–99 °C) type. Cyclic hydrocarbons such as cyclohexane (BP 71–85 °C) are also used. Such solvents are highly flammable and great care is necessary in their use. Non-flammable solvents such as trichloroethylene (BP 86·5 °C) have also been used but they are toxic and so also difficult to handle and with certain products the spent cake is itself toxic to cattle. Carbon disulphide has been used for olive oil extraction and acetone and ethyl ether for fish livers. Recently considerable interest has been expressed in the use of isopropyl alcohol and ethyl alcohol as solvents. Batch extractors are only used for relatively small scale, or specialised operations. Most oil extraction plants include some type of moving-bed extractor. All the types described in Section 8.1.5.3 find application in this field. Pretreatment of the feed, such as size reduction and heating, can greatly influence yield and quality of the product. Quite a complex series of operations are necessary to recover the solvent from the solution and the spent solid as exemplified by the flow sheet for soybeans in Fig. 8.18. Soybeans, peanuts, cottonseed and flaxseed are among the materials from which oil is extracted by solvent extraction.[8, 9]

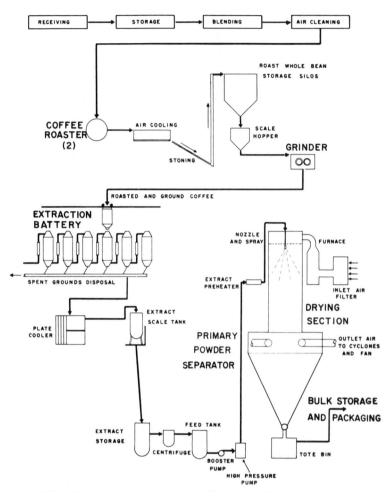

FIG. 8.19. Flow diagram of instant coffee plant. (Reproduced from *Food Dehydration*[10] by courtesy of AVI.)

8.1.6.3. Manufacture of instant coffee.

A typical flow diagram for the manufacture of instant coffee is shown in Fig. 8.19. Extraction is an important stage in such a process. The ground, roasted beans are extracted with hot water to produce a solution containing about 25–30 % solids. Extraction is usually carried out in a countercurrent, multistage, static-bed system, consisting of from 5 to 8 units. At any one point in time one cell is isolated from the circuit while the spent solid is discharged and fresh grounds introduced. Tall cylindrical pressure vessels are used with heat exchangers interposed between cells. When first introduced into the battery, the grounds are extracted with water at a temperature less than 100 °C. As extraction proceeds the solution temperature is raised up to a maximum of about 180 °C. In the latter stage of extraction some hydrolysis of insoluble carbohydrate material occurs resulting in an increase in soluble solids. The rate and degree of extraction are influenced by many factors. An increase in temperature can result in increased yield of solubles but too high a temperature may impart an undesirable flavour to the product due to excess hydrolysis. A small particle size favours a high rate of extraction, but if the grind is too fine movement of solution in the towers is impaired and excess oil may be released into the solution. Cycle times, usually in the range $\frac{1}{2}$–1 h, and the ratio water:coffee grounds, usually in the range 7:2–5:1, also influence extraction. Some specially designed, continuous extractors are also used for the extraction of coffee grounds.[10–12]

8.1.6.4. Manufacture of instant tea. Extraction of dried, blended leaves with hot water is an essential stage in the manufacture of instant tea. Extraction may be accomplished in a 3–5 stage, static-bed system. Temperatures usually range from 70 °C in the initial stages of extraction to 90 °C in the final stages. To improve the rate of flow of solution through the cells they may be evacuated after filling with leaves and the pressure restored to atmospheric level with carbon dioxide gas. The final solution usually contains from 2·5 to 5 % solids. Some continuous, countercurrent towers and moving-bed extractors, somewhat similar in principle to the Rotocel (Fig. 8.17), are also used for this purpose. The solution of soluble tea solids is then stripped of volatile aroma constituents and concentrated by vacuum evaporation, to a solids content of from 25 to 50 %. The aroma constituents are added back and the solution dried by spray, vacuum-belt or freeze drying.[10, 11]

Other applications for solvent extraction include: the extraction of essential oils from flowers; the separation of cell fragments from hydrolysed yeast; the recovery of grape sugar from pomace and the extraction of oil from wheat germ, rice bran, coconut and other sources.

8.2. EXPRESSION

8.2.1. INTRODUCTION

Many materials—fruits, vegetables and seeds—contain valuable liquid constituents within the cell structure composing them.

Groundnuts, coconuts, soya beans, sunflower seeds and olives, for example, yield edible oils and fats, while juices from a variety of fruits are used in the manufacture of various soft drinks and wines. The cell walls normally require disruption before this liquid constituent can be separated and some form of pre-treatment such as pulping or heating is often required.

Though interest has centred on the liquid being extracted, in some cases the residues have found use as animal feed. In traditional oilseed processing priority has been given to the production of oil rather than to the oilseed residue. Recent interest in protein utilisation has highlighted the possibility of the oilseed wastes as alternative sources of protein for human food sources.[13] To avoid protein denaturation during processing it may be necessary to modify the traditional extraction methods.[14] Traditionally, separation is accomplished by either solvent extraction—as in the recovery of fats from animal and vegetable materials[15]—or by mechanical expression. Expression, the unit operation considered here, is the separation of liquids from solids by the application of compressive forces and is often used in the food and beverage industries.

Three methods of expressing the liquid from the solid–liquid matrix are employed:

(i) hydraulic pressing,
(ii) roller pressing,
(iii) screw pressing.

Hydraulic presses are widely used in fruit juice processing whereas roller presses have not really been accepted.[16] Roller presses are universally used in expressing juices from sugar cane.[17]

Screw presses are being used in fruit juice expression but here they tend to be used as 'finishers', following a prior pulp thickening process using other thickening techniques. A recent process uses a basket centrifuge for pre-thickening before expression.[18, 19] Both hydraulic and screw presses are used in the extraction of oils during oil milling, the oil being expressed from cleaned oil bearing seeds after cooking and conditioning in steam cookers.[15] In general, hydraulic presses are used for batch type operations while roller and screw presses find their main application in continuous processing.

The efficiency of an expression process depends on several factors including:

(i) The yield stress of the solid phase (*i.e.* its resistance to deformation).
(ii) The porosity of the cake formed.

(iii)   The viscosity of the liquid expressed.
(iv)   The compressive force applied.

The rate of flow of liquid through the interstices of the cake or 'pomace' will depend on the thickness of the cake and on its porosity, both quantities which can vary with the degree of compression applied.

The nature of the pulp itself depends on its type and previous history. Fruit pulp for example varies with the particular variety of a fruit, with the climatic and soil conditions under which it was grown, its maturity at picking and any metabolic changes occurring during the interval between picking and processing.

8.2.2. HYDRAULIC PRESSING

Two types of hydraulic press are in common use.

(*a*) *Plate press.* The pulp to be expressed is placed in heavy cotton filter bags, or cloths, which are placed between grooved pressure plates

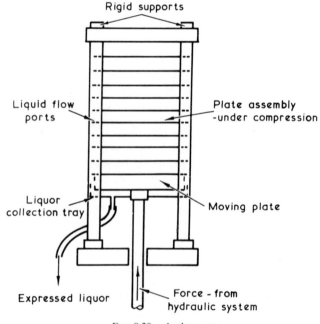

Fig. 8.20.   A plate press.

arranged in a vertical stack. Hydraulic pressure is applied across the ends of the stack, pressures of 31–62 MN/m² (2–4 tons/in²) being developed. The pulp, in the form of relatively thin layers, experiences a compressive force. Keeping the layers thin permits reasonably rapid draining of liquor through the cake interstices and across the grooved plate faces to a common receiver (Fig. 8.20).

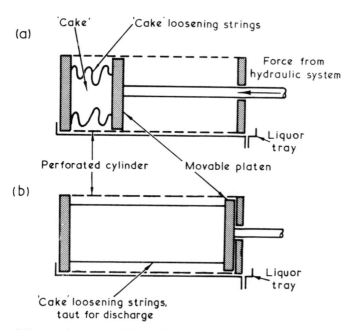

FIG. 8.21.   A cake press. (a) Cake under compression. (b) With hydraulic pressure released for cake discharge.

Filling, pressing, opening and cleaning of these batch units requires a high labour usage. In an attempt to achieve maximum extraction more economically, presses capable of exerting increasing pressures in several stages have been developed. In these units the assembly of plates moves beneath a series of pressure heads each exerting a higher pressure than the preceding head. The pressure should be increased gradually, since rapid changes can lead to sharp decreases in bed voidage with a consequent drop in drainage rate.

(*b*)   *Cage press*. For this type of press, a finely perforated cylinder carries an internal pressure plate (platen) which can be moved backwards and forwards within the cylinder, hydraulically (Fig. 8.21).

The design of the system allows close control over the pressure exerted
on a pulp charge inside the cylinder. Liquid expressed from the cake
on compressing passes through the perforations. Plastic strings
connected between the pressure plate and the closed end of the
cylinder act as drainage channels during compression, thus assisting
the rate of expression. Older presses may have chains or ropes fitted in
place of plastic strands. With some cage presses, the pressure plate is
withdrawn after an initial compression. The strings, on tightening,
loosen the cake. Combining this action with rotation of the cylinder
breaks down the cake, which can then be recompressed. Several
pressings are normally performed on a given charge.

8.2.3. CONTINUOUS PRESSES

To reduce the high labour requirements associated with hydraulic
expression, continuous presses have been developed.

(*a*) *Roller press.* In this type of unit, a compressive force is applied
by passing the pulp between heavy rollers. Modifications of this
method have been developed to improve the separation of liquid from
solid. For instance simple crushing rolls of the type used for

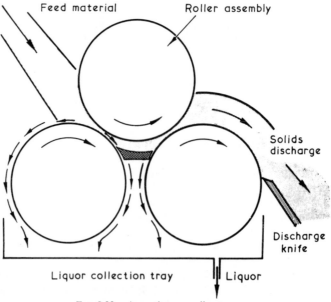

FIG. 8.22. A continuous roller press.

expressing juice from sugar cane have directional drainage grooves (Menchaerts grooves) on the roller surfaces. These grooves direct the liquors away from the compressed cake thus reducing re-wetting.[17] Pulp is fed between the rollers as shown in Fig. 8.22. Liquid is expressed from the pulp and flows to a collection launder. Solid passes to the third delivery roller where it is removed by a 'doctor' knife. In other types of roller presses, drums similar in design to those used in

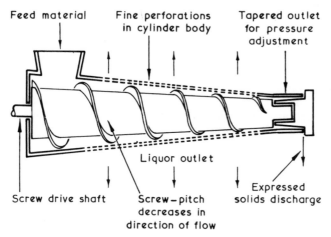

FIG. 8.23.   A continuous screw press.

drum filtration are used. The face of the drum is perforated and covered by a filter cloth. Dewatering rollers bear against the face of the drum. Pressing takes place between the drum and the rollers. Liquid is drawn through the filter cloth and into the perforated drum the interior of which may be maintained under reduced pressure to aid flow. The cake is removed by 'doctor knife' or 'string discharge'.

Roller presses used in fruit juice expression are discussed in Ref. 16.

(*b*) *Screw press*. In this unit, known in the oil milling industry as an 'expeller',[15] fruit pulps or oilseed meals are fed to a thick-walled cylinder containing a rotating polished screw having a gradually decreasing pitch. Material trapped between the screw and the inside of the cylinder barrel passes through a gradually reducing flow area, experiencing an increasing compressive force. The walls of the cylinder contain fine perforations or slots covered by adjustable screens, through which expressed liquor drains from the cake. The expressed cake leaves the unit through an adjustable discharge port (Fig. 8.23). Power consumption in these units is high. Power is dissipated in friction and may raise the product temperature appreciably. The risk of thermal degradation to heat sensitive materials can be reduced by the use of hollow water-cooled screws. The degree of compression achieved can be varied by adjusting the area of the discharge port and by varying the speed of rotation of the worm. Shaft speeds fall in the range 5–500 rev/min, depending on application, and barrel pressures of 138–276 MN/m^2 (20 000–40 000 psi) are achieved. Good separations at throughputs of up to 8500 kg/h (200 tons/24 h) are reported with the residual cake containing 4–5 % of liquid. With certain fruits, passage of fine particles with the liquid can present problems. In such cases, subsequent clarification by centrifugation or filtration may be required.

The application of various types of expression device in fruit juice processing is discussed by Crowe.[19] This author predicts the demise of the hydraulic press in fruit-juice processing in favour of the perforated, scroll centrifuge.

8.2.4. CONICAL SCREEN CENTRIFUGE

In principle this device is a 'screen-conveyor centrifuge' (*see* Fig. 7.16). Crushed fruit (or pre-extracted fruit) is fed into the machine and conveyed, by means of the rotating scroll, downwards over the inside of the conical basket wall. A centrifugal force of about 1800 g is developed which drives the juice through the perforated wall. The solids pass out as shown. The capital cost of this machine is not high when compared to the modern (automatic) batch hydraulic press and it offers considerable savings in labour.

REFERENCES

1. Foust, A. S., Wenzel, L. A., Clump, C. W., Maus, L., and Anderson, L. B., 'Principles of Unit Operations'. (Wiley: 1960.)
2. Coulson, J. M., and Richardson, J. F., 'Chemical Engineering', 2nd ed. (Pergamon Press: 1968).
3. Brown, G. G. (Ed.), 'Unit Operations'. (Wiley: 1955).
4. Charm, S. E., 'The Fundamentals of Food Engineering', 2nd ed. (AVI: 1971).
5. Perry, R. H., and Chilton, C. H. (Eds). 'Chemical Engineers' Handbook', 5th ed. (McGraw-Hill: 1973).
6. McCabe, W. L., and Smith, J. C., 'Unit Operations of Chemical Engineering', 2nd ed. (McGraw-Hill: 1967).
7. McGinnis, R. A., 'Beet-Sugar Technology'. (Reinhold: 1951.)
8. Clarke, R. J., 'Process Engineering in the Food Industries'. (Heywood: 1957.)

9. Swern, D. (Ed.), 'Bailey's Industrial Oil and Fat Products', 3rd ed. (Interscience Publishers: 1964).
10. Van Arsdel, W. B., Copley, M. J., and Morgan, A. I. Jr (Eds), 'Food Dehydration', 2nd ed., Volume II, Practices and Applications. (AVI: 1973.)
11. Masters, K., 'Spray Drying'. (Leonard Hill Books: 1972.)
12. Sivetz, M., and Elliott Foote, H., 'Coffee Processing Technology', Volume I, Fruit—Green, Roast and Soluble Coffee. (AVI: 1963.)
13. Worgan, J. T., 'World Supplies of Protein from Unconventional Sources', *in* Porter, J. W. G., and Rolls, B. A. (Eds) 'Proteins in Human Nutrition', 47–74. (Academic Press: 1973.)
14. Dunning, J. W., 'Mechanical Preparation of Vegetable Seeds for Edible Protein Concentrates', *in* Bieber, H. (Ed.) 'Engineering of Unconventional Protein Production'. Chemical Engineering Progress Symposium Series No. 93, Vol. 65, 46–48. (American Institute of Chemical Engineers: 1969.)
15. Bailey, A. E., 'Industrial Oil and Fat Products', 3rd ed. (Interscience: 1964.)
16. Swindells, R., and Robbins, R. H., 'Extraction of Fruit Juices'. Process Biochem., 1(9), 457–469 (1966).
17. Hugot, E., 'Handbook of Cane Sugar Engineering', 2nd ed. (Elsevier: 1972).
18. Durkee, E. L., Hamilton, W. E., and Morgan, A. I., 'Thick Cake Extraction'. Fd Engng, 36(12), 48–50 (1964).
19. Crowe, D. S., 'Extraction of Fruit Juices—Squeeze or G's'. Fd Technol. Aust., 22(10), 556–559 (1970).

CHAPTER 9

CRYSTALLISATION

9.1. INTRODUCTION

Crystallisation processes are used for two purposes in the food industry. A liquid material may be separated by crystallisation into a solid and liquid phase differing in composition, one or both fractions becoming products of the process. Alternatively no separation of the solid phase is attempted and all the raw material is retained in the product.

If separation is to be effected, it is necessary to obtain the maximum deposition of one component in crystalline form, to remove substantially all the crystals formed from the liquid and to carry out these operations so that the minimum of liquid is removed either through wetting the surface of the crystals or by being trapped within them. In order to separate the crystals from their 'mother liquor' it is desirable to have the crystals of comparable size. Uniformity of crystal size may also be aesthetically desirable. Hence crystallisation procedures involving separation are generally designed to produce individual crystals of a specified size and shape. In crystallisation procedures not involving separation the control of crystal size is also important. For instance the texture of confectionery such as fondant creams and fudges is dependent on the size of the crystals produced during their manufacture, as is also the texture of butter (see Chapter 5).

The process of crystallisation can be initiated either by cooling or by evaporation. To illustrate the differences between these two methods, consider a solution of sucrose in water. From the equilibrium diagram for a sucrose–water system (Fig. 9.1) it can be seen that the quantity of ice or crystalline sucrose that can be recovered in the pure state by cooling a solution is limited. At a temperature fractionally above the 'eutectic temperature' (θ_c) the system consists of crystals of one component in equilibrium with a solution at the eutectic concentration (C), while at a temperature fractionally below θ_c the equilibrium state is a single solid phase. The saturation line for sucrose, i.e. the line separating the 'solution' and 'solution + sucrose' zones, is very steep over the range shown in the diagram. Therefore a saturated solution of sucrose in water, over this range, has a concentration only very slightly above the eutectic concentration *C* and the yield of sucrose from cooling such a solution will be correspondingly limited. On the other hand, over 80 % of the water in a 20 % solution of sucrose in water can be recovered as ice by freezing.

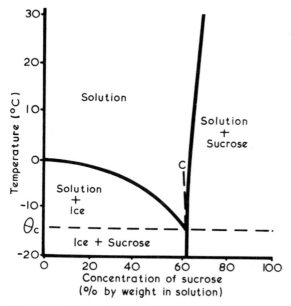

FIG. 9.1.   The equilibrium diagram for the sucrose–water system.

Since only the water is volatile in the sucrose–water system this component may be driven off by heating, so raising the concentration to that level at which crystallisation of sucrose occurs. In this instance the solution could be evaporated to dryness and all the sucrose recovered in crystalline form, an operation which could not be accomplished by cooling the solution.

The sucrose–water system has a particularly simple equilibrium diagram. Even two component systems may have more complex diagrams, *e.g.* in a case such as NaCl, where an aqueous solution of the material can crystallise both in hydrated and anhydrous forms. Systems having more than two components will exhibit a more complex pattern of behaviour and the desired product may no longer be a single component but a mixture of several. Crystallisation in such systems can still be promoted by cooling and/or evaporation, and crystallisation processes may be classified on the basis of the method used.

In these more complex systems the degree to which separation can be achieved (*i.e.* the extent to which desirable material may be concentrated in the fluid or removed with the crystals) depends on the composition of the system. In many instances, particularly with aqueous solutions in the food industry, the solution may be regarded as being composed of a solute, a solvent and certain impurities. The impurities may increase or decrease the solubility of the solute in the solvent. Occasionally impurities have no significant influence and sometimes a mixed crystal is formed. A solubility coefficient (c) can be defined by:

$$c = \frac{\text{solubility of solute in impure solution at given temperature}}{\text{solubility of solute in pure solvent at same temperature}}$$

If the impurities are such that c is greater than unity these are said to 'salt in' the solute and if c is less than unity the solute is said to be 'salted out'. It is interesting to note, in this connection, that the normal impurities found in sugar cane juice are such that $c < 1$ while the reverse is true for beet sugar juices.[1]

9.2. NUCLEATION

If a solution of a solute in a solvent is progressively cooled, or if the solvent is progressively evaporated, crystallisation does not commence immediately the concentration of one component of the solution increases above its saturation value at the temperature of the solution. The immediate effect is to produce a supersaturated solution in which crystal nucleation may, or may not, occur. The degree of supersaturation of a solution is measured in terms of the supersaturation coefficient (S) where:

$$S = \frac{\text{concentration (w/w) of solute in solvent at given temperature}}{\begin{array}{c}\text{concentration (w/w) of solute in solvent in a saturated}\\ \text{solution at the same temperature}\end{array}}$$

Obviously the solution is supersaturated if $S > 1$ and $S = 1$ defines the solubility curve.

Crystallisation in supersaturated solutions may be initiated by the addition of solute crystals. Crystallisation may then proceed by the deposition of material on the faces of these added crystals alone, without nucleation of new crystals. Alternatively, the presence of the added solute crystals may give rise to the formation of additional crystal nuclei in the solution (secondary nucleation—see below). Alternatively crystals of similar structure to the solute crystals, dust or gas bubbles may also initiate crystallisation, as may the application of mechanical shock or ultrasonic vibrations (heterogeneous nucleation). In supersaturated solutions free, as far as possible, from any crystalline material or foreign particles, crystallisation can still take

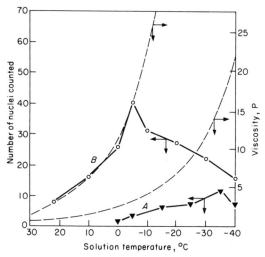

Fig. 9.2. Spontaneous nucleation in supercooled citric acid solutions in relation to the degree of supercooling and the viscosity of the solution. (From Mullin and Leci, *J. Crystal Growth*, **5** (1969), 75.)

place, nuclei being generated from the solution itself (homogeneous nucleation). The rate at which homogeneous nucleation occurs is a function of the supersaturation. Figure 9.2 shows the results of experiments on the rate of nucleation in supersaturated citric acid solutions. Solution A had a concentration equivalent to 4·6 kg of citric acid monohydrate per kg excess water giving a saturation temperature of 62 °C. Solution B was more concentrated (7 kg/kg; saturation temperature 85 °C). As may be seen, when the solution was held at progressively lower temperatures (and so the supersaturation increased) the rate of nucleation also increased up to a maximum value, after which a fall was observed. This fall in nucleation rate occurs when the viscosity of either solution is higher than 15 P (1·5 Pa s). It has been observed in some other systems, particularly in melts, which generate high viscosity at high supersaturations or supercoolings. Thus the stability of the supersaturated sugar solutions that compose high-boiled confectionery (*e.g.* barley sugar) is attributed to the very high viscosity of the product. When high-boiled sweets are 'pulled' (*i.e.* as occurs in the manufacture of peppermint rock) the air bubbles incorporated in the mass act as sites for nucleation.[2]

The nucleation behaviour shown by the experiments mentioned above is shown in generalised diagrammatic form in Fig. 9.3. The

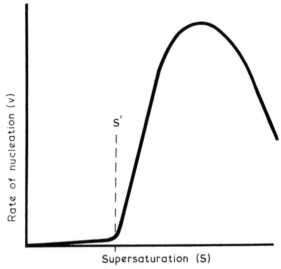

FIG. 9.3. Diagrammatic representation of the relationship between the rate of nucleation in a solution and supersaturation of the solution.

nucleation rate (v) is zero at $S = 1$ and increases only very slowly at first as the supersaturation increases. The rate then rises much more rapidly and then finally may fall again.

A theoretical explanation for the rapid rise in nucleation rate with increasing supersaturation may be obtained as follows.[3] The solubility (L) of a small spherical crystal of radius r is given by the Ostwald–Freundlich equation as:

$$L = L_\infty \exp\left(\frac{2\sigma M}{dRTr}\right) \tag{9.1}$$

where L_∞ = value of the solubility over extended plane surfaces of the material (*i.e.* the values normally quoted); σ = solid–liquid interfacial surface energy per unit area; d = density of the crystal; R = molar gas constant; M = molecular weight of the crystal material; T = absolute temperature of the system.

Equation (9.1) is similar to the Gibbs–Thomson equation describing the vapour pressure over a small droplet and it indicates that the solubility of a small crystal is greater than that of a large one. From equation (9.1) the radius (r^1) of the smallest spherical crystal stable in a solution of supersaturation S ($= L/L_\infty$) is given by:

$$r^1 = \frac{2\sigma M}{dRT \ln(S)} \tag{9.2}$$

Thus if crystal formation is to occur spontaneously in a solution, crystal nuclei of radius r^1 or greater must be formed. If the minimum energy to effect this is W, kinetic considerations suggest that the rate of nucleus formation (v) will be given by:

$$v = k \exp\left(-\frac{W}{RT}\right) \tag{9.3}$$

The value of W can be deduced to be:

$$4/3 \, \pi (r^1)^2 \, \sigma$$

—so, substituting for r^1 from equation (9.2), equation (9.3) may be rewritten:

$$v = k \exp\left\{-\frac{16\pi}{3}\left(\frac{\sigma}{RT}\right)^3\left(\frac{M}{d \ln(S)}\right)^2\right\}. \tag{9.4}$$

The rise in the nucleation rate is so rapid that, in practice, a certain supersaturation (S' in Fig. 9.3) may be defined so that, effectively, no spontaneous nucleation occurs at supersaturations below S'. This supersaturation defines the 'supersolubility curve' (Fig. 9.4). At supersaturations above S' (the 'labile zone') nucleation occurs spontaneously in the solution. At supersaturations between S' and unity (the 'metastable zone') spontaneous nucleation is negligible though crystals of solute added to the solution ('seed material') will grow in size by crystallisation on their surfaces. In the impure sucrose solutions handled during sugar refining the value of the critical supersaturation defining the supersolubility curve is found to increase as the purity decreases.[1]

Two basic approaches are possible to nucleation in industrial processes. First, finely divided solute crystals may be added to a solution which is maintained in the metastable zone of supersaturation and these seed crystals grown to finished size without any further nucleation. If it is assumed that each seed crystal supplied grows to a finished crystal of the same shape, the mass of seed material required for a given finished weight of product with a given average crystal size will rise as the cube of the characteristic linear dimension of the seed particles. Clearly, very finely divided seed material is required if its mass is to be kept to reasonable proportions.

Secondly, nuclei may be formed from the solute already in the solution either spontaneously, from solutions in the labile zone, or by secondary nucleation. If crystals are present in a supersaturated solution, particularly when the solution is agitated and in the upper ranges of supersaturation of the metastable zone, a supply of new

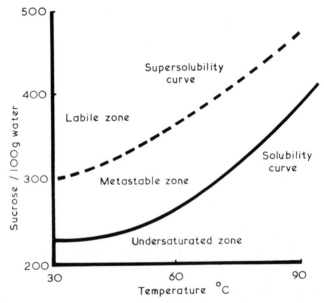

FIG. 9.4. Approximate supersolubility diagram for sucrose.

crystals can be formed. The supersaturation of the solution has to be sufficiently high that the nuclei formed from the existing crystals do not redissolve in the solution. There are several explanations for this secondary nucleation, some of which may fit the facts better in one situation than in another. For instance, small fragments may be broken from the existing crystals as they collide with each other, with the walls or agitators. Foreign particles which have not heretofore taken part in the process could become activated by contact with a crystal face and then serve as crystal nuclei. Alternatively, partly integrated units, weak outgrowths or weak conglomerates may be stripped off the crystal surfaces or torn apart by the viscous drag of passing fluid. It has been shown that in some systems the existing crystals have to be greater than a certain size to cause secondary nucleation, perhaps because they have to be large enough to induce sufficiently strong eddies for this last process to take place. Two further courses are then possible. Either the supersaturation may be maintained high enough for nucleation to continue or the supersaturation of the nucleated solution can be reduced to such a degree that nucleation ceases and growth of the existing nuclei takes place. Which method is employed in a particular situation depends to a large extent on the relative rates of nucleation and crystal growth in the system and on the degree to which the size of the finished crystals must be controlled. Also it is clear that procedures in which nucleation is arrested are best suited to batch processing.

Since the degree of supersaturation of a solution influences its nucleation behaviour, control of supersaturation is important. This is particularly true in the sugar industry where direct-reading electrical instruments have been developed to measure supersaturation. The measurement of this quantity involves the determination of both the temperature and concentration of the solution. While the former measurement is straightforward, the latter must be approached indirectly. Boiling point elevation, viscosity and electrical conductivity have been used as indications of the concentration of sugar solutions.[3]

9.3. CRYSTAL GROWTH

Subsequent to nucleation or the addition of seed material, crystals will grow in a supersaturated solution, drawing material from the liquid phase. The rate of growth of a crystal in a solution depends both on the transport of material to the surface of the crystal and on the mechanism of surface deposition. Stirring the solution during crystallisation will reduce the effect of the first factor but, even when there is no mechanical agitation, transport of material to the surface is not necessarily the rate-determining factor. Experimental evidence suggests that the rate of growth of sucrose crystals is diffusion controlled only above 40–45 °C and sodium chloride crystals above 50 °C. The presence of impurities may also affect the rate of crystal growth, generally reducing it, though the reverse effect has been reported.

The external form, or 'habit', of a crystal depends on the conditions of growth. The different faces of a growing crystal do not all advance at the same rate. This can lead to a fast-growing face being overlapped by slower-growing faces on its boundaries and 'growing out'; that is, being absent from the finished crystal (Fig. 9.5). Crystals grown rapidly from highly supersaturated solutions tend to develop extreme habits, the crystals growing into long needles or having a dendritic (tree-like) structure.

The reason for this is that crystals of this shape have a high specific surface and so can more easily dissipate the heat released as material

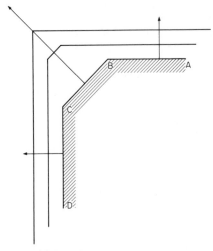

FIG. 9.5.   The modification of the shape of a crystal due to the differential growth rates of its surfaces. The diagram shows a section through the corner of a crystal. The initial crystal has a face BC growing at three times the rate of faces AB and CD. These latter faces overlap the former during the growth of the crystal, as shown.

in solution deposits on the crystal in a lower energy state. In the case of deposition from the vapour phase, say in the deposition of frost on the evaporator of a mechanical refrigerator, the energy release is higher than from a solution and crystals of extreme habit are very frequently formed.

The presence of 'impurity' compounds in the solution can also affect the shape of the crystals by selectively influencing the growth rates of different crystal faces. Materials that have this effect are known as 'habit modifiers'. A habit modifier may be a naturally occurring impurity or a material deliberately added to produce habit modification. As an example of the first category the effect of raffinose in beet sugar production can be cited. Raffinose occurs naturally in sugar beet and its concentration is increased by prolonged cool storage. In the extracted sugar syrups it has the effect both of slowing the rate of growth of the sucrose crystals and modifying their habit.[4] Up to 0·5 % of raffinose in the sucrose has no significant effect.

Between 0·5 and 1·0 % raffinose gives the sucrose crystals a distinctive cubic appearance. Peculiar flat crystals are produced as the level reaches 2 % and above this concentration the presence of the raffinose leads to thin, narrow, plates of sucrose, sometimes almost needle-like. These changes affect both the appearance of the product and its bulk density.

Examples of the deliberate addition of habit modifiers are given in Section 9.5, but it should be appreciated that the actual solvent itself may be regarded as a habit modifier. It is, after all, a material foreign to the crystal. Thus crystals of one material, formed from different solvents, can have different habits. An extreme form of habit modification is crystal inhibition, where growth is reduced to negligible proportions on all faces.

Modification of the shape of the growing crystal also occurs when such crystals come together and adhere. This gives rise to 'twinned' crystals, when the original crystals join together at a definite mutual orientation, and to crystal aggregates when the original crystals join in random orientation. When a fraction of the crystals formed in a solution aggregate, the irregular and comparatively large crystals formed influence both the subsequent processing operations and the final product. Furthermore, some of the solution from which they developed can be trapped in the interstices of the aggregated crystals, reducing the purity of the crystalline phase of the system. The formation of aggregates depends on the extent and duration of crystal–crystal contacts during the process of crystallisation. Stirring during crystallisation reduces the tendency to aggregate formation, as does the presence of surface active agents and a high dielectric constant in the crystallising solution.[5]

9.4. POLYMORPHISM

Some substances can crystallise in a variety of different forms due to differing molecular arrangements within the crystal lattice. These forms can be distinguished by their physical properties, and X-ray diffraction has been widely used in their investigation. This phenomenon, which is quite distinct from the modifications to crystal shape due to differing growth habits, is known as polymorphism. Two types of polymorphism are distinguished, reversible (enantiotropism) in which there is a reversible transition between two forms at a definite transition temperature and irreversible (monotropism).

In the food industry polymorphism is of particular technological importance in fat crystallisation. Many triglycerides can crystallise in a distinct number of crystal structures, each giving a solid of a different melting point. Almost all triglyceride polymorphism is monotropic. In this irreversible type of polymorphism a lower melting point crystal can only transform into a form with a higher melting point. It is easy to supercool fats down to the temperature of fusion of the lowest melting point form (*i.e.* the least stable form). Thereupon, crystallisation takes place rapidly in the lowest melting point form of crystal. These crystals can then transform to crystals in the higher melting point forms, the rate of transformation being a function of temperature. If the crystals are melted and the liquid fat recooled, low melting point crystals can again be produced.

9.5. CRYSTALLISATION PROCESSES IN THE FOOD INDUSTRY INVOLVING SEPARATION

9.5.1. OPERATIONS IN WHICH THE LIQUID PHASE IS THE DESIRED MATERIAL

The winterisation of salad oils and freeze concentration are examples of such processes, which essentially involve crystallisation by cooling.

9.5.1.1. Winterisation of oil. Vegetable oils—particularly cottonseed oil and lightly hydrogenated (105 iodine value) soybean oil—are used as proprietary salad oils and in the manufacture of mayonnaise. These oils contain some glycerides with melting points sufficiently high that they deposit solid crystals at the temperature of a cool larder (say 5 C). This would spoil the appearance of a salad oil and impair its pouring properties. It could also break the emulsion in a mayonnaise. The winterisation process[6] removes sufficient of these high melting point glycerides by fractional crystallisation to prevent this turbidity occurring during low temperature storage of the oil. The major difficulty of the process lies in growing the glyceride crystals in such a way that, on removal, they entrain as little as possible of the oil product. Large crystals are found to be the most favourable form for this process, so the cooling is carried out very slowly keeping the degree of supercooling, and hence the rate of crystal nucleation, low. The cooling and crystallisation process is spread over a period of two or three days and once nucleation has occurred, to prevent crystal breakdown, the crystallising oil is not stirred. At the end of the crystallisation process the mixture must be moved to filters in such a way that crystal damage is again minimised.

An alternative fractional crystallisation process for dividing oils and fats into two fractions involves crystallisation from a volatile solvent such as, for example, acetone or hexane. Suitable glyceride crystals are more quickly and easily formed from such a solution and a more complete glyceride separation is achieved since the liquid phase is of lower viscosity.

The addition of, for instance, lecithin can further reduce the possibility of fat crystallisation from winterised oil. This material acts as a crystallisation inhibitor (see Section 9.3).

9.5.1.2. Freeze concentration. This process involves the fractional crystallisation of ice from liquid foods. Although this process is traditional (it has long been used to enhance the alcoholic content of cider) it has heretofore found only limited and spasmodic use in the food industry. It has been employed, or recommended, for producing citrus juice concentrates to be preserved by freezing, for concentrating alcoholic beverages and adjusting the alcohol content of wines, for concentrating vinegar and for the preliminary concentration of liquid foods prior to freeze drying.

The advantage of this method of concentration is that heat degradation is eliminated and high quality products may be produced. Its disadvantages are twofold: the degree of concentration achievable is limited (see Section 9.1) and the process has in the past proved more expensive than evaporation. The capital cost of the plant is not the only feature contributing to the economics of the process, since the fraction of the soluble solids of the feed material discharged with the ice crystals or melted water rather than with the concentrate is highly important. Process improvements in recent years have much reduced this loss.[7]

The problem to be solved is the generation of ice crystals substantially free of inclusions of mother liquor and the separation of these from the system clean of any adhering concentrate. One recent process attempts this operation by first passing the solution to be concentrated through a scraped surface cooler (Fig. 9.9) to produce a slurry of crystal nuclei. In this unit the fluid to be cooled flows through the annular space between the cylindrical cooling surface and the axial rotor (or 'mutator') revolving within it. Blades mounted on the rotor bear against the cooling surface and continuously scrape the cooled product from it. The slurry from this unit is then fed into a crystalliser vessel, where it rises through a fluidised crystal bed. Here the nuclei from the cooler redissolve, because of their higher solubility, the water depositing on the larger ice crystals forming the bed. The solution, freed of its load of nuclei and so concentrated, is mixed with new feed-stock and recycled. The crystals in the fluidised bed, through impact, become abraded to spheroids, the debris either redepositing or forming new crystals. The system is generally similar to that shown in Fig. 9.8 except that crystals are formed by cooling instead of by evaporation. As a crystal increases in size it falls towards the base of the bed and is removed together with concentrated liquor.

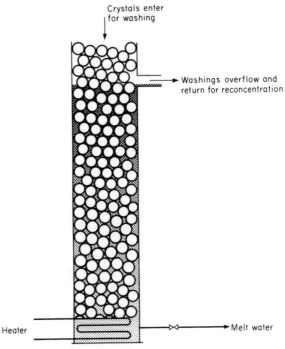

Crystals enter
for washing

Washings overflow and
return for reconcentration

Heater

Melt water

FIG. 9.6.   Diagrammatic view of the wash column. The crystals are shown enlarged to clarify the mode of operation.

The crystals must now be freed from this concentrate, which is the product, and their large size and spherical shape aid this process.

First the majority of the liquor is drained, pressed or centrifuged from the crystals to form the product. The crystals are then taken to a wash column for purification. This device is shown diagrammatically in Fig. 9.6. The heater at the base of the column melts the crystals, the majority of the melt water escaping at the base of the column. However, the rate of outflow is controlled so that some melt water rises through the crystal bed, in countercurrent flow to the crystals, washing their surfaces as it goes. The washings from the column can then be returned to the system.

9.5.2. OPERATIONS IN WHICH THE SOLID PHASE IS THE DESIRED MATERIAL

The manufacture of many crystalline compounds used in food processing (*e.g.* sodium chloride, sucrose, lactose, citric acid, monosodium glutamate, etc.) involves this operation. Also fractional crystallisation of fats (see Section 9.5.1.1) may be carried out to yield either the crystalline fraction or the liquid fraction as the desired product, *e.g.* a commercial cocoa butter substitute is crystallised from a solution of palm kernel oil in acetone. Another process which has reached pilot scale operation is the inverse of freeze concentration—the production of potable water from saline or brackish water by the crystallisation and separation of ice. Nevertheless the prime examples of this crystallisation operation are in the manufacture of salt and sugar.

9.5.2.1. Salt manufacture. In coastal areas with high insolation (*i.e.* exposed to considerable solar radiation), sea water is evaporated in shallow lagoon-like salt pans by natural agencies. Elsewhere factory methods are employed for salt production. Much salt was heretofore

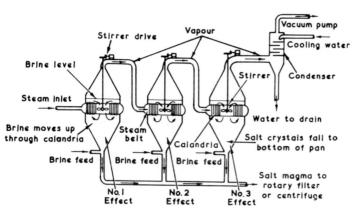

FIG. 9.7. Diagrammatic representation of a triple effect salting evaporator. (By courtesy of I.C.I. Mond Division.)

made by evaporation of brine at, or just below, its boiling point in open pans to give coarse crystals ('pan salt'). This process is wasteful of heat and labour and is being increasingly replaced by the use of multiple effect vacuum evaporators (see Fig. 9.7 and Chapter 12).

A temperature difference of about 13 C across each calandria is sufficient to maintain adequate heat transfer in salt manufacture and the presence of the salt in the boiling solution raises the boiling point of the water about 9 °C. Thus the vapour given off is superheated by this amount and will condense at a temperature 9 °C lower in the calandria of the next effect. There will therefore be a temperature difference of about 22 °C in the boiling temperature of the solutions in adjacent effects and, in the triple effect evaporator shown in Fig. 9.7, about 44 °C between the boiling temperatures in the first and third effects. In the third effect an adequate crystallisation rate is obtained with a boiling temperature of 46 °C and the vapour produced can be condensed with water at ambient temperature. The boiling temperature in the first effect will be about 90 °C, which is quite acceptable since salt is completely stable at this temperature.

The crystals formed in such units are suspended in the circulating brine and grow until they are large enough to settle to the base of the evaporator body. The system is continuous but, due to the build-up of impurity salts in the evaporating brine, the latter must be completely replaced periodically. The normal crystal form of 'vacuum salt' is cubical. The addition of a trace of potassium ferrocyanide to the brine as a habit modifier results in a dendritic form of crystal. A coarse crystal of rounded form ('Granular Salt') is also produced. Crystals of this form may be manufactured in an Oslo-type crystalliser (see Fig. 9.8) in which a salt-solution, supersaturated by flash evaporation, passes through a fluidised bed of growing crystals. Granular and dendritic salt are replacing pan salt for purposes where coarse and absorbent crystal forms are required, for instance in the curing of hides and sausage casings.

9.5.2.2. Sugar manufacture. Sucrose solutions cannot be boiled above 85 °C because coloured impurities are produced. Below 55 °C the crystallisation rate is unsatisfactorily slow. The boiling point elevation of the crystallising syrup will be about 10 °C and, due to the high thermal resistance in the fluid on the solution side of the calandria, the temperature difference across the calandria would have to be in excess of 20 °C. Thus it is not possible to use multiple effect evaporation in crystallising sugar and single effect, short-tube evaporators are normally employed. The high fluid viscosities and the requirement for uniform crystal size also lead to batch operation. The normal procedure today is to draw a quantity of syrup into the evaporator, sufficient to cover the calandria, and concentrate this to a metastable supersaturated solution. Finely ground sugar is then added and subsequent operations are conducted so that crystallisation takes place only by growth of this seed material. Syrup is added as the process proceeds, the syrup/crystal mixture (or massecuite) level rising in the evaporator body. At the end of the process the syrup/crystal ratio is allowed to fall ('tightening the massecuite') to a

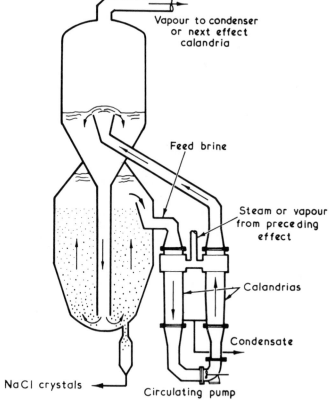

FIG. 9.8. Diagrammatic view of a 'Krystal' evaporative crystalliser for sodium chloride. (By courtesy of A. W. Bamforth, Crystallization Specialist, Stockton-on-Tees.)

degree limited by the need to maintain the massecuite sufficiently fluid.

After the finished massecuite has been discharged from the pan it is centrifuged to separate the crystals from the syrup and the latter is fed to another evaporator pan. Between two and four evaporation stages may be used, the syrup becoming increasingly impure as it passes from stage to stage and crystal growth becoming consequently slower. In the final stage of crystallisation in the manufacture of raw cane sugar, crystal growth is so slow that it is uneconomic to complete this process in the pan and the massecuite is discharged into crystallisers. These are tanks where the massecuite is cooled in a controlled manner to maintain the syrup in the metastable zone in order to complete the crystallisation process. The tanks are equipped with stirring apparatus designed to minimise crystal breakage.

9.6. CRYSTALLISATION PROCESSES IN THE FOOD INDUSTRY NOT INVOLVING SEPARATION

9.6.1. GENERAL

A number of food manufacturing processes involve a crystallisation operation in which no separation of the crystals is desired. Such operations occur in the production of frozen foods (including ice cream), of sweetened condensed milk, butter, margarine, chocolate and certain sugar confectionery. A common requirement for such processes is that the crystals produced should be below a certain critical size. Fondant and candy manufacture are to some extent a departure from this general rule in that, though the sugar crystals involved are quite small, their size may be controlled to give the desired texture to a particular confectionery item.

As examples of the processes involved, the crystallisation of ice, lactose and fat in food products is considered in more detail below.

9.6.2. THE CRYSTALLISATION OF ICE IN FOODS

The texture of thawed frozen foods is influenced, among other things, by the size of the ice crystals formed during freezing. The more rapid the cooling, the higher the rate of nucleation and therefore the smaller are the crystals formed. Additionally, it is found that, with slow cooling of materials such as fruit, vegetables, meats or fish which have a cellular structure, comparatively sparse nucleation of ice occurs in the spaces between the cells and these nuclei are fed with water by diffusion through the cell wall. The cells distort due to dehydration and the pressure of large external ice crystals. With more rapid cooling, the nucleation rate is higher but now nucleation occurs within the cell itself.

Ice cream, which is eaten in a partly frozen condition, requires small ice crystals for a smooth texture. The requisite intense nucleation can be achieved in a scraped-surface heat exchanger (Fig. 9.9). Here the ice cream mix is rapidly cooled to a temperature where nucleation occurs freely. The mechanical agitation not only speeds the cooling but leads to conditions favouring secondary nucleation. The frozen product leaves this heat exchanger in a plastic condition, where it can be formed into the required portions. Subsequently it may be hardened by further prolonged cooling. This is a process of crystal growth.

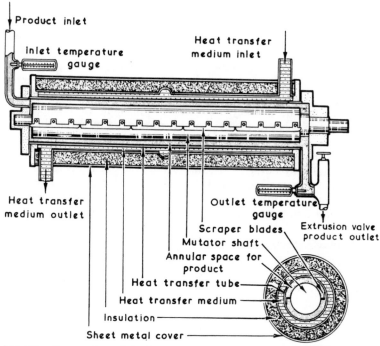

Product inlet

Inlet temperature gauge

Heat transfer medium inlet

Heat transfer medium outlet

Outlet temperature gauge

Scraper blades

Mutator shaft

Annular space for product

Heat transfer tube

Heat transfer medium

Insulation

Sheet metal cover

Extrusion valve product outlet

FIG. 9.9. Cross-sections of the 'Votator' type scraped surface heat exchanger. (By courtesy of A. Johnson & Co.)

It has already been noted that solubility is a function of crystal size (equation 9.1). This has an important bearing on the storage of products where crystal size has to be a minimum, such as frozen foods. Consider such a material stored under conditions of fluctuating temperature. As the temperature rises, some of the ice present will melt and, because of the enhanced solubility of small crystals, these will melt first. As the temperature falls, ice will again be frozen out, but will deposit on the larger crystals as the supersaturations involved are insufficient to generate new nuclei. Thus, under these conditions, large ice crystals will form at the expense of small and product quality is lost.

To retard this recrystallisation in ice cream, and to help inhibit the growth of large ice crystals during primary freezing, a stabiliser is added to the mix.[8] This stabiliser is a gel-forming agent, such as carboxymethylcellulose (CMC) which reduces the mobility of the liquid water and acts as a habit modifier, reducing the rate of growth of the ice crystal faces.[3]

9.6.3. LACTOSE CRYSTALLISATION IN FOODS

There is about 5 % lactose in cows' milk and it contributes about 40 % of the total solids. A saturated aqueous solution at 20 °C contains 16 % lactose and this solubility is reduced in the presence of sucrose. Thus in products with a high milk solids content lactose crystallisation can be a problem. Lactose crystals dissolve slowly in the mouth and if they are over 30 μm long they impart an objectionable sandy texture to the product. For a satisfactorily smooth texture crystals should be no more than 10 μm long.[9]

In ice cream, the growth of objectionably sized lactose crystals will be promoted by storage, particularly at fluctuating temperatures (see Section 9.6.2) and so is not a problem in ice cream consumed immediately on freezing. For products which will be stored, the milk-solids-not-fat content must be limited to prevent too high a lactose concentration.[8]

In sweetened condensed milk the excess lactose is crystallised out as small crystals by cooling to a temperature where the product is supersaturated with lactose but not too viscous (say 30 °C), seeded with fine lactose crystals and then held at a constant temperature with agitation to obtain secondary nucleation. Alternatively, the hot product may be pumped through cooling coils which may be precoated with an already treated batch of material to provide the initial supply of crystals for secondary nucleation.

9.6.4. FAT CRYSTALLISATION

Margarine is a water-in-oil emulsion, the oil phase of which contains a mixture of different base materials and thus a whole range of differing triglycerides. At room temperature a finished table margarine will have only about 20–25 % of the triglycerides in solid form and these solid fat crystals will be of the order of 3–10 μm. Too large crystals will give a grainy texture, too small will give a product lacking in plasticity.[10]

To produce the desired crystal formation, the emulsion is spread on the surface of a chilled drum or passed through a scraped surface heat exchanger (Fig. 9.9), where it will rapidly supercool and nucleate. The material emerging from this process is too hard, with too much solid triglyceride. Slight warming and mechanical working of the material causes recrystallisation to the required final composition.

Peanut oil is liquid at room temperature and can separate from peanut butter. Peanut butter is therefore stabilised by producing a matrix of fine crystals of added solid fat in the material. These crystals are produced with extreme habits to complex as much oil as possible. Hydrogenated peanut oil was used for this purpose, but it can lose some of its stabilising power in storage due to enantiotropic recrystallisation (see Section 9.4). Other fats are therefore now used.[6]

Monotropic recrystallisation is also a problem in chocolate manufacture. Not only must the fat crystals produced when chocolate solidifies be sufficiently small to give the product a good appearance, but they must also be in a stable form so that subsequent recrystallisation, resulting in loss of surface appearance ('fat bloom') is avoided. This operation of producing suitable fat crystal nuclei in the molten chocolate is known as tempering. The triglycerides in chocolate heated to 49 °C will all be liquid. On cooling to 27 C unstable nuclei are formed. On re-heating to 31–32 C, these are converted to stable (β) polymorphs and subsequent crystal growth, as the chocolate is cast or enrobed, will be in this form.

REFERENCES

1. Hugot, E., 'Handbook of Cane Sugar Engineering', 2nd ed. (Elsevier: 1972).
2. Lees, R., and Jackson, E. B., 'Sugar Confectionery and Chocolate Manufacture'. (Leonard Hill: 1973).
3. Mullin, J. W., 'Crystallisation', 2nd ed. (Butterworths: 1972).
4. McGinnis, R. A. (Ed.) 'Beet Sugar Technology', 2nd ed. (Beet Sugar Development Foundation: 1971).
5. Van Hook, A., 'Crystallisation, Theory and Practice', A. C. S. Monograph No. 152. (Reinhold: 1961).
6. Weiss, T. J., 'Food Oils and Their Uses'. (AVI: 1970).
7. Thijssen, H. A. C., Proceedings of the 3rd International Congress of Food Science and Technology, 491. (I.F.T.: 1971).
8. Hyde, K. A., and Rothwell, J., 'Ice Cream'. (Churchill Livingstone: 1973).
9. Webb, B. H., and Whittier, E. O. (Eds.) 'Byproducts from Milk'. (AVI: 1970).
10. Anderson, A. J. C., and Williams, P. N., 'Margarine', 2nd ed. (Pergamon: 1965).

CHAPTER 10

HEAT PROCESSING I

10.1. INTRODUCTION

The manufacture of foods involves two broad types of conversions—those concerned primarily with physical changes and those in which irreversible chemical changes are the main purpose of the activity. Physical conversions, such as size reduction and centrifugation, are conventionally regarded as *unit operations*. Conversions in which the main effects are chemical in nature are referred to as *unit processes*.

Using these conventions, the subject of food processing may be rationalised. Thus, instead of considering foods on a commodity basis, it is more convenient to deal with these in groups, each of which is based on a common, physical or chemical, conversion activity. The unit process of 'heat processing' embraces baking, boiling, frying, grilling, blanching and other conversion activities where the application of heat is used primarily to effect chemical changes in the food. This chapter is concerned with the food engineering aspects of the unit process of heat processing.

10.2. MODES OF HEAT TRANSFER INVOLVED IN HEAT PROCESSING OF FOODS

Heat flow, in some foods, is susceptible to analysis on the bases of the classical theories of conduction, convection or radiation (*see* Appendix II). However, in many cases, combinations of two or all three modes of heat transfer are effective simultaneously, and mathematical treatments become either very involved or impracticable. The situation is further complicated by the fact that heat processing, in changing the chemical nature of the food, also brings about changes in its *physical* properties. Thus, viscosity and density change, often continuously, during heating, and such changes profoundly affect the thermal behaviour of the food. Added to this is the fact that there is a dearth of knowledge relating to the physical and thermal properties of foods. Finally, foods are seldom of simple geometric shape or of homogeneous composition. From the foregoing, the difficulties of applying any precise mathematical treatment to heat flow in most practical systems becomes obvious. Nevertheless, much progress has been made in the mathematical treatment of heat transfer. These treatments, although invaluable in assisting our understanding of the interaction of the factors controlling heat flow in foods, are either excessively generalised or too specific or too empirical.[1]

10.3. METHODS OF HEAT GENERATION FOR HEAT PROCESSING

Heat is generated from four main sources of energy:

(i)   Solid fuels, *e.g.* coal, coke or wood.
(ii) Liquid fuels, *e.g.* fuel oils, paraffin or kerosene.
(iii) Gaseous fuels, *e.g.* coal gas, natural gas, petroleum gases, etc.
(iv) Electrical energy generated from solid, liquid, gaseous or nuclear fuels or by water power.

The selection of the source of heat for the heat processing of foods involves consideration not only of the general economic properties of the source of energy but also of the effects of the fuel and its by-products on the food. In general, the best compromise must be arrived at considering the following requirements:

(i)   The lowest fuel cost per unit of useful heat.
(ii)   The lowest capital and maintenance costs for combustion and transfer equipment.
(iii) The lowest direct labour cost per unit of useful heat.
(iv)   The lowest fire and explosion hazard in dusty conditions.
(v)   The lowest risk of product contamination by the fuel and its by-products.
(vi)   The maximum of flexibility in operation and control.
(vii) The maximum of reliability in continuity of supply.

10.3.1. SOLID FUEL

Coal, of various types, represents the most abundant source of primary energy in the major industrial countries of the world. In 1975 coal contributed about 40 % of the total primary energy consumed in

Food Engineering Operations

the UK. Supplies of North Sea gas and oil are expected to reach a peak by the mid-1980s. Current estimates suggest that stocks of these fuels should last for 30–40 years. Depending on price, this could mean a temporary reduction in the use of coal as an energy source followed by an increase as stocks of other fossil fuels fall.

TABLE 10.1
Average properties of UK fuels

	Gross calorific value (MJ/kg)	Sulphur (%)	Moisture (%)	Ash (%)
Solid				
Anthracite	32·5	1	8	8
Coal	29	2	5–10	8
Coke	28	1	0·5–5	1–5
Wood (air dried)	14	–	12	4–5
Liquid				
Kerosene	46·5	0·2 max.	neg.	–
Gas oil 34 sec[a]	45·5	0·75 max.	0·05 max.	0·01 max.
Fuel oil 220 sec[a]	43·5	3·2 max.	0·5 max.	0·05 max.
Fuel oil 950 sec[a]	43	3·5 max.	0·75 max.	0·07 max.
Fuel oil 3 500 sec[a]	42·5	3·5 max.	1·00 max.	0·10 max.
Gaseous				
Town Gas[b]	18·6 MJ/m^3	neg.	neg.	neg.
Natural Gas (North Sea)	37·2 MJ/m^3	neg.	neg.	neg.

[a] Viscosity, seconds Redwood I at 100 °F (38 °C).
[b] Blend from various sources (coal, coke oven, water gas, oil based etc.).

The average properties of solid fuels, compiled from various sources, are compared in Table 10.1. From this it may be seen that these fuels are characterised by high sulphur and ash contents. Additionally, coal and anthracite often contain traces of volatile, toxic materials like lead and arsenic compounds and they are dusty to handle. These facts contra-indicate the use of such fuels in food processing other than for steam raising or indirect fired equipment. In any application it is vital to prevent product contamination by the fuel, its fumes or its ash, by isolating the burners and the fuel storage bunkers from the production area.

10.3.2. LIQUID FUELS

Table 10.1 indicates the properties of some typical liquid fuels. Of these, petroleum-derived fuel oils of various viscosities represent the most widely used group of industrial heating fuels. British Standard Specifications[2] are accepted as basic requirements for oil fuels sold in the UK, whilst in the USA specifications are laid down by the American Society for Testing and Materials (ASTM). The gross calorific values of these fuels are reasonably constant, whatever the grade, at around 41 MJ/litre (175 000 Btu/Imp. gall). The price of fuel oils decreases as the viscosity increases but the higher viscosity oils must be kept hot enough to allow them to be pumped from storage to the burners. The lower price is, therefore, offset, to a certain extent, by the capital and maintenance costs of the additional equipment involved.

When used in the food industry, liquid fuels are best restricted to use in indirect fired equipment since, although the combustion gases are substantially free from toxic materials, their high sulphur dioxide content may lead to product contamination. Additionally, there is an ever-present risk of contamination by odours and smuts arising as a result of incomplete combustion. Finally, fuel oils are characterised by pungent odours so that it is imperative to ensure that valves and pipelines are completely leakproof and that the oil storage area is isolated from the production area.

10.3.3. GASEOUS FUELS

Table 10.1 lists the properties of the two main gaseous heating fuels. Town gas in the UK is a variable blend of gaseous fuels, the blend itself being standardised to a gross calorific value of $18 \cdot 6 \, MJ/m^3$ (500 Btu/cu ft). Various gases, as available, are used. For instance, in 1965 the gas sources were as follows:

coal gas (retort) 35 %, oil gas 14 %, coke-oven gas 12 %, water gas 11 %, liquefied petroleum-gas 11 %, refinery gas 8 %, natural gas 7 %, other gases 2 %.

North Sea gas is 90 % methane; it is practically free from water, sulphur and other impurities; it has a high calorific value and is non-toxic. No on-plant storage of gas is required (*cf.* solid and liquid fuels), but its use presents a fire and explosion risk. Natural gas differs from town gas in several respects, notably in possessing a lower flame-propagation rate, and this calls for special burner design to ensure flame stability.

In the food industry, the properties of gas—combined with its flexibility, ease of control and low labour involvement—make it an attractive fuel for both direct and indirect fired equipment.

10.3.4. ELECTRICITY

Although electricity is not a primary source of heat energy it is widely used for industrial heating. Due to the low efficiency of conversion of primary energy in electricity generation (only about 40 % in the UK), electricity is a costly source of heat. This is offset, to a certain extent, by the high thermal efficiencies obtainable in electrical heating systems. In the food industry, electricity offers excellent flexibility and control, low fire and explosion risk and excellent hygiene and cleanliness properties.[3]

10.4. METHODS OF APPLYING HEAT TO FOOD

10.4.1. INTRODUCTION

Foods are heated by indirect or direct methods. In indirect heating, heat is applied to the food through heat exchangers, the products of combustion being isolated from the food. In direct systems the heat energy is passed directly into the food without the intervention of heat exchangers, the products of combustion being in direct contact with the food. The methods of heat application in use and under development for the heat processing of foods may be classified as follows:

(i)   Indirect heating by:

    (a) Vapours or gases such as steam or air.
    (b) Liquids such as water and organic heat exchange liquids.
    (c) Electricity, in resistance heating systems.

(ii) Direct heating:

    (a) Using gas, oil and solid fuels.
    (b) Using infra-red energy.
    (c) Using electricity, by dielectric or microwave methods.

10.4.2. INDIRECT HEATING METHODS

These systems comprise, basically, four components: (i) a combustion chamber where the fuel is burnt and its products of combustion disposed of; (ii) a heat exchanger where the heat of combustion is taken up by a heat transfer fluid; (iii) a transfer system in which the heated transfer fluid is passed to the heat user and (iv) a

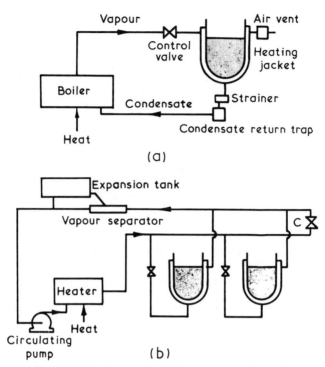

FIG. 10.1. Simple fluid heating systems. (a) Vapour system. (b) Liquid system—the control valve C automatically maintains a constant pressure between the delivery and return manifolds.

heat exchanger at the user-end of the system where the transfer fluid exchanges its heat with the food. Figure 10.1 illustrates typical vapour and liquid systems serving jacketed heat-users. Components (i) and (ii) above constitute a boiler in these cases. Types of boiler, their design and application are discussed elsewhere.[4]

Variations of this basic system include:

(i) the use of gaseous transfer media such as air or steam which are passed into or over the food;

(ii) heating the food by contacting it directly with a heat exchanger.

10.4.2.1. Indirect heating of foods by vapours or gases. Saturated steam and air are commonly used heat transfer media. Steam may be used for heating in either its saturated or its superheated form; it may also be used to operate electrical generators and vacuum ejectors and as a motivator for machinery. No other material possesses these unique properties, and for this reason a source of steam is an essential requirement in most food plants.

Thermodynamically, saturated steam is also exceptional. When applied as a heat transfer medium it has a high latent heat and a high thermal conductivity, which are advantageous. On the other hand, it has a high vapour pressure and low critical point which are disadvantageous. In its other properties, steam has much to recommend it to the food processer: it is non-toxic, fire and explosion proof and odourless; it is produced from a cheap and abundant raw material. In normal practice, saturated steam is used for food processing up to temperatures in the region of 200 C. Above this, the cost of the necessary high pressure equipment starts to become unduly high. Perry[4] gives much useful information relating to steam as a heating vapour.

At temperatures above its saturation temperature, steam behaves as any other gas and, although it has somewhat better thermal properties than air, it is comparable with the latter as a heat transfer medium. Superheated steam, therefore, finds little heating application in the food industry although the Dole aseptic canning process uses superheated steam to effect sterilisation of cans and lids (Section 11.4.2.1).

Air is a poor heat transfer fluid since it has low specific heat and thermal conductivity. Nevertheless, air is used for the heating of canned foods in the Ekelund cooker (Section 11.3.3.2), for baking (Section 10.5.2) and in fluidised bed cooking.[26] In all these cases transfer is by forced convection. In hot-air driers, air acts both as a heat and mass transfer medium (Section 13.2.2). Air is, of course, non-toxic and non-contaminating although it can bring about deterioration in foods which are sensitive to oxidation.

10.4.2.2. Indirect heating of foods by liquids. Liquids such as water, mineral oils, chlorinated hydrocarbons and fused salts are used for general process heating. With the exception of water, these liquids find application in high temperature processing since they have the advantage of low vapour pressures. The more important properties of some typical heating liquids are set out in Table 10.2.

High temperature hot water is a most useful medium at temperatures up to 200 C when advantage may be taken of its high specific heat and thermal conductivity. Additionally, in the absence of oxygen, there is little corrosion and, since evaporation is absent, scale formation is minimal. The other liquids all possess odours so that great care must be taken to prevent leaks if product contamination is to be avoided.

TABLE 10.2
Properties of some heat exchange fluids

	M.pt. (°C)	B.pt. (°C)	S.ht.[a] (kJ/kg °C)	Enthalpy[a] above 0°C (kJ/kg)	Thermal conductivity (J/m s °C)	Vapour pressure at °C (kN/m²)	Practical operating range (°C)
Water	0	100	4·3	625	0·68	1 540 (200)	0 → 200
Steam	—	—	2·0	2 740	0·17	—	100 → 200
Air	—	—	1·0	150	0·03	—	—
o-Dichlorobenzene	−22	180	1·6	490	0·11	600 (260)	−17 → 260
Mineral oil	—	—	2·3	350	0·12	10 (316)	10 → 320
Chlorinated diphenyls	—	> 320	1·3	180	0·09	30 (315)	10 → 320
Organosilicate	—	> 320	2·0	300	0·13	13 (316)	10 → 320
Diphenyl/Diphenyloxide	12	260	2·2	580	0·13	1 500 (400)	15 → 400

[a] Measured at 150°C.

10.4.2.3. Indirect heating of foods by electrical resistance heating.
The generation of heat by the flow of current through a resistor is
known as resistance heating. Process vessels may be heated in this
manner by attaching resistors to the vessel walls or by immersing
sheathed resistors in the material to be heated (immersion heating). The
heating elements used are generally made from spirally wound,
nickel–chromium wires. They may take the form of rigid platens fixed
to the vessel wall or may comprise flexible jackets for vessels or tapes
for pipelines and valves. These elements work at temperatures up to
800 °C so that, since heat transfer into the food is primarily
conductive, high rates of transfer may be produced at the point where
it is required and with a high degree of control.[16] Resistance-heated
baking ovens are common; resistor banks are located within the oven
cavity, heat being conveyed to the food by a combination of
conduction, convection and radiation.

10.4.3. DIRECT HEATING METHODS

The risks attendant upon the direct heating of foods by solid,
gaseous and liquid fuels have been indicated (Section 10.3) but
numerous direct fired baking ovens, malt kilns and driers are
encountered in the food industry. Solid fuels, gas and fuel oil are used
in this way, gas being favoured because of its freedom from potential
contaminants.

Direct heating, by means of electrode boilers,[16] finds some use in
special steam-raising applications when steam is required either
intermittently or at a user-point uneconomically remote from the
main steam source. This method, although of high thermal efficiency, is
only an economic possibility in special circumstances or when a cheap
source of electric power is available.

Induction heating, that is heating in a material by means of the
currents induced in that material by an alternating magnetic field,[6] is
only applicable to electrically conducting substances. Thus, although
widely used in many other branches of industry, induction heating
finds little application in the food industry. Inductively heated
reaction vessels would appear to have applications in food processing
because of their precisely-controllable area-heating characteristics
and fast heating properties.

Direct heating by infra-red energy generated by radiants heated
either electrically or by fuels is important in food processing both as a
heating method and as a contributor in equipment heated by other
direct and indirect systems.

Two other methods of direct electrical heating—dielectric heating and microwave heating—have been the subject of intense investigation by the food industry over the last decade. These are now well established as valuable heating methods in certain fields of heat processing. Additionally, these methods appear to have considerable potential, as yet unexploited, in several new applications. Both methods use high-frequency energy and, to avoid interference in radar, television and radio transmissions, the frequencies permitted for use for industrial, scientific and medical purposes are regulated by international agreement (Table 10.3).

TABLE 10.3
High frequencies for industrial, scientific and medical purposes
(International Telecommunication Union. Radio Regulations, Geneva 1976)

Frequency (MHz)	Wavelength	
13·56 ± 0·05 %	22·1 m	
27·12 ± 0·6 %	11·1 m	
40·68 ± 0·05 %	7·4 m	
433·92 ± 2·0 %	69·2 cm	⎧Allocated only to Region 2 (Greenland
915 ± 25[a]	32·8 cm	⎨ and N. and S. America)
2 450 ± 50	12·2 cm	⎩
5 800 ± 75	5·2 cm	
22 125 ± 125	1·4 cm	

[a] *Note.* The Wireless Telegraphy Regulations 1971 (SI.1675. HMSO) permits the use of the frequency range 886–906 MHz in radio frequency heating apparatus subject to limitations on the maximum radiated field strength and maximum terminal voltage of the apparatus.

10.4.3.1. Infra-red heating of foods.

This is carried out by means of banks of radiant heaters located in a tunnel through which food is conveyed. Electrically heated radiants are of two types, medium temperature heaters and high temperature heaters. In medium temperature heaters, filaments operating at 500–1000 °C are sheathed in metal or silica tubes. These generate energy at an intensity of around 15 kW/m². High temperature radiators comprise either tungsten filament lamps or filaments sheathed in quartz tubes. These operate at filament temperatures of about 2500 °C and are available with energy outputs of 10–65 kW/m² depending on type. Although some of the heat is transferred convectively, the majority of the energy is radiated in the infra-red with a range of wavelengths between 0·75 and 350 μm (Fig. 10.2).

Radiant energy is transformed into heat only on absorption, a process described by Beer's Law which states:

$$I = I_0 \exp(-\alpha x) \qquad (10.1)$$

where I is the amount of radiation and α is the absorption coefficient.
incident intensity of radiation and α is the absorption coefficient.
Practical systems involve selective radiators (*see* Appendix II) so that
absorption varies from zero ($\alpha \to 0$) at some wavelengths, to complete
absorption ($\alpha \to \infty$) at other, selective wavelengths. Only wavelengths
up to about 50 μm are of practical importance in food heating. Water

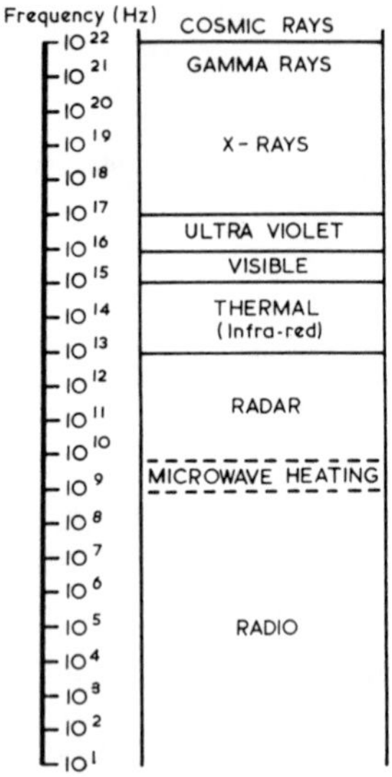

Frequency (Hz)	
10^{22}	COSMIC RAYS
10^{21}	GAMMA RAYS
10^{20}	
10^{19}	X - RAYS
10^{18}	
10^{17}	
10^{16}	ULTRA VIOLET
10^{15}	VISIBLE
10^{14}	THERMAL (Infra-red)
10^{13}	
10^{12}	
10^{11}	RADAR
10^{10}	
10^{9}	MICROWAVE HEATING
10^{8}	
10^{7}	
10^{6}	
10^{5}	RADIO
10^{4}	
10^{3}	
10^{2}	
10^{1}	

FIG. 10.2.   The electromagnetic spectrum.

and aqueous systems absorb best at wavelengths around 1 μm.
Ideally, for maximum absorption, it is necessary to produce an
intense, narrow spectrum tuned to the absorption bands of the
substance to be heated but, in practice, realisation of this can only be
partial. The relevant theory is discussed briefly in Appendix II.3 and
more fully elsewhere.[5]

When absorption of infra-red energy occurs, it is characterised by
low penetration, and produces rapid surface cooking of the food. This
results in rapid sealing and browning of the outer layers. Water and
volatile flavours tend to be retained, making the food more juicy and
flavoursome. Penetration to the centre of the food-piece is mainly by
conduction, which is often a slow process. It is important, therefore,
when using this method of heating, to ensure that an adequate final
centre-temperature is obtained. Radiant heating has many
applications in food processing such as: grilling; toasting; baking;
cooking; specialised dehydration procedures, *e.g.* drying of sugar

cubes and nuts and in freeze drying; melting of fats and as a component of other heating methods, *e.g.* in direct fired boilers and ovens.[5, 16]

10.4.3.2. Dielectric heating of foods

Dielectric heating theory. Dielectric heating is defined[6] as heating in an electrically insulating material by the losses in it when subjected to an alternating electric field. The material to be heated constitutes a dielectric sandwiched between capacitor plates connected to a capacitative, high-frequency, alternating generator. Heating is brought about by molecular friction due to the rapid orientation of the electric dipoles under the influence of the high-frequency alternation of the applied field.

The power (P) developed in a parallel plate capacitor is given by the relationship:

$$P \propto E^2 . f . \frac{A}{d} . \varepsilon_r . \tan \delta \qquad (10.2)$$

where E = electrical field strength, f = frequency, A = area of the dielectric, d = thickness of the dielectric, ε_r = relative dielectric constant of the dielectric, $\tan \delta$ = loss tangent of the dielectric. ($\varepsilon_r \tan \delta$ is referred to as the 'loss factor' of the dielectric.)

For P to be maximal, E, f, A and $\varepsilon_r \tan \delta$ must be as high as possible whilst d should be as small as possible. The system is, however, subject to the following restraints:

(i)   The applied voltage is limited by the dielectric strength of the material being heated, and by the occurrence of 'flash-over' between the capacitor plates. For these reasons industrial equipment is usually limited to about 15 kV.

(ii) Designers of equipment are limited in the frequencies they may use and also by the fact that the cost of high-frequency capacitative generators increases steeply at frequencies above about 100 MHz. Commercial dielectric heaters therefore use the lower frequencies, 27 MHz being a common frequency.

(iii) The dimensions 'A' and 'd' of the food-piece are often predetermined, *e.g.* biscuits, fish pieces and so on. There is some flexibility in the case of bulk fluid foods, but according to Absil[7] the maximum dimension (L) of a capacitor is limited by $L < \lambda / 16 \sqrt{\varepsilon_r}$ where λ is the wavelength involved. The thickness d is limited by 'flash-over' between the plates.

(iv) The loss factor, '$\varepsilon_r \tan \delta$', is a property of the dielectric (the food) and is both frequency and temperature dependent.

Equipment design. Dielectric heating equipment generally comprises a low-loss belt which conveys the food at a controlled rate between the plates of the capacitor. The top plate may be raised or lowered to control the heat generated in the product, and power input is also variable. It is usual to fit traps at the input and outlet points of the conveyor in order to limit R.F. leakage. Heaters capable of dissipating 30 kW of energy in the food with an efficiency of about 50 % are usual, although units generating hundreds of kilowatts have been constructed.

Characteristics of dielectric heating. This type of heating has the following characteristics:

(i)   The rate of heating is very fast compared with conventional methods.

(ii)   The fastest heating point occurs at some depth below the surface of the food so that heat losses are minimised.

(iii)   Local overheating is minimised and this, in conjunction with (i), reduces heat damage to the food.

(iv)   Because of its speed, dielectric heating saves working space.

(v)   It is clean, continuous in operation and is well suited to automatic control.

(vi)   There is no surface browning of the food.

(vii)   Energy is generated directionally so that the orientation of the food unit in relation to the capacitor plates is of great importance in determining the magnitude of the ratio A/d.

Food-processing applications of dielectric heating. Dielectric heating is used to thaw frozen eggs, meat, fruit juices[8] and fish[9] and to melt fats, chocolate and butter.[8] The method finds application in the baking of biscuits (Section 10.5.2.1). Other applications include the heating of peanuts for confectionery manufacture and the drying of sugar cubes and crispbread.[10]

Obviously, since about 2 kWh of energy is required to evaporate 1 kg of water, this method is unsuitable for the removal of water in bulk.

10.4.3.3. Microwave heating of foods. Microwaves are regarded as those electromagnetic radiations having frequencies in the range of 3–300 000 MHz.[11] For reasons already discussed, industrial equipment is limited to the frequencies given in Table 10.3; 897 and 2450 MHz are commonly used frequencies.

Microwave heating theory. As in the case of dielectric heating, only the briefest outline of the relevant theory can be given here but excellent descriptions are available elsewhere.[11, 12]

Although, as in dielectric heating, microwaves generate heat by molecular-dipole vibration, the former is electrostatic whereas the latter is a radiation phenomenon. Microwave heating differs from dielectric heating only in using higher frequencies and these dictate the use of a different type of equipment. The basic power equation (equation 10.2) applies, but the considerations involved differ in the following respects:

(i) Because of the higher energy associated with the higher frequencies used in microwave heating, the same energy input may be achieved by the application of a lower voltage. Hence dielectric stress within the food is reduced and 'flash-over' is largely eliminated.

(ii) The food dimensions 'A' and 'd' are no longer restraints. The shape and size and orientation of the food are of importance only in respect of ensuring adequate 'through heating'.

(iii) Loss factors are higher at the higher frequencies used in microwave heating. This implies a lower voltage stress on the food for the same energy input.

(iv) In microwave heating we are particularly concerned with the penetration of the radiation. If the food is transparent then no heating results. It is convenient to measure the penetration in terms of the penetration depth 'D' at which the energy is reduced to 1/eth of its incident value.[12]

Penetration depth is given by the following equation:

$$D \simeq \frac{\lambda_0}{2\pi(\varepsilon_r \tan \delta)^{1/2}} \tag{10.3}$$

where λ_0 = wavelength in free space.
Penetration is, therefore, inversely proportional to frequency. For example, for water at 95 C, D = 29·5 cm at 915 MHz and 4·8 cm at 2450 MHz.

For the foregoing reasons it will be clear that the frequency selected for use in a purely radiative phenomenon, such as microwave heating, is a matter of great importance if the best result is to be obtained.

Equipment design. Microwave heaters comprise a high-frequency generator (such as a magnetron) from which energy is transported by means of a hollow, rectangular waveguide or by a coaxial cable to a heating chamber (Fig. 10.3). This latter may be either a metal oven or tunnel, effectively water-trapped at each end, through which passes a low-loss belt carrying the food to be heated. In either case the heating cavity must be accurately matched to the generator, otherwise the resulting mismatch causes overheating of the power tube which could be damaged as a consequence.

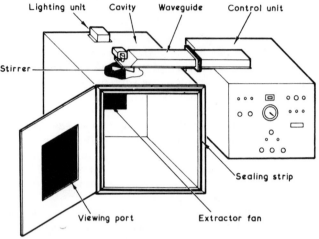

Fig. 10.3. A microwave oven. (By courtesy of Elliott Electronic Tubes Ltd, Borehamwood, England.)

Alternatively, food may be conveyed through the waveguide which then becomes the heating chamber. Movement of the food through the heating zone counteracts field inequalities which, in fast-heating processes such as microwave heating, result in large temperature gradients within the food.

Domestic and catering ovens operating at 1 or 2 kW are now common. Magnetrons generating up to 5 kW at 897 MHz and up to 30 kW at 2450 MHz are available and these, used singly or in combination, provide the processor with considerable flexibility. Industrial heaters generating as much as 130 kW have been reported.[16] Clearly, equipment of this power must be carefully safeguarded to prevent energy leakage and the design of microwave heating equipment has received much attention.[14, 15]

Food-processing applications of microwave heating. Microwaves are used to heat precooked, frozen foods and, in conjunction with the browning effect of infra-red heaters, for the cooking of food in canteens and hospitals where speed is important. Industrially, microwaves are used for precooking chicken, for apple-juice evaporation and in potato-crisp finishing. Investigational work has indicated promising applications, *e.g.* in the pasteurisation of fruit juices; in reducing mould counts in bread, cakes and jam; in bread baking and in accelerated freeze drying (Section 13.3.4).[13, 14, 16]

Safety considerations in the use of microwaves. The human body is a 'lossy' entity and current indications are that exposure to microwaves results predominantly in thermal effects, the eyes and testicles being specially susceptible to heat change. It is reported that non-thermal biological effects such as enzyme inactivation and protein modification have been demonstrated in animals exposed to microwave energy.[11] A situation of uncertainty exists regarding human sensitivity and more information is required on this important subject. In the USA a maximum R.F. leakage level of $5\,mW/cm^2$ is specified,[12] and equipment is engineered to ensure that this limit is not exceeded. As indicated previously, the energy source is tuned to match the heating cavity so that a leak of any magnitude would result in a mismatch causing the magnetron to stop working. Modern microwave equipment is fitted with foolproof safety devices and may be regarded as inherently safe.

10.5. FOOD CONVERSION BY HEAT PROCESSING

10.5.1. THE BLANCHING PROCESS

Blanching is an important heat process in the preparation of vegetables (and some fruits) destined for canning, freezing or dehydration. Primarily, blanching is carried out to inactivate enzymes or to destroy enzyme substrates such as peroxides. Blanching is effected by heating the food *rapidly* to a predetermined temperature, holding it at this temperature for a predetermined time and then either *rapidly* cooling the material or, alternatively, passing it to subsequent processing without delay. If unblanched food is processed (*e.g.* as a canned conduction-heating pack) it may well be an appreciable time in reaching a temperature sufficiently high to inactivate enzymes. In low-temperature processes, such as vacuum evaporation, spray drying and freeze drying, enzyme inactivation temperatures may not be reached at all. In both these cases, residual enzyme activity in the food may cause the development of undesirable odours, flavours and colours during processing and storage.

In addition to destroying enzymes, blanching also brings about the following changes:

(i)   The raw material is cleaned and the bacterial load is reduced.

(ii)   Cellular gases are expelled, reducing can corrosion and assisting the attainment of adequate headspace vacua during canning.

(iii) The food is softened and shrinks, so filling of containers is facilitated.

(iv) Texture may be improved, especially in dehydrated foods.

(v)   Undesirably, blanching may lead to loss of heat-sensitive vitamins and to leaching out of water-soluble nutrients.[17] Over-blanching causes texture damage.

The two methods of blanching in general use are: (i) immersion blanching using hot water, and (ii) steam blanching. Immersion blanching involves passing the food at a controlled rate through a perforated drum rotating in a tank of water thermostatically controlled to the blanching temperature (75–100 °C). Alternatively, the food is suspended in water, heated to blanching temperature and is then pumped through a serpentine holding tube (pipe blancher). Immersion blanching leads to high loss of solubles in some foods, and scrupulous plant hygiene is necessary if thermophile contamination is to be avoided.

Steam blanchers utilise saturated steam at atmospheric or at low pressure ($150 \, kN/m^2$). The food is conveyed through the steam chamber on a mesh belt or by means of a helical screw, the residence time being controlled by the conveyor speed. The blanched product is discharged through an outlet lock to a washer and cooler. Steam blanching tends to give lower blanching losses than immersion blanching but has a reduced cleaning effect on the food so that an 'after washer' is necessary. Generally, steam blanchers are easier to sterilise than water blanchers.

Microwave blanching has been applied to fruits and vegetables packaged in film bags[18] and would appear to offer some advantages, such as microbiological cleanliness and low losses of nutrients. The method, although costly, may well find specialised applications.

The main problems concerning blanching are, firstly, in ensuring uniform heat-treatment and, second, in controlling blanching losses and the effluent disposal difficulties caused by these. 'Individual Quick Blanching' (IQB) claims to alleviate these problems.[19] This is a modified three-stage steam-blanching process in which pieces of food are rapidly heated as a thin layer ($\sim 5 \, kg/m^2$) followed by holding as a deep bed, where equilibration takes place, after which the food is cooled by chilled air. This permits shorter retention time, giving improved yield and quality and reduces effluent volumes and strength.

10.5.2. THE BAKING PROCESS

The baking of farinaceous foods like bread, biscuits and cakes, is an important food-conversion activity. In yeast-raised foods such as bread, which is the biggest preoccupation of the baker, a series of complex, temperature-dependent chemical reactions take place during baking (Fig. 10.4). Since these reactions determine the

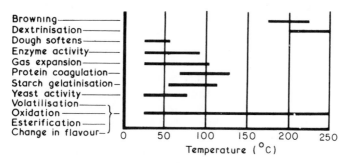

FIG. 10.4. The reaction in bread during baking.

properties of the converted food, the heating must be carefully controlled if the desired colour, flavour, aroma and texture are to be obtained. The chemical changes taking place are discussed, in detail, publications.[20-22]

Baking ovens form an important group of heat processing equipment and include a wide array of types which may be classified on the following bases:

Heating Method: (i) Indirect by solid fuel, oil, gas or electricity.
(ii) Direct by gas, air or electronically.

Design Types: (i) Batch—peel or draw-plate ovens.
(ii) Continuous—rotary hearth, reel, tunnel and multicycle tray ovens.

10.5.2.1. Heating of baking ovens. In indirectly fired ovens the food is heated mainly by radiant heat transfer. Hot combustion gases or electrical energy are used to heat the walls of batch ovens or to heat radiators located above and below the baking band in continuous ovens.

Conventional direct heating by gas is effected by locating ribbon-type gas burners above and below the baking band. Heat transfer, in this case, is by a combination of radiation and natural convection.

In direct forced-convection baking, air, drawn from the baking chamber, is heated directly by gas burners. The hot gases are then forced by a recirculating fan back into the chamber through nozzles located above and below the baking band.[22, 23] According to Gales and Petty[23] the relationship $Nu \propto Re^x . Pr^y$ for forced convection (Appendix II) approximates, in this system, to $h \propto G^{0.78}$ (where h = heat transfer coefficient and G = mass flow of heated air) when air velocities around 0·5 m/s are used with moderate nozzling. The advantages of this type of oven are: shortened baking times, high thermal efficiency and excellent control (since h is roughly proportional to the air-speed). Additionally, changing the oven temperature or heating up from cold is speeded since the thermal mass of the system is low.

Dielectric heating is firmly established in the post-baking of biscuits. In thin food sections, such as biscuits, browning and dehydration down to about 10% moisture may be effected in the first 60% of travel through conventional tunnel ovens. The rest of the baking time is required to reduce the moisture content to around 2% whilst retaining the desired biscuit colour. This last stage may be performed rapidly (15–20 s) by passing the partly finished biscuits through a dielectric oven. This has the effect of increasing the throughput of highly expensive tunnel ovens and is, therefore, financially attractive. Additionally, better control over moisture contents is claimed.[24]

10.5.2.2. Types of baking oven. Batch ovens, heated directly or indirectly, are in general use and consist of a baking cavity into which the food is charged either singly, on a long-handled shovel (or peel), or in batches on trays. Charging and discharging is facilitated by fitting this oven with a sliding hearth (the draw-plate oven).

The smaller continuous ovens include the rotary-hearth oven in which the food is charged on to a heated sole plate which rotates horizontally. The speed of rotation is adjusted so that the baked product may be removed continuously as fresh material is charged. In the reel oven the food is conveyed within the oven chamber on trays slung between two wheels which rotate vertically, using the ferris wheel principle. Charging and discharging takes place at the same point. These two types of oven give uniform baking results, the effects of local hot-spots being minimised by the movement of the food.

The multicycle tray oven conveys the food on a serpentine path through the baking chamber, the food being carried on trays suspended from chains. Loading and unloading is usually carried out at the same point. Such ovens are characterised by high capacity and economic use of floor space.

In tunnel ovens the food is carried on an endless conveyor belt which passes, at controlled speed, through a series of independently controllable heating sections. The food enters at one end of the tunnel, which may be 60 m long, and is discharged at the other end. Tunnel ovens are expensive to buy and occupy a large floor area, but their capacity, flexibility and accuracy of control has established their wide application in large-scale baking. There is an extensive literature on baking oven design.[20–22, 25]

REFERENCES

1. Cutting, C. L., 'Food Manufacturing Aspects of Heat Transfer'. Chemy Ind., 1004–1011 (1963).
2. Anon., 'Petroleum Fuels for Oil Engines and Burners'. B.S.2869: 1970 (British Standards Institution).
3. Hoskin, R. D., 'Electricity in the Food Industry'. Industrial Monograph G.1. The Electricity Council, E.D.A. Division, London (1967).
4. Perry, J. H. (Ed.) 'Chemical Engineers' Handbook', 5th ed. (McGraw-Hill: 1973).
5. Ginzburg, A. S. and Growchowski, A., 'Applications of Infra-Red Radiation in Food Processing'. (Leonard Hill, London: 1969).
6. Anon., 'Glossary of Terms Used in Industrial High Frequency Induction and Dielectric Heating'. B.S.2759. Section 1 (British Standards Institution: 1956).
7. Absil, L., 'Le Préchauffage des Matières Thermodurcissables par Pertes Dielectriques'. Revue Belge des Matières Plastiques No. 4, 283–294 (1963).
8. British Patents: 833714, 20323/60, 5120/59, 14186/61 (Radyne Ltd., Wokingham, Berkshire, England.
9. Jason, A. C., 'Rapid Thawing of Foodstuffs'. IFST Proceedings, **7**(3), 146–157 (1974).
10. Anon., 'High Frequency Heating Gains'. Fd Engng, **37**(11), 62–3 (1965).
11. Tape, N. W., 'Application of Microwave Energy in Food Manufacture'. Can. Inst. Fd Technol., **3**(2), 39–43 (1970).
12. Copson, D. A., 'Microwave Heating', 2nd ed. (AVI: 1975).
13. Decareau, R. V., 'Microwave Energy in Food Processing Applications'. Critical Reviews in Food Technology (CRC: 1970).
14. Goldblith, S. A., 'Basic Principles of Microwaves and Recent Developments', *in* Chichester, C. O., Mrak, E. M., and Stewart, G. F. (Eds) 'Advances in Food Research', Vol. 15. (Academic Press: 1966.)
15. van Dijk, J. E. M., 'Design Considerations in Some Types of Microwave Heating Equipment'. Fd Trade Rev., **37**(3), 57–60 (1967).
16. Anon., 'The Role of Heat Transfer in the Food Industry', Symposium Proceedings No. 19. British Food Manufacturing Industries Research Association (1973).
17. Lee, F. A., 'The Blanching Process', *in* Mrak, E. M., and Stewart, G. F. (Eds) 'Advances in Food Research', Vol. 8. (Academic Press: 1958.)
18. Anon., 'Microwaves in Heat Processing of Foods in Plastic Packages'. Fd Process., **24**(12), 79 (1963).
19. Lazar, M. E., Lund, D. B., and Dietrich, W. C., 'IQB—a New Concept in Blanching'. Fd Trade Rev., **42**(2), 13–15 (1972).

20. Matz, S. A., 'Bakery Technology and Engineering'. (AVI USA: 1972.)
21. Smith, W. H., 'What Happens in the Baking Oven'. Bisc. Mkr., 17(9), 652–6 (1966).
22. Brunson, B., 'Advanced Methods of Heat Transfer and Control in Modern Band Ovens'. Bakers' Dig., XL(1), 65–9 (1966).
23. Gales, D. R., and Petty, M. H., 'Oven Design—The Forced Convection Oven'. Technologists' Conference. The Cake and Biscuit Alliance Ltd, 157 Victoria Street, London, S.W.1 (1960).
24. Holland, J. M., 'High Frequency Baking'. Technologists' Conference. The Cake and Biscuit Alliance Ltd, 157 Victoria Street, London, S.W.1 (1962).
25. Anon., 'Developments in Continuous Baking Ovens'. Food Processing and Marketing, London, 36(424), 16–22; 36(425), 57–61 (1967).
26. Sachsel, G. F., 'Fluidised Bed Cooking'. Fd Process., 24(11), 77–8 (1963).

PART III
PRESERVATION OPERATIONS

CHAPTER 11

HEAT PROCESSING II

11.1. MICROBIOLOGICAL CONSIDERATIONS

11.1.1. INTRODUCTION

When foods are preserved by heat, the heating process serves to reduce the concentration of micro-organisms in the food. It may also inactivate enzymes present (see Section 10.5.1). The heating operation forms only part of the total preservation process, which can include, *e.g.* the addition of chemical preservatives, suitable packaging of the product or storage at reduced temperatures. It is not a necessary requirement of the heating operation that it should eliminate all viable organisms from the material. Sound cans of food, particularly cans of cured meat products, frequently contain viable organisms.[1] What is required is that the resulting product should be both acceptable to the consumer and safe to eat at the end of a predetermined storage period under defined conditions.

It is convenient to divide heat processes into three categories, involving heating (i) to temperatures below 100 °C; (ii) to a temperature of 100 °C; (iii) to temperatures above 100 °C.

Heat processes below 100 °C are usually termed pasteurisation processes and generally they are designed to kill all pathogenic organisms and some, but not necessarily all, of the spoilage organisms which, if present, would be capable of growing in the food under defined storage conditions. Milk technology affords good examples of their use. Liquid milk for domestic consumption is distributed frequently and a short storage life can be accepted. A pasteurisation process can destroy pathogens in the milk while leaving its organoleptic properties effectively unimpaired. The pasteurisation of milk for cheese-making destroys organisms that would compete with the desired fermentation.

Nicholas Appert (1750–1840), the inventor of the process of preservation by heating in sealed containers, recommended the heating of containers of food in boiling water in a bain-marie and holding them there for prescribed periods of time. In other words, the

251

earliest bottling and canning processes belonged to the second class above.

Processes of this type are still in use for home bottling and for the commercial canning of acid products such as fruit (say in the pH range 3·7–4·5). For products of less acidity the holding times at 100 °C required to produce a microbiologically acceptable pack are very long and it is desirable to heat to temperatures above 100 °C to achieve a shorter process with improved product quality. This third class of

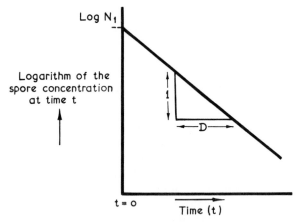

FIG. 11.1.   The relationship between the spore concentration and the time of heating at a constant temperature.

heat process was developed in the mid-nineteenth century; first baths of boiling salt solution and then steam under pressure in a retort being used as the heating medium.

As may be seen from the above, the pH of the material strongly influences the nature of the heat process required to produce an acceptable product. Preserved foods range in pH from neutrality to about pH 3·0. The inhibiting effect of acids on spoilage organisms starts to become apparent at pH 5·3, whilst *Clostridium botulinum* and other food-poisoning organisms are inhibited at pH 4·5. Below pH 3·7 only fungi are likely to grow. The important demarcation point occurs at pH 4·5. For low acid foods (pH ≥ 4·5) the requirement to destroy food poisoning organisms such as *C. botulinum* leads to the use of the severest class of heat processing, treatment above 100 °C; such processes are frequently described as 'sterilisation'—a term to which some objection can be raised, since it implies complete absence of viable microflora. A better term is 'commercial sterilisation' (see Section 11.1.2) which may be defined as heat processing designed to kill substantially all micro-organisms and spores which, if present, would be capable of growing in the food under defined storage conditions.

The pH is not the only factor which influences the nature of the heat process required for the product. The presence of osmotically active ingredients like salt or sugar will affect the growth properties of the microflora. Again, the organoleptic properties of large cans of ham would be impaired by normal heat processing; the use of refrigerated post-processing storage enables a sound product to be marketed following a mild heat process. Products with a very low pH, such as acid pickles, or with low water activity, such as sweetened condensed milk or dried foods, provide environments so hostile to spoilage micro-organisms that no heat processing is needed for their preservation. In such cases, however, it is possible that a mild pasteurisation process might be needed to inactivate enzymes.

11.1.2. THE THERMAL DESTRUCTION OF SPOILAGE MICRO-ORGANISMS

The microbiological stability and eating quality of heat processed foods are affected both by the temperature and duration of the thermal process. Under-processed food will be liable to bacterial spoilage, and over-processed food will be nutritionally and organoleptically inferior. The parameters of a suitable thermal process may be estimated on the basis of assumptions regarding the heat resistance of the spoilage micro-organisms and a knowledge of the temperature history of the food during processing.

For all practical purposes, bacterial spores (as also vegetative cells) may be assumed to have a logarithmic order of death,[2] *i.e.* when a given spore preparation is held at a constant temperature sufficiently high for thermal destruction to occur, the number of spores per unit volume decreases as shown in Fig. 11.1. Clearly, from Fig. 11.1, if the spore concentration is N_1 spores/ml of suspension at time $t = 0$ and N spores/ml at time $t = t$:

$$\log \frac{N}{N_1} = -\frac{t}{D} \qquad (11.1)$$

where D is a constant known as the 'Decimal Reduction Time' and is the time over which the spore concentration is reduced tenfold (log 10 = 1). For the purposes of heat process calculations the decimal reduction time is assumed to be independent of the initial spore concentration but a function of temperature. It is also dependent not only on the strain of the species of bacterial spore and the medium in which the spores are heated, but also on the previous history of the spores and the techniques used for detecting survivors (what is always measured is the number of surviving spores that grow under the experimental conditions, which is not necessarily an absolute measure of the 'number of survivors').

An immediate result of equation (11.1) is that since N can become equal to zero only when t becomes infinite, it would appear to be impossible to sterilise a spore concentration with absolute certainty. From this the concept of 'commercial sterility' has arisen. If the concentration of a given strain of bacteria or bacterial spores in a batch of food product is reduced to below a certain value (N_0/ml), just low enough to present a commercially acceptable spoilage hazard, the product is said to be 'commercially sterile' with respect to that organism. If N_1 is taken to be the initial concentration of a particular bacterial spore in a certain food material before heat processing, then we may write:

$$m = \log \left(\frac{N_1}{N_0} \right)$$

This has been termed the 'reduction exponent'[1] since, *e.g.* for $m = 5$ the process reduces the spore concentration by a factor of 10^5. Table 11.1 gives frequently adopted values of m for different spoilage organisms. It should be noted that these figures are based on a value of N_1 resulting from good hygienic practice in the preparation of the product. Furthermore, the values of m adopted are such that the validity of equation (11.1) is implicitly assumed at spore concentrations far below those for which it has been experimentally verified. Thus it may be seen that the methods of thermal process calculation described subsequently are justified mainly by their success in practice.

11.1.3. THE EFFECT OF VARYING TEMPERATURES

Consider a suspension of bacterial spores of equal heat resistance held at a temperature which is uniform but varies with time. Suppose that at the start of the process ($t = 0$) the spore concentration is N_1 and at the end of the process ($t = t_f$) it has been reduced to N_f. From equation (11.1):

$$\log \frac{N_f}{N_1} = - \int_0^{t_f} \frac{dt}{D} \tag{11.2}$$

For commercial sterility to be achieved N_f must be no greater than N_0 or in other words:

$$\log \frac{N_f}{N_1} \leq \log \frac{N_0}{N_1} \qquad (11.3)$$

So that, from equation (11.2):

$$\int_0^{t_f} \frac{dt}{D} \geq m \qquad (11.4)$$

Referring to Fig. 11.2, suppose the upper graph represents the temperature-history of the spore suspension. At any arbitrary time t,

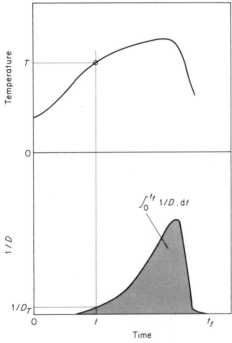

Fig. 11.2. The evaluation of the integral in equation (11.4).

let the temperature of the suspension be T. If the variation of the decimal reduction time with temperature is known from experimental data, the decimal reduction time, D_T, at temperature T can be determined (say from a graph of experimental results) and the point $(t, 1/D_T)$ plotted on the lower axes as shown. Repeating this operation for a number of different values of t will enable the graph of $1/D$ against t

to be drawn. The area under this graph (shown shaded) will then be equal to the left hand side of the inequality (11.4). This area can then be compared with m, as indicated by the inequality, to see if commercial sterility has been achieved with respect to this organism.

If we can express the decimal reduction time as an explicit function of temperature, the inequality (11.4) can be developed further. One approach, following a suggestion of Bigelow[4] is to assume an empirical relationship in which the logarithm of the decimal reduction

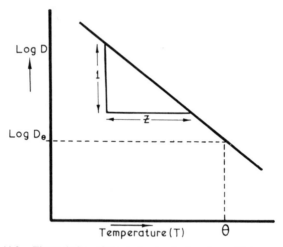

FIG. 11.3.   The variation of the decimal reduction time with temperature.

time is a linear function of temperature (Fig. 11.3). Thus if the decimal reduction time at some reference temperature, θ, is equal to D_θ, the decimal reduction time, D, at temperature T is given by:

$$\log \frac{D}{D_\theta} = -\frac{T - \theta}{z} \tag{11.5}$$

where z is the temperature range over which the decimal reduction time changes tenfold. Thus equation (11.4) may be re-written:

$$\frac{1}{D_\theta} \int_0^{t_f} 10^{\frac{T - \theta}{z}} \, dt \geq m \tag{11.6}$$

or, putting $L = 10^{\frac{T - \theta}{z}}$, as:

$$\int_0^{t_f} L \, dt \geq m D_\theta \tag{11.7}$$

The inequalities of equations (11.4) and (11.7) offer alternative, though related, ways of assessing the severity of a thermal process since, if the inequality is satisfied, commercial sterility of the suspension has been achieved. In both cases the left hand side may be evaluated by graphical integration.

An alternative approach, advocated by Gillespy[5] and Diendoerfer[6] is to assume an Arrhenius-type relationship between the decimal reduction time and temperature the logarithm of the decimal reduction time being a reciprocal of the absolute temperature. Gillespy[5] points out that, although this relationship is quite different to that assumed in Fig. 11.3, over a limited range of temperature both assumptions lead to predictions in reasonable agreement with each other. It can be seen from Fig. 11.2 that, in practice, the majority of the sterilising effect accrues over a narrow temperature range near the maximum temperature experienced by the suspension. Thus, providing the assumed relationship of decimal reduction time and temperature is based on experimental data for that appropriate temperature range, either assumption will lead to acceptable results. In the treatment given below equations (11.5)–(11.7) are used, rather than those derived from an Arrhenius-type relationship, since the former have achieved wide currency in canning technology.

To make use of equation (11.7), it is necessary to have a table relating the lethal rate L to the temperature T, assuming a certain z-value for the organism and a suitable reference temperature. From what has been said before, it is clear that this last should be approximately equal to the maximum temperature experienced by the suspension. For suspensions processed at $100\,°C$, the reference temperature should be taken as that. For products processed in a retort it has, in the past, been a general convention to take $250\,°F$ as a reference temperature. In terms of the Celsius scale this is $121\cdot11\,°C$. This temperature is still used, although it would clearly be preferable to adopt a more rational reference temperature when working with the Celsius scale—say $120\,°C$. Because of its present currency, however, it has been retained in Table 11.1, where a selection of the thermobacteriological constants of important food spoilage organisms are listed.

With selected values of z and θ, a table of L against T can be constructed (a 'Lethal Rate' table as it is frequently termed). Tables 11.2 and 11.3 have been constructed assuming $z = 10\,°C$, which is an average value among those listed in Table 11.1. Table 11.2 assumes the traditional reference temperature of $121\cdot11\,°C$ ($250\,°F$) while Table 11.3 is constructed on the basis of a reference temperature of $120\,°C$.

The integral on the left hand side of equation (11.7) has the dimensions of time, and has been called the 'equivalent time' of the

TABLE 11.1
Approximate heat processing data for some important spoilage organisms[a]

Organism	$\theta\,^\circ$C	D_θ (Min)	$z\,^\circ$C	m	Type of product needing protection against spoilage by this organism
C. botulinum	⎫	0·1–0·3	8–11	12	Low acid foods (pH > 4·5)
C. sporogenes	⎪	0·8–1·5	9–11	5	Meats
B. stearothermophilis	⎪	4–5	9·5–10	5	Vegetables and milk
C. thermosaccharolyticum	⎬121·11	3–4	7–10·5	5	Vegetables
B. subtilis	⎪	~0·4	6·5	6	Milk products
B. coagulans	⎪	0·01–0·07	10	5	Foods of pH 4·2–4·5, e.g. tomatoes
C. pasteurianum	⎭ 100	0·1–0·5	8	5	Foods of pH 4·2–4·5, e.g. pears

[a] These figures are intended to be indicative only. The nature of the foodstuff affects the thermal resistance of spoilage organisms, so the specialist literature should be consulted for more precise information on particular products.

process and denoted by the symbol F. Since this time is calculated with respect to a particular value of z and a particular reference temperature θ, these values are often used respectively as superscripts and subscripts to the symbol for equivalent time, thus: F_{120}^{10}.

In the particular case of equivalent times calculated with respect to $z = 10\,^\circ$C and $\theta = 121\cdot11\,^\circ$C, important for reasons which are discussed in the following subsection, the symbol F_0 is used.

TABLE 11.2
L values for $z = 10\,^\circ$C and $\theta = 121\cdot11\,^\circ$C ($= 250\,^\circ$F)

C	0	1	2	3	4	5	6	7	8	9
100	0·01	0·01	0·01	0·02	0·02	0·02	0·03	0·04	0·05	0·06
$^\circ$C	0·0	0·1	0·2	0·3	0·4	0·5	0·6	0·7	0·8	0·9
110	0·08	0·08	0·08	0·08	0·08	0·09	0·09	0·09	0·09	0·10
111	0·10	0·10	0·10	0·10	0·11	0·11	0·11	0·11	0·12	0·12
112	0·12	0·13	0·13	0·13	0·13	0·14	0·14	0·14	0·15	0·15
113	0·15	0·16	0·16	0·17	0·17	0·17	0·18	0·18	0·19	0·19
114	0·19	0·20	0·20	0·21	0·21	0·22	0·22	0·23	0·23	0·24
115	0·24	0·25	0·26	0·26	0·27	0·27	0·28	0·29	0·29	0·30
116	0·31	0·32	0·32	0·33	0·34	0·35	0·35	0·36	0·37	0·38
117	0·39	0·40	0·41	0·42	0·43	0·44	0·45	0·46	0·47	0·48
118	0·49	0·50	0·51	0·52	0·54	0·55	0·56	0·57	0·59	0·60
119	0·62	0·63	0·64	0·66	0·67	0·69	0·71	0·72	0·74	0·76
120	0·77	0·79	0·81	0·83	0·85	0·87	0·89	0·91	0·93	0·95
121	0·97	1·00	1·02	1·04	1·07	1·09	1·12	1·15	1·17	1·20

TABLE 11.3
L values for $z = 10\,°C$ and $\theta = 120\,°C$

°C	0	1	2	3	4	5	6	7	8	9
100	0·01	0·01	0·02	0·02	0·03	0·03	0·04	0·05	0·06	0·08
°C	0·0	0·1	0·2	0·3	0·4	0·5	0·6	0·7	0·8	0·9
110	0·10	0·10	0·10	0·11	0·11	0·11	0·11	0·12	0·12	0·12
111	0·13	0·13	0·13	0·13	•0·14	0·14	0·14	0·15	0·15	0·15
112	0·16	0·16	0·17	0·17	0·17	0·18	0·18	0·19	0·19	0·19
113	0·20	0·20	0·21	0·21	0·22	0·22	0·23	0·23	0·24	0·25
114	0·25	0·26	0·26	0·27	0·28	0·28	0·29	0·30	0·30	0·31
115	0·32	0·32	0·33	0·34	0·35	0·35	0·36	0·37	0·38	0·39
116	0·40	0·41	0·42	0·43	0·44	0·45	0·46	0·47	0·48	0·49
117	0·50	0·51	0·52	0·54	0·55	0·56	0·58	0·59	0·60	0·62
118	0·63	0·65	0·66	0·68	0·69	0·71	0·72	0·74	0·76	0·78
119	0·79	0·81	0·83	0·85	0·87	0·89	0·91	0·93	0·95	0·98
120	1·00	1·02	1·05	1·07	1·10	1·12	1·15	1·17	1·20	1·23
121	1·26	1·29	1·32	1·35	1·38	1·41	1·45	1·48	1·51	1·55

The evaluation of the equivalent time, F, follows the same course as that of the evaluation of $\int_0^{t_f} \dfrac{dt}{D}$ (see Fig. 11.2). First a graph of L against time is drawn up, using the temperature history of the suspension and a suitable lethal rate table, to give a curve as shown in Fig. 11.4. Next the area beneath that curve is measured. An easy way of measuring such areas is by counting squares. For instance, using

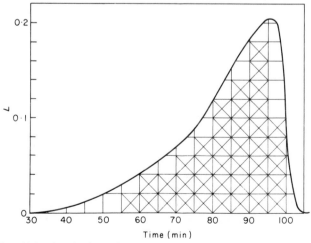

FIG. 11.4.   Graph of L v. time showing how the integral is evaluated.

the squares ruled in Fig. 11.4, the area beneath the curve amounts to 39 whole squares (marked by crosses) and parts of squares which have a total area amounting approximately to 15 squares more. Each square represents an area 5 min wide by 0·02 units high (*i.e.* of 5 × 0·02 min), so the total area beneath the curve is approximately

$$5 \times 0·02 \times (39 + 15) = 5·4 \, \text{min}$$

11.1.4. THE PRACTICAL APPLICATION OF THE THEORY TO THERMAL PROCESS CALCULATIONS

The theory given in Section 11.1.3 relates only to a spore suspension in which the temperature varies with time but not location. It may be possible to regard a fluid foodstuff undergoing processing in, say, a plate heat exchanger as made up of elementary volumes each experiencing a substantially identical temperature history as it flows through the apparatus. Nevertheless for food in containers such as cans heated and cooled by external agencies, the temperature in the food during the process varies from point to point. Some writers have suggested that in this situation the probability of spore survival should be integrated over the contents of the can.[2] Such a procedure is possible only if the temperature history of every particle of food in the can can be inferred. In practice a more simple, though less logical, convention is often employed: calculations are based on the temperature history determined at the slowest-heating point within the can. In packs where heat transfer within the can is by conduction, this point is at or slightly above the geometric centre of the can. In other cases its location is best determined experimentally.

Experimental determinations of temperature histories (or 'heat penetration' experiments, as they are termed) are most conveniently made with thermoelectric thermometers. Several thermocouples specifically designed for this purpose are available commercially. Temperature probes are even available which link to a special computing device which displays the accumulated *F*-value as processing proceeds. While it is desirable to use a thermocouple which is robust, mounts conveniently in the test can and allows the can to be filled and closed conventionally, nevertheless it is essential that the presence of the thermocouple and its mounting should not disturb significantly the temperature distribution within the can. Heavy metal fittings are therefore to be avoided.

So far, attention has been given only to suspensions containing organisms of identical thermal resistance. While unprocessed cans contain a varied microflora, certain spoilage organisms are of particular importance either because they are the most heat resistant

TABLE 11.4

F_0 values that have been successfully used commercially for products on the UK market

Product	Can sizes	F_0 values
Babyfoods	babyfood	3–5
Beans in tomato sauce	All	4–6
Peas in brine	up to A2	6
	A2 to A10	6–8
Carrots	All	3–4
Green beans in brine	up to A2	4–6
	A2 to A10	6–8
Celery	A2	3–4
Mushrooms in brine	A1	8–10
Mushrooms in butter	up to A1	6–8
Meats in gravy	All	12–15
Sliced meat in gravy	Ovals	10
Meat pies	Tapered, flat	10
Sausages in fat	up to 1lb	4–6
Frankfurters in brine	up to 16Z	3–4
Curried meats and vegetables	up to 16Z	8–12
Poultry and Game, whole in brine	A2½ to A10	15–18
Chicken fillets in jelly	up to 16oz	6–10
'Sterile' ham	1 and 2lb	3–4
Herrings in tomato	Ovals	6–8
Meat soups	up to 16Z	10
Tomato soup, not cream of	All	3
Cream soups	A1 to 16Z	4–5
	up to A10	6–10
Milk puddings	up to 16Z	4–10
Cream	4/6oz	3–4
	16Z	6
Evaporated milk	up to 16oz	5
Petfoods	up to 16Z	15–18

(Reproduced by courtesy of *Food Manufacture*, London.)

present or because, for safety reasons, their final concentration must be reduced to an exceptionally low level. Thus it is possible to restrict attention to one of the organisms present in the pack, this organism being the critical one for the particular foodstuff involved. For instance, while all packs with a pH above 4·5 must be processed sufficiently to protect them against *C. botulinum*, meat packs, in which *C. sporogenes* may prove a problem, will require a more severe heat process to protect them from spoilage by the latter organism. Furthermore, since many of the important spoilage organisms have a z-value of about $10\,°C$, the commercial process for many canned foods can be conveniently specified by giving the F_0 value (see Section 11.1.3) which should be achieved over the process. A number of these values are listed in Table 11.4.

11.1.5. INOCULATED PACKS

It may be deduced from equation (11.2) that a thermal process will reduce the spore concentration of a given bacterial species by a fixed factor. For normal levels of initial infection, a process giving commercial sterility will reduce the spore concentration by such a factor that infected cans will rarely be found after processing. If the initial concentration is increased to such a level that a measurable fraction of the processed cans spoil, a measure of the reduction ratio of the spore concentration may be obtained. Techniques developed from this[1] are available for checking the results of thermal process calculations and for evaluating processes in cases where temperature history measurements are impractical (for instance in hydrostatic sterilisers).

11.1.6. FORMULA METHODS OF THERMAL PROCESS EVALUATION

Consider a can of food heated by a medium at a constant temperature T_r. If the initial temperature at the slowest heating point within the can is T_0 and the temperature at this point at any given time

TABLE 11.5

The function $-Ei(-x)$

x	$-Ei(-x)$	x	$-Ei(-x)$	x	$-Ei(-x)$
0·0	$+\infty$	1·5	·10002	3·0	·01305
0·1	1·82292	1·6	·08631	3·1	·01149
0·2	1·22265	1·7	·07465	3·2	·01013
0·3	·90568	1·8	·06471	3·3	·00894
0·4	·70238	1·9	·05620	3·4	·00789
0·5	·55977	2·0	·04890	3·5	·00697
0·6	·45438	2·1	·04621	3·6	·00616
0·7	·37377	2·2	·03719	3·7	·00545
0·8	·31060	2·3	·03250	3·8	·00482
0·9	·26018	2·4	·02844	3·9	·00427
1·0	·21938	2·5	·02491	4·0	·00378
1·1	·18599	2·6	·02185	4·1	·00335
1·2	·15841	2·7	·01918	4·2	·00297
1·3	·13545	2·8	·01686	4·3	·00263
1·4	·11622	2·9	·01482	4·4	·00234

(From Selby, S. M. (Ed.), *Handbook of Mathematical Tables*, 1st edn. (Chemical Rubber Publishing, Cleveland, Ohio).)

is T, then a dimensionless temperature (see Appendix II) can be defined as:

$$V = \frac{T_r - T}{T_r - T_0}$$

If log V is plotted against time, the resulting curve is often found to become asymptotic to a straight line (see Fig. 11.5). Further, it is often the case that thermal destruction of the spores of the critical bacterial

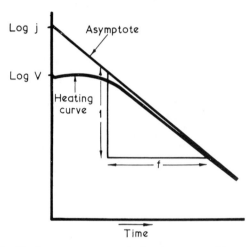

FIG. 11.5. The linear asymptote to the heating curve and its parameters.

species occurs substantially during the period when the linear asymptote forms a good approximation to the true heating curve. This asymptote can be specified by the 'lag factor', j, and the 'slope', f (see Fig. 11.5). The equation to the asymptote provides a relationship between T and t to substitute into equation (11.7). If the equivalent time of the heating phase of the process is denoted by F_h and the value of $T_r - T$ at the end of the heating phase is denoted by g, the left hand side of equation (11.7) can be integrated to give:

$$F_h = Mf \, \exp\left(\frac{T_r - \theta}{Mz}\right)\left\{-Ei\left(-\frac{g}{Mz}\right)\right\} \qquad (11.8)$$

where $M = \log e = 0{\cdot}4343$

and the exponential integral $-Ei\,(-x) = \displaystyle\int_x^\infty \frac{e^{-t}}{t}\,dt.$

Values of $-Ei\,(-x)$ can be read from Table 11.5.

Since in many instances the majority of the F-value of the overall process is accumulated during the heating phase, the contribution due to the cooling phase is sometimes treated as a safety margin and F_h taken as the total equivalent time. On the other hand Ball[3] and others have attempted to obtain equations similar to (11.8) for the cooling phase. While this 'formula' method of calculation offers some advantages when changes of can size or retort temperature are being considered for existing processes, the assumptions made concerning the physics of heat processing limit its applicability.

11.2.   PRELIMINARY OPERATIONS FOR STERILISATION IN CONTAINERS

Two general methods of sterilisation are used: (i) sterilising in containers, and (ii) sterilisation of the food before placing in the containers (see Fig. 11.6). All these procedures involve temperatures in excess of 100 °C, hence pressures above atmospheric are generated.

The containers used are cans, glass jars and film pouches. Considerable development of sterilisable containers has taken place in recent years. Cans are now available with easy-open ends and with

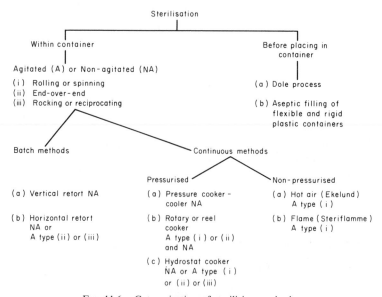

FIG. 11.6.   Categorisation of sterilising methods.

'necked-in' flanges (to control post-process infection). The use of tin-free steel cans is also of interest. Sterilisable plastic containers are obtainable in rigid, semi-rigid and flexible forms in wide material varieties and combinations.[7] Heat penetration in these packs is controlled by the geometry of the pack and by the thermal properties of the food, the container and the heating medium. For these reasons, in-pack sterilisation, particularly where conduction heating foods are involved, is slow compared with external sterilisation where high-speed heat exchangers may be used.

Irrespective of the type of container used, heat processing is preceded by filling, exhausting and closing, and these operations exert considerable influence over the rate of heat penetration and the effectiveness of the heat process. The methods of carrying out these preliminary stages and their effect on the process and on the food are considered, briefly, in the following sections. These refer, specifically, to canned foods, but the underlying principles are applicable to other types of container.

11.2.1. FILLING INTO CONTAINERS

Containers and lids are supplied in a 'commercially clean' condition. This guarantees nothing and it is vital, therefore, to ensure that containers are cleaned before filling. Cans and glass containers are washed by inversion over hot water sprays or by rotary brushing. They are then conveyed upside down for draining and, to limit recontamination, should remain inverted until just before filling.

Filling machines vary, depending on whether the material filled be a liquid, a paste, or a solid, but all fillers must:

(i)   ensure accurate fill,
(ii)   avoid slopping even at maximum fill-rate,
(iii) include a 'no can—no fill' device,
(iv) be flexible for different sizes and fill-rates, and
(v)   be of good sanitary design.

11.2.1.1. Liquid fillers. Liquids include brines (*i.e.* salt solutions) and syrups, or sugar solutions. Syrup strengths in canned and bottled fruits are controlled either by Codes of Practice or by legislation. Sugars are relatively expensive so that, apart from specification considerations, it is important to control syrup strengths within narrow limits. The hardness of the water used to make syrups and brines is often an important factor controlling the texture of canned fruits and vegetables (see Chapter 18).

Syrups and brines have the following desirable attributes:

(i)   they improve heat transfer to food packed with them;
(ii)   being osmotically active, they help to preserve the food;
(iii) they displace air and gases from solid or paste ingredients, assisting heat transfer within them and reducing pressure strain in containers during processing;
(iv)   they improve flavour and acceptability;
(v)   they provide a convenient means of incorporating small-quantity ingredients such as flavours and colours;
(vi)   in some foods (*e.g.* apples, pears, potatoes) they inhibit browning.

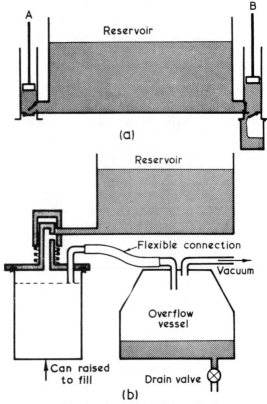

FIG. 11.7. The operating principles of typical liquid fillers. (a) A piston filler—the piston rises (A) charging a metering cylinder and falls (B) filling the can. (b) A vacuum filler—the can headspace (dotted) is determined by the depth of the vacuum line beneath the can mouth.

Liquids may be filled by multi-head rotary fillers of the piston or vacuum type[8] (Fig. 11.7), or by rotary pumps feeding through nozzles attached to a rotating filling head. These latter fillers work on a volume/time basis and high accuracy is claimed for them.

11.2.1.2. Paste fillers. Viscous and semi-liquid foods—fish and meat pastes, purées, preserves—may be filled using fillers fitted with screws or with piston plungers[9] (Fig. 11.7). Alternatively, rotary pump fillers similar to the liquid filler described previously may be used. Viscous or paste-like foods tend to carry entrapped air into the can, reducing heat transfer to the food and causing uneven filling. This difficulty is overcome by pre-vacuumising or blanching the food before filling.

11.2.1.3. Solid fillers. The method adopted for filling solids depends largely on the nature of the food. Delicate fruits and foods where shape imposes difficulty (asparagus or rhubarb), or packs such as sliced beetroot (where the rings tend to disintegrate), are packed by hand. Other foods can be filled by means of a semi-automatic hand-pack filler. This comprises a rotating coned table with a central discharge port to which is fitted an adjustable cut-off plate. The container is located, automatically, beneath this port which then opens, filling the can. An operator ensures that the table is kept supplied with food. Other types of solids fillers include auger fillers and special types of piston filler.[10]

It is important when filling any material into cans, but particularly so with solid ingredients, to ensure that the can flange is left in a clean condition. Food trapped between the lid and body of the can may lead to infection after processing.

11.2.2. EXHAUSTING OF CONTAINERS

11.2.2.1. The development of internal pressure during heat processing. When a closed container (*e.g.* a can of food) is heated, internal pressure is generated owing to the following effects:

(i)   the can contents expanding,
(ii)   the water vapour pressure increasing, and
(iii)   the air and other gases, in the headspace and in the food, expanding.

This internal pressure is partially balanced by the expansion of the can and by the outwards movement of the can ends, which are provided with expansion rings for this purpose. However, a completely filled can would be subjected to excessive strain when sterilised and, to obviate this, a free space (headspace) must be established above the food in the can. The headspace, apart from accommodating liquid and gaseous expansion, facilitates heat transfer during agitated processing. For glass containers processed at 115–121 °C it is recommended that the headspace should occupy not

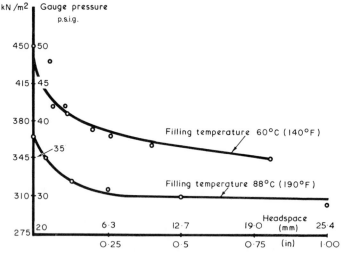

Fig. 11.8. The effect of headspace and filling temperature on the internal pressure in cans during processing. The curves are drawn from measured values of pressure generated in 16Z cans (300 × 410) filled with water to the headspace indicated and processed at 127 °C (260 °F). (By courtesy of The Metal Box Co. Ltd., London.)

less than 6 % of the container volume measured at normal sealing temperature (55 °C).[11] This recommendation would also appear to be an appropriate lower limit for sterilisation in other rigid containers. As a general rule, the headspace should not exceed 10 % of the container volume.

The vapour pressure within the container is determined by the processing temperature, but the partial pressure of the air in the can during processing may be reduced: (i) by ensuring that the food is freed from entrapped gases (by blanching or pre-vacuumising), and (ii) by producing a vacuum in the headspace (exhausting) before closing. In addition to reducing pressure strain (Fig. 11.8) de-gassing and exhausting lowers the oxygen tension within the can, thus reducing can corrosion, limiting oxidation of the food and inhibiting the growth of aerobic organisms. Four methods of exhausting are in general use: mechanical exhausting, hot filling, hot exhausting and steam flow closing.

11.2.2.2. Mechanical exhausting. This is applied to heat-sensitive or dry foods, and comprises closing of the cold-filled container under mechanically produced vacuum (*e.g.* using a pump). Both batch and continuous vacuum seamers are in use and, to ensure adequate degassing of liquid foods, vacuum filling should precede mechanical exhausting wherever practicable. This method is not suitable for viscous foods which tend to froth when vacuumised, and should not be used for foods which liberate gas on heating (*e.g.* strawberries in syrup).

11.2.2.3. Hot filling. An aqueous food, hot filled near the boiling point of water, generates about one atmosphere of water vapour pressure in the can headspace so that, on closing without delay and cooling, a vacuum is produced within the can. This method effectively removes gases—in the headspace and trapped in the food—and provides useful preheating which reduces processing time. Disadvantageously, unless the can and its lid are heated before filling, localised cooling and loss of vacuum results. Any delay between filling and closing also causes loss of vacuum.

11.2.2.4. Hot exhausting. In 'hot exhausting', the filled cans, either open or with their lids clinched on (Section 11.2.3), are conveyed through a thermostatically controlled water bath or steam chamber where they are heated to 80–95 °C. The exhausted cans are then double seamed immediately after leaving the exhauster. The method gives reproducible results because there is no local condensation, as occurs with hot filling. Exhausting times may be excessive with conduction-heating foods, and there is a considerable risk of contamination through the open top or, to a lesser extent, through the clinched lid. Hot exhausting is often used in conjunction with hot filling.

11.2.2.5. Steam-flow closing. For slow-heating foods (*e.g.* canned meats and fish pastes), the headspace gases may be displaced by steam jets directed into the top of the filled can. After a pre-set time the lid, which is also heated by steam, is automatically positioned and the can is closed (steam-flow closing).[12] Obviously, there is no removal of entrapped gases by this method so pre-vacuumising or hot filling should precede steam-flow closing.

11.2.3. CLOSING OF CONTAINERS

Clearly, the storage life of foods preserved in containers is dependent on the protection provided by the closure. Industrially, can seaming is carried out in two stages (double seaming). The can and lid may be rotated in contact with a chuck which holds the lid firmly on the can body. The first seaming operation is then carried out by engaging a seaming roller which is profiled to form mating hooks on

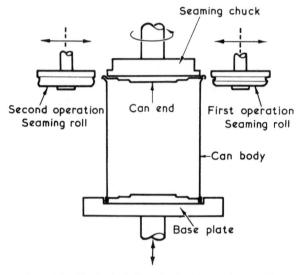

FIG. 11.9.   The basic design of a double-seaming machine.

the can and its lid. Tightening of these hooks is then completed by engaging a second-operation roller (Fig. 11.9). In high-speed machines of this type, centrifugal spillage of the can contents is prevented by arranging for the first- and second-operation rollers to rotate around the stationary can, lid and chuck. In the differential double seamer, a different principle is employed.[13] The can, lid and chuck are rotated and are driven forward between profiled, curved seaming rails. As before, seaming is carried out in two stages. Can seams are formed at high speeds and must conform to narrow dimensional tolerances.[14]

Clinching of can lids, as employed in hot exhausting, involves attaching the lid by a first-operation roller. The lids should be just loose enough to allow gases to be vented whilst limiting contamination by exhauster water or condensate. After exhausting, double seaming is completed. Clinching must be carried out so that the final seam is of the correct dimensions.

Glass containers are hermetically sealed by a number of different patterns of closure. The seal is established by holding the closure against a compressible gasket located between the closure and the neck of the container. The closure may be held in contact by a metal band or by crimping the closure over the container neck. Special types of screwed closure are also used. In most cases, a headspace vacuum is established by an appropriate method such as hot filling or steam-flow closure.

11.3. METHODS OF HEAT STERILISATION IN CONTAINERS

Heat processing of food in containers may be effected: by indirect heating by saturated steam; by hot air under forced convection; or by direct flame contact (cans only). Of these, heating in saturated steam is the most commonly used method.

11.3.1. GENERAL CONSIDERATIONS

Low-acid foods (Section 11.1.1) are sterilised at temperatures above 100 °C (usually 115–127 °C), and this requires the use of pressurised sterilisers. As with any other type of process using steam, it is important to ensure adequate venting of air from the retort and from the container surfaces.[16, 17] This is particularly important in the case of food sterilisation where any reduction in heat transfer rate could result in under-processing.

Retorting in steam, under pressure, must be carried out so as to minimise thermal shock to the food and to limit pressure strain on the containers.[18] The internal pressure developed on heating, when the food approaches retort temperature, is partly balanced by the pressure of the steam surrounding the containers. However, during the heating-up stage the food is below retort pressure and the containers are under compression, whereas during sterilising and cooling the food is above retort pressure and the containers are under tension. This pressure strain is reduced by controlling the heat-up and cool-down rates and by applying a balancing air pressure to the retort during the cooling stage (pressure cooling).

Thermal shock to glass containers is controlled by processing under water. The application of a superimposed air pressure during heating and cooling is used to counteract pressure strain.[11, 15] This

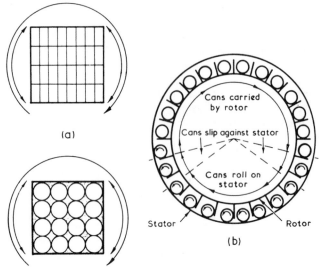

FIG. 11.10.   Common methods of agitating cans during processing. (a) Rotary or oscillatory, axial or end-over-end movement of crated cans in a batch retort. (b) Axial rotary movement of cans in a continuous steriliser.

method is also applied to cans which have large areas of flat surface (*e.g.* rectangular corned-beef cans) and to foods packaged in flexible pouches.[7, 19]

In many conduction heating packs, agitation of the container is used to produce movement of the food and, hence, accelerate the rate of heat transfer.[3] Agitation may be produced by any of the following methods:

   (i)   Rotation about the long axes of the cans by rolling them along tracks.
   (ii)   End-over-end rotation, the cans being rotated with their long axes aligned as the spokes of a wheel.
   (iii) Imparting a reciprocating or rocking motion to the containers (Fig. 11.10).

11.3.2. BATCH STERILISERS

Non-agitating batch retorts are used extensively in spite of their high labour requirements. They can accommodate containers of different sizes and are suitable for different types of process but steam and water consumptions are high compared with modern continuous retorts. The vertical (top loading) types (Fig. 11.11) require less floor-space than horizontal (side loading) retorts, but the latter are more convenient to charge and discharge. The design and operation of batch sterilisers are considered in Reference 15 and 16.

Batch sterilisers equipped for end-over-end rotation, for reciprocating and for rocking action of the containers are available.

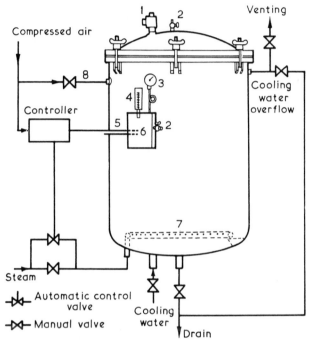

FIG. 11.11.   A vertical batch retort equipped for cooling under air pressure. 1, safety valve; 2, petcocks to maintain a steam bleed from retort during processing; 3, pressure gauge; 4, thermometer; 5, sensing element for controller; 6, themo-box; 7, steam spreader; 8, air inlet for pressure cooling.

The Orbitort* steriliser is an automatic, batch-type cooker-cooler operating at steam pressures of 350–415 kN/m² (25–45 p.s.i.g.). Cans are charged, with their long axes horizontal, at 45 cans/min *via* an air-operated gate valve, into the annular space between two concentric reels equipped with spiral guides. The reels are housed in a cylindrical pressure-shell about 1·5 m diameter and 8 m long. When charging is complete (around 600 cans depending on size), the retort is closed automatically, the reels are clamped together to hold the cans

* FMC Corp. San Jose, Calif., USA.

and the assembly is rotated within the shell at a controlled speed so that the headspace bubble passes through the can contents once each revolution, inducing stirring. The cooking and pressure-cooling is then controlled by a programmer, the cooled cans being discharged through an air-operated gate valve at the outlet end as a fresh charge is introduced at the inlet valve. The complete cycle, charge to discharge, is automatic.[21]

Reduced operating costs, better space utilisation and better processing of viscous foods compared with other batch retorts are claimed for the Orbitort which is now widely used in the USA and in many other parts of the world.[4, 7]

11.3.3. CONTINUOUS STERILISERS

Continuous sterilisation may be effected under pressure (using steam) or at atmospheric pressure (using hot air or direct flame heating). This latter method is restricted to use for small cans capable of withstanding the considerable pressure developed.

11.3.3.1. Continuous pressure sterilisers. The main types of continuous pressure sterilisers are: (i) the continuous pressure cooker-cooler, (ii) the continuous rotary steriliser, and (iii) the hydrostatic steriliser. The Hydrolock* continuous cooker-cooler is a recent addition to this class of steriliser.

The continuous pressure cooker-cooler is a non-agitating steriliser. The containers are carried on a roller track or chain conveyor through the preheating, sterilising and cooling sections. Transfer between the sections, which are at different pressure, is effected by means of pressure locks.

In the *rotary* (*or reel*) *steriliser* (Fig. 11.12) the containers are carried in a helical track affixed to the inner walls of each of three cylinders. Flanges, attached to the periphery of a slowly rotating hollow drum, convey the containers around and along each cylinder. Pressure locks effect transfer into and out of the machine and between the three sections. Agitation occurs by a combined rolling and sliding action as the containers travel around the helix (Fig. 11.12).

Continuous sterilisers of these types have good capacity (up to 500 cans/min) and give excellent uniformity of process, providing special care is taken in controlling product viscosity and can head-space conditions.[20] Disadvantageously, a large number of cans are undergoing processing at any one time so that a breakdown, such as may occur at the transfer locks, is serious. Pressure strain and thermal

---

* Ateliers et Chantiers de Bretagne. Paris, France.

shock, particularly at the transfer valves, may also be considerable in these sterilisers.

In *the hydrostatic steriliser*[15, 21, 22] (Fig. 11.13), the containers are conveyed through a steam tower, pressurised by means of water columns. The conveyor consists of slowly moving (~ 2 m/min) twin roller-chains to which are attached transverse carriers of various types (*e.g.* 'I' or 'C' section channels or perforated tubes). Containers are

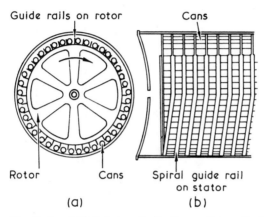

Guide rails on rotor   Cans

Rotor   Cans   Spiral guide rail
on stator

(a)   (b)

Fig. 11.12. The Mather & Platt Automatic Continuous Rotary Steriliser. (a) End view of rotor. (b) Side view, showing how the lead is confined to the lower part of the spiral so that the cans move forward only when they are in the rolling position. (By courtesy of Mather & Platt Ltd., Manchester, England.)

normally carried with their long axes horizontal, thus assisting convective heat transfer within the can.

Although, primarily, the Hydrostat is a non-agitating steriliser, a degree of agitation may be imparted. Devices for affecting this include:

(i)   Cans conveyed in carriers equipped with sprockets which mesh with a separate chain running parallel with the main conveying chains. This causes the carriers to rotate, inducing end-over-end or axial can motion depending on the orientation of the cans in the carriers.

(ii)   Mechanical vibration of the chains carrying the cans.

(iii) Permanent magnets set along the carrier-tube guides cause the tubes to rotate as they adhere to the guides during conveyance.

Other facilities include can-driers and the provision of over-riding

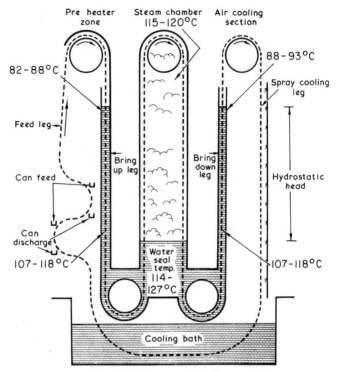

Fɪɢ. 11.13. Diagram showing the operating principle of the 'Hydron' hydrostatic steriliser. (By courtesy of Chisholm-Ryder International Ltd., Middlesex, England.)

air pressure to allow effective processing of foods packaged in plastic pouches and glass containers.

The expanding use of this type of steriliser, since its introduction into Europe in 1936 (there are now several hundred in use throughout the world), is due to its numerous advantages which are as follows:

(i)   Its minimisation of thermal and pressure shock to the food and container.
(ii) Its suitability for all types of sterilisable containers.
(iii) Its amenability to a high degree of automation.
(iv) Its efficient use of steam and water.
(v)   The excellent uniformity and control of processing of which it is capable.
(vi) Its mechanical reliability.
(vii) Its economic use of floor space (about 40 m² for an output of 1000 cans/min). Although a height of 20 m is necessary, only

the bottom section, where charging and discharging takes place, needs to be enclosed.

(viii) Its relative flexibility for different can sizes.

(ix) Its availability in a wide range of capacities (within the range 60–1000 cans/min).

The capital investment involved in these sterilisers, together with their ancillary equipment such as feeders, and control gear, is considerable. Additionally, there is a high in-process stock at any one

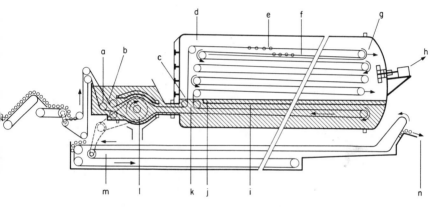

FIG. 11.14. The Hydrolock steriliser: (a) water seal; (b) carrier chain; (c) retort water-level; (d) steam space; (e) cans in carriers; (f) can track; (g) direction-changer; (h) steam–air mixing fan; (i) insulating partition separating steam space from water space; (j) pre-cooling water; (k) transfer slot; (l) water-sealed rotary valve; (m) air cooling; (n) discharge. (By courtesy of Ateliers et Chantiers de Bretagne, Paris, France.)

time. For these reasons, the hydrostatic steriliser is of particular application in high-capacity plants processing long runs of materials requiring similar heat processes.

The Hydrolock steriliser[21, 23] (Fig. 11.14), introduced around 1966 comprises a horizontal, cylindrical pressure vessel into which 'sticks' of cans or glass jars, contained in chain-driven carriers, are conveyed via a rotary valve. This valve is sealed partly mechanically and partly by the water in which it is submerged. The containers are preheated as they pass through the valve and then ascend into the top of the pressure cylinder where they are conveyed horizontally, back and forth, under pressure in saturated steam for the required sterilising time. The cans are then pre-cooled as they pass through a slot in a hollow, insulating partition into a water layer in the base of the retort. After pre-cooling the cans are discharged by the rotary valve to final, atmospheric cooling and are then unloaded.

Axial rotation of the cans is effected by rolling them along tracks located below the carriers. Alternatively, these tracks may be disengaged to give non-agitated cooking. Sterilising temperatures up to 143 °C are possible (allowing shorter processing times) and the retort may be used with an air-overpressure for processing glass or plastic containers. In this case a fan, mounted in the pressure shell, is used to promote intimate mixing of the steam and air to offset, partly, the poor thermal properties of the latter.

Advantages claimed for this machine are economic use of steam, water, labour and space. Disadvantageously, it is to be expected that pressure strains at the rotary valve during charging and discharging would be appreciable.

11.3.3.2. Continuous atmospheric-pressure sterilisers. *The Ekelund hot-air steriliser* has been used successfully in Sweden for the sterilisation of canned milk. The milk is preheated and is then filled into sterilised cans. The cans are closed and are then conveyed into the top of a hot-air chamber where they roll down tracks (9 passes at 10 m each). The chamber is heated by forced convection with air at 145 °C and at a flow-rate of 10 m/s. Sterilising time is about 15 min, after which the cans are water cooled. The steriliser has a capacity of 3200 cans per hour.[24] Pressure strain is considerable and the process would appear to be limited to small cans for this reason. Successful trials on the canning of fruits and vegetables using this method have also been reported.[25]

Flame sterilisation (the Steriflamme Process) has been used for canned milk, peas, beans, carrots and mushrooms.[21, 26] The cans are preheated in a steam chamber whence they are conveyed into a sterilising chamber where the cans are spun (120 rev/min) over gas flames at 1300 °C. Thus the can contents are heated rapidly to sterilising temperature (97–125 °C in 45 s) after which they are conveyed to a steam-heated holding chamber and finally through a water cooler. Recent equipment modifications include improved agitation using 'shuttle-bar' movement of the cans[27] and pulsing of the heating cycle to allow equilibration of temperatures within the can.[29] The steriliser is uncomplicated in concept and operation and the fast, high temperature process gives high-quality products. Problems exist in can temperature measurement and in the absence of pressure-balancing, this restricting the method to small cans. The heat transfer, thermal processing and quality aspects of Steriflamme processing have been the subject of recent, detailed study.[28]

11.4. STERILISATION OF THE FOOD OUTSIDE THE CONTAINER

Sterilising methods of this type take advantage of the fact that high temperature processing (up to 150 °C) by means of high-speed heat exchangers may be used. This results in a substantial reduction in processing time with consequent general improvement in product quality. Processes using rapid sterilising at these high temperatures are referred to as high-short processes and should not be confused with the H.T.S.T. process used for milk pasteurisation.

11.4.1. THE EFFECTS OF HIGH-SHORT PROCESSES ON FOOD QUALITY

What little information there is suggests that the destruction of vitamins and food colours or the inactivation of enzymes in foods follows much the same course as the destruction of bacterial spores. but with a z-value considerably higher.[2] This has important consequences. Consider a food that requires an equivalent time.

$$F_{120}^{10} = 10 \, \text{min for commercial sterilisation}$$

This could be provided by heating the food instantaneously to 120 °C, holding it at that temperature for 10 min and instantaneously cooling it again. Alternatively the food could be heated instantaneously to 140 °C and instantaneously cooled after a holding time of only 0·1 min.

Suppose that this food contains an enzyme with a z-value of 50 °C which requires holding for 4 min at 120 °C for inactivation. Clearly the 10 min process at 120 °C will both sterilise the food and inactivate the enzyme. However, at 140 °C (by adapting equation 11.5) the enzyme can be calculated to require

$$4 \times 10^{\frac{120 - 140}{50}} = 1·6 \, \text{min for inactivation.}$$

Thus the process of 0·1 min at 140 °C will produce a commercially sterile product, but not inactivate the enzyme.[30] This simple illustration demonstrates why high temperature-short time processing, while giving acceptably sterile products of high organoleptic quality and with good vitamin retention, can experience enzyme regeneration problems.[31]

In general, therefore, high-short processing gives improved quality products. Exceptions to this include meat based products[32] in which flavour and colour development are the results of extended cooking (as in conventional canning) and canned pulses which are tenderised by lengthy in-container cooking.

11.4.2. METHODS OF STERILISING OUTSIDE THE CONTAINER

In processes of this type, the preheated food is rapidly heated in a high-speed heat exchanger to about 150 °C and is then passed to a holding section. After the requisite holding time, which is only a matter of seconds with the high 'L values' (Section 11.1.3) obtaining at this temperature, the food is rapidly cooled and is then sealed in sterile containers. This process, which is completed in a few minutes when carried out under aseptic conditions, is known as 'aseptic processing'.

Various types of heat exchanger are used depending on the nature of the food. Low-viscosity foods may be heated indirectly, using steam heated, spiral-tube, or plate-type heat exchangers (Fig. 12.10), or, directly, using in-line injection of 'live' steam. High-viscosity foods are best heated by scraped-surface heat exchangers (Fig. 9.9). Cooling, after holding, may be effected by passage through a vacuumised flash-chamber (which also de-aerates the product), or a continuous cooler of suitable design may be used. The sterilised food may then be submitted to other processes such as straining or homogenisation before being filled aseptically into sterile containers.

Aseptic processes are now well established and their application is expanding. The more important industrial methods are described below.

11.4.2.1. The Dole Process.[*][33] This process has been in use, mainly in the USA, since 1951, and has been applied to milk products, purées, some soups and to yoghourt and sour cream.[7, 21] This process is applied in a closed, inter-connecting system which carries out the sequence of operations described in Section 11.4.2 and provides an uninterrupted passage of the food through the steriliser. The plant is pre-sterilised with superheated steam at about 300 °C and a slight positive pressure is maintained during operation to retain sterility. The cans and ends are sterilised with superheated steam at 225 °C, briefly cooled by spraying the can-bottoms with sterile water and are then filled through a slit-filler with the cooled, aseptically-sterilised food. Fill-in weights are controlled by using a positive displacement pump to feed the slit-filler. The filled cans are then double seamed using seamers of standard design modified to allow shrouding for sterilisation and to withstand the high temperatures involved. Cans may be handled at 450–500/min in retail sizes and packs ranging from

---

* The James Dole Engineering Co., San Francisco, USA.

125 ml cans to 22·5 litre drums can be processed. Development of a Dole Aseptic Steriliser for glass containers has reached an advanced stage.[7, 21, 35]

11.4.2.2. Aseptic filling of bulk containers. In the USA pumpable food products such as fruit purées and tomato concentrates are now filled aseptically into specially designed large cans and drums.[7, 21] In one such system, two retorts are used alternately. A drum and its cover, which is fitted with a small filling hole, are placed in the retort, sterilised with steam at $800 \, kN/m^2$ (~ 100 psig) and is filled, under vacuum, with cooled aseptically-sterilised food. The filling hole is then closed, with the filled drum still in the retort, the vacuum is released and the sealed drum is removed. The two retorts are operated in sequence and the system can fill 24 55 gallon (US) drums/h.

Another bulk filler sterilises the drum and lid by jetting with steam at $207 \, kN/m^2$ (15 psig) for $1\frac{1}{2}$ min with venting followed by a further 1 min with the vent closed. The sterilising jet is then retracted and replaced by a filling tube through which cool, sterilised food is introduced. At the completion of filling, the tube is withdrawn and the filling hole is automatically closed in an aseptic manner.

The advantages claimed for bulk packs are: reduced handling, labour and transportation costs; reduced product hold-up in empty packages and better space utilisation in storage.

11.4.2.3. Aseptic filling of plastic containers. Aseptic filling of rigid and flexible plastic containers is the subject of intensive investigation.[7, 34] Serious problems have been encountered regarding the integrity of the materials and seams. Meticulous attention must be given to the sterilisation of the containers, which, in general, are not amenable to heat treatment. Treatments with ethylene oxide, hot and cold hydrogen peroxide, ionising radiation and sterile air are advocated. Aseptic filling procedures using form-fill-seal equipment (Section 11.4.2.4), glove-boxes and/or 'clean-room' techniques have been reported.

11.4.2.4. Milk sterilisation. In-pack sterilisation of milk is widely practised but the colour, flavour and sterility of the product leave much to be desired. High-short aseptic processes give much improved quality [36] and extended storage life and numerous processes have been developed. These differ in the method of heating (*e.g.* 'live' steam injection or indirect plate heating, etc.) and in the times and temperatures used for sterilisation. Cooling and filling are carried out aseptically, the containers being cans, bottles and cartons of various types.[37] The 'Tetra-Pak' and 'Tetra-Brik' Systems (AB Lund,

Sweden) have achieved considerable use in the production of long-life milk and coffee whiteners. Composite packs made from laminates of polythene/paperboard/aluminium foil/polythene are used in a process which forms the container, fills it aseptically and seals it in a continuous manner in a single piece of equipment.[7] This is known as 'form-fill-seal' packaging.

11.5. PASTEURISATION BY HEAT PROCESSING

11.5.1. GENERAL CONSIDERATIONS

This heat process (Section 11.1.1) was developed by Pasteur in 1864 for preventing abnormal fermentations in wine. Pasteurisation is now applied to a wide range of foods: milk, cream, ice-cream, canned and bottled fruits, fruit juices, pickles, beers, wines, and canned liquid egg. In some countries, and for some foods, pasteurising procedures are specified in legislation. Where legal standards do not exist, suitable pasteurisation processes may be calculated using the principles set out in Section 11.1.

Sterilisation is concerned with spore destruction, whereas in pasteurising the major concern is with the destruction of vegetative organisms and yeast and mould spores. Owing to the relatively low temperatures used ($< 100\,^\circ\text{C}$) in pasteurisation, foods preserved by this method suffer less heat damage than foods preserved by sterilisation. However, processing at these lower temperatures for times adequate for pasteurisation may leave the food with residual enzyme activity. This may cause spoilage of the food during storage (*e.g.* in pickles[38] and fruit juice[39]). The oxygen concentration within the food, apart from determining the extent of oxidative deterioration, also controls the growth of some micro-organisms (particularly moulds) in pasteurised foods.[39] For these reasons, pasteurisation processes should be such as to ensure: (i) adequate microbiological control, (ii) destruction of undesired enzymes and (iii) low oxygen tension in the food.

11.5.2. PASTEURISING METHODS

Both batch and continuous methods are used and pasteurisation may take place before or after placing in the container. In all cases the equipment is less complex than that used for sterilisation since pasteurisation is carried out at atmospheric pressure.

11.5.2.1. Batch pasteurisation. Bulk foods such as milk and fruit juices may be pasteurised in individual batches in stirred, jacketed, stainless steel vessels.[40] The jacket may be used both for heating (using steam or hot water) and cooling (using chilled water or brine). Very often, since rapid cooling is advisable in order to limit the growth of thermophilic organisms, the pasteurised food is passed through a separate cooler. Foods sealed in containers may be batch pasteurised in water or steam baths followed by water-spray cooling.

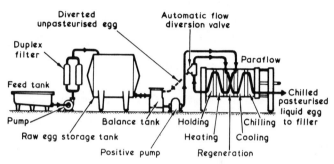

Fig. 11.15.   Flow diagram of a typical APV Paraflow liquid egg pasteurising plant. (By courtesy of The APV Company Ltd., Crawley, England.)

11.5.2.2. Continuous pasteurisation. Bulk liquid foods may be pasteurised by passage through plate heat exchangers which usually comprise four stages—preheating (regeneration), heating, holding and cooling (Fig. 11.15). Pasteurisers of this type are available with capacities up to 35 000 litres per hour. Ancillary equipment may include flash-vacuum deodorisers for cream and de-aerators for fruit juices.

Continuous, non-agitating pasteurisation of food in containers is carried out by conveying them through an atmospheric pressure cooker-cooler. The containers may be heated by immersion in hot water, or by spraying with hot water, or by exposure to steam at atmospheric pressure. The pasteuriser is usually divided into sections which are heated and thermostatically controlled individually. This minimises thermal shock and improves thermal efficiency since countercurrent heating may be used. The hydrostatic cooker (Fig. 11.13) may also be used for the continuous pasteurisation of foods in containers.

The rotary, atmospheric pressure cooker-cooler is used for the continuous, agitating pasteurisation of canned foods. This is of similar design to the pressure steriliser illustrated in Fig. 11.12 but is of simpler construction since pressurisation is unnecessary.

Microwave heating (Chapter 10) is finding some application as a continuous pasteurisation method for packaged foods such as bread and cakes,[41] and has been studied as a possible method for continuous sterilisation of foods.[42]

REFERENCES

1. Hersom, A. C., and Hulland, E. D., 'Canned Foods–an Introduction to their Microbiology (Baumgartner)' 5th ed. (Churchill: 1963).
2. Stumbo, C. R., 'Thermobacteriology in Food Processing', 2nd ed. (Academic Press: 1973).
3. Ball, C. O., and Olson, F. C. W., 'Sterilization in Food Technology'. (McGraw-Hill: 1957).
4. Bigelow, W. D., J. Infectious Dis., **29**(5), 528 (1921).
5. Gillespy, T. G., J. Sci. Fd Agric., **2**, 107 (1951).
6. Diendoerfer, F. H., Applied Microbiology, **5**, 221 (1957).
7. Brody, A. L., 'Food Canning in Rigid and Flexible Packages'. Critical Reviews in Food Technology (Chemical Rubber Co.: 1971).
8. Fechheimer, P. R., 'Filling Liquid Products'. Mod. Packag. Encycl., **40**(13A), 446–459 (1967).
9. Minard, E. S., 'Filling Viscous Products'. Mod. Packag. Encycl., **40**(13A), 460–469 (1967).
10. Blackwell, J. S., 'Filling Dry Products'. Mod. Packag. Encycl., **40**(13A), 436–445 (1967).
11. Anon., 'Processes for Low Acid Canned Foods in Glass Containers'. Bull. Nat. Cann. Ass., No. 30-L(1963).
12. Coleman, G., 'Steam Flow Closure–a Re-examination'. Tech. Memo. No. 73, Fruit Veg. Preserv. Res. Ass. (undated).
13. Geeson, R. E., 'Trends in the Design of High Speed Can Closing Machinery'. Ed. Leitch, J. M. Vol. 4. (Gordon and Breach, London: 1965).
14. Anon., 'Double Seam Manual'. The Metal Box Co. Ltd., England: 1973.
15. Anon., 'Canned Foods. Principles of Thermal Process Control and Container Evaluation'. National Canners' Association, USA: 1973.
16. Hickman, A., and Robinson, D. J., 'Batch Sterilizing Cans'. Process. Biochem., **8**(7), 21–2 (1973).
17. Anon., 'Air in Steam Heated Plant' and 'The Air Venting of Large Steam Spaces'. Information Sheet Nos. 10 and 19. (Spirax-Sarco, Gloucestershire, England: 1960).
18. Adams, H. W., and Owen, W., 'Internal Pressure of Cans'. Fd Technol., **26**(7), 28–30 (1972).
19. Trautmann, L., '1975—Year of the Retort Pouch'. Fd Engng, **46**(12), 69–72 (1974).
20. Hersom, A. C., 'Sterility Problems Associated with Rotary Cooker Coolers', Proc. Int. Fd Ind. Cong., 63–66. (Grampian Press: 1964).
21. Lopez, A., 'A Complete Course in Canning', 10th ed. (The Canning Trade, Maryland, USA: 1975).
22. Nair, J. H., 'Hydrostatic Sterilisers'. Fd Engng, **36**(12), 37–42 (1964).
23. Lawler, F. K., 'New Sterilizer Made in France', Fd Engng, **39**(7), 73–5 (1967).
24. Sporle, C. H., 'Sterilizing Milk by Hot Air'. Fd Process. Packag. **24**, 232–3 (1955).
25. Gillespy, T. G., 'Ekelund Hot Air Cooker. Heat Penetration and Canning Trials'. Tech. Memo. No. 28, Fruit Veg. Cann. Quick Freez. Res. Ass. (1958).

26. Lawler, F. K., 'French Process Boosts Quality Cuts Costs'. Fd Engng, **39**(7), 65–8 (1967).
27. Casimir, D. J., 'New Equipment for Thermal Processing of Canned Foods'. Fd Technol. Aust., **22**(1), 8–19 (1970).
28. Leonard, S. *et al.* Various Titles. J. Fd Sci., **40**(2), 246–258 (1975).
29. Johnson, A. H., and Peterson, M. S. (Eds.) 'Encyclopaedia of Food Technology'. (AVI. USA: 1974).
30. Stumbo, C. R., 'Fundamental Considerations in High Temperature Short Time Processing of Foods', *in* Tilgner, D. J., and Borys, A. (Eds.). Proc. 2nd Int. Cong. Fd Sci. Technol. (Ars Polona, Foreign Trade Enterprise, Warsaw: 1966).
31. Esselen, W. B., and Anderson, E. E., 'Thermal Destruction of Peroxidase in Vegetables at High Temperatures'. Fd Res., **21,** 322–5 (1956).
32. Luh, B. S., *et al.*, 'Aseptic Canning of Foods. (5) Chemical and Flavour Changes in Strained Beef'. Fd Technol., **18**(2), 90–94 (1964).
33. Martin, W. M., 'Aseptic Canning System Embodying Short-High Temperature Sterilization'. Paper presented to Inst. Fd Technol., Chicago (1950).
34. Toledo, T. R., and Chapman, J. R., 'Aseptic Packaging in Rigid Plastic Containers'. Fd Technol., **45**(11), 68–76 (1973).
35. Rees, J. A. G., 'Practical Aspects of Aseptic Processing'. Fd Mf., **48**(9), 48–51 + 86 (1973).
36. Kent, N., 'Aseptic Canning for Milk-Based Desserts'. Fd Process. Ind., **45**(530), 34 and 36 (1976).
37. Davis, J. G., 'A Dictionary of Dairying'. (Leonard Hill: 1965).
38. Dakin, J. C., 'Pasteurization of Acetic Acid Preserves', *in* Hawthorn, J., and Muil Leitch, J. (Eds.) 'Recent Advances in Food Science', Vol. 2. (Butterworths: 1962).
39. Meyrath, J., 'Problems in Fruit Juice Pasteurization', *in* Hawthorn, J. and Muil Leitch, J. (Eds.) 'Recent Advances in Food Science', Vol. 2. (Butterworths: 1962).
40. Anon.. 'Pasteurizing Plant Manual'. 2nd ed. (Soc. Dairy Technol., London: 1966).
41. Evans, K. A., and Taylor, H., 'Microwaves Extend Shelf Life of Cakes'. Fd Mf., **42**(10), 50–1 (1967).
42. Kenyon, E. M., 'The Feasibility of Continuous Heat Sterilization Using Microwave Power', Tech. Rep. 71–8–F.L. US Army Natick Laboratories, Mass., USA: 1970.

CHAPTER 12

EVAPORATION

12.1 USES OF EVAPORATION

Evaporation—the concentration of a solution by boiling off solvent—has three major applications in the food industry:

(i)   Pre-concentration of a liquid prior to further processing, *e.g.* before spray drying, drum drying, crystallisation, etc.

(ii) Reduction of liquid volume to reduce storage, packaging and transport costs.

(iii) To reduce 'water activity', by increasing the concentration of soluble solids in food materials, as an aid to preservation, *e.g.* in sweetened condensed milk manufacture.

12.2. BASIC EVAPORATOR CONSTRUCTION

Industrial evaporator systems normally consist of

(i)   a heat exchanger to supply sensible heat and latent heat of evaporation to the feed. In the food industry saturated steam is usually used as the heating medium.

(ii) a separator in which the vapour is separated from the concentrated liquid phase.

(iii) a condenser to effect condensation of the vapour and its removal from the system. This may be omitted if the system is working at atmospheric pressure.

In the food industry, risk of heat damage to the concentrating liquid often arises if evaporation is carried out at atmospheric pressure. It is usual to evaporate food liquids at reduced pressures. In this case ancillary equipment—vacuum pump or steam jet-ejector and extraction pumps and/or barometric legs—will be required (Section 12.7).

12.3. FACTORS INFLUENCING LIQUID BOILING POINT

The driving force for heat transfer in the heat exchanger of an evaporator is the temperature difference between the heating medium and the liquid being heated. The temperature of the latter is influenced by several factors including the following.

12.3.1. EXTERNAL PRESSURE

A liquid boils when the vapour pressure it exerts equals the external pressure to which it is subjected. In the case of food materials the solvent is usually water—a substance for which vapour pressure–temperature relationships are readily available.

12.3.2. DISSOLVED SOLUTE—BOILING POINT RISE (BPR)

The boiling point of a solution is higher than that of the pure solvent at the same pressure. The more concentrated the solution, the higher the boiling point. As evaporation proceeds the liquid concentration increases and the boiling point rises. This change leads to a progressively decreasing temperature difference and hence rate of heat transfer. This decrease in rate of heat transfer must be taken into account in the design of commercial evaporators. The value of the BPR must be subtracted from any value of the temperature difference based on the boiling point of pure solvent. The actual elevation of the boiling point with change in concentration can often be obtained from Dühring's rule. This empirical rule states that the boiling point of a solution is a linear function of the boiling point of the pure solvent at the same pressure. Dühring plots show the boiling points of the solution at various concentrations, plotted against the boiling point of pure solvent at the same pressures. Differing concentrations are represented as a family of curves, and the boiling points of solutions of various concentrations are obtained by interpolation. A Dühring plot for sucrose solutions is shown in Fig. 12.1. The rule is not exact over wide ranges of pressures although it finds wide application in industrial calculations. Dühring plots for food materials are not readily available.

12.3.3. HYDROSTATIC HEAD

At any level beneath its free surface, liquid is subjected to a pressure equal to the sum of the pressure on the surface and the pressure

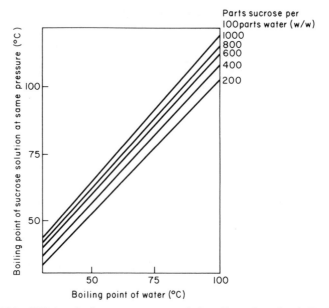

FIG. 12.1.   Dühring plot for aqueous sucrose solutions (drawn from data in Honig[1]).

corresponding to the hydrostatic head—the vertical distance from the free surface to the level in question. Thus the boiling temperature of the liquid in an evaporator varies with depth. This increase in boiling temperature with increasing depth lowers the temperature difference between the heating medium and the boiling liquid and may lead to overheating of the process liquid, which can become superheated. Overheating can give rise to heat damage in a unit designed to operate at a specific temperature which is unknowingly exceeded. The influence of hydrostatic head becomes more pronounced in vacuum evaporation and can be a problem in long-tube evaporators (Section 12.6.3). Commonly the average boiling temperature for liquid, based on the pressure at a liquid level halfway up the evaporator, is used in design calculations.

12.4.   THE HEAT LOAD

The overall rate of heat transfer, Q, from the heating medium to the boiling liquid across the intervening wall and surface films, is often known as the 'heat load' and is given by

$$Q = UA\Delta T \qquad (12.1)$$

U is the overall heat transfer coefficient, based on the outside or inside surface area, A, and ΔT is the temperature difference between the heating medium and boiling liquid. The value of U depends on a number of factors and cannot be predicted with any accuracy (see Section 12.4.3).

In the design, selection and operation of evaporators, an important requirement is a knowledge of the heat load. This may be obtained from heat and material balances.

12.4.1. HEAT BALANCE

Ideally a heat balance should be constructed on the basis of enthalpy–concentration data. Such data is not readily available for food materials and a modified heat balance using mean specific heats of the materials is often used.

Referring to Fig. 12.2:

L_i is the feed liquor flow rate in kg/s, the liquors containing a mass fraction x_f of solids.

L_o is the product liquor flow rate in kg/s, the liquors containing a mass fraction x_p of solids.

V_i is the mass of steam (kg/s) condensed in the steam chest.

V_o is the mass of solvent (kg/s) vaporised in the evaporator (the 'evaporative capacity').

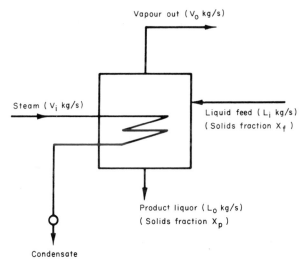

FIG. 12.2. A simple mass balance diagram for one effect of an evaporator.

λ_s is the latent heat of condensation of the inlet steam (J/kg).
C_p is the mean specific heat of the feed stream (J/kg °C).
λ_v is the latent heat of vaporisation of the vapours produced (J/kg).

Heat losses from the system are omitted from Fig. 12.2. These losses are due almost entirely to convection and radiation from hot surfaces. For efficient operation, heat losses should be minimised by lagging exposed surfaces and by avoiding steam leaks. The cost of such losses is discussed by Lyle.[2] Neglecting heat losses, so that all the heat given up by the condensing steam is transferred to the process liquors, the heat balance becomes:

Heat given up by condensing steam

$$= \text{sensible heat gained} \atop \text{by liquid feed} + \text{latent heat of vapour} \atop \text{produced}$$

or

$$V_i\lambda_s = L_iC_p(T_b - T_i) + V_o\lambda_v \qquad (12.2)$$

T_b is the boiling point of the liquid and in general rises with increasing concentration (Section 12.3.2).
T_i is the temperature of the feed stream.

No account has been taken of the heat in the condensate leaving the steam chest. This is only a very small fraction of the total heat transferred. The heat given up by the condensing steam is transferred to the liquid, *i.e.*

$$V_i\lambda_s = Q = UA\Delta T \qquad (12.3)$$

12.4.2. MATERIAL BALANCES

The rate of vapour production, V_o, during evaporation is obtained from a material balance.
Two equations are required which may be solved for V_o.
The overall material balance:

$$L_i = V_o + L_o \qquad (12.4)$$

The material balance on the liquid:

$$L_i(1 - x_f) = L_o(1 - x_p) + V_o. \qquad (12.5)$$

12.4.3. FACTORS INFLUENCING THE OVERALL HEAT TRANSFER COEFFICIENT

The value of U may be calculated (see Appendix II) knowing:

(a) The condensing film heat transfer coefficient on the steam side of the heat exchanger.
(b) The boiling liquid film coefficient on the liquid side of the heat exchanger.
(c) The scale or fouling factors on both inner and outer walls bounding the heat transfer surfaces.
(d) The thermal resistance of the wall material.

Film coefficients for steam condensing both inside tubes and on tube banks are well known[3] and fall in the range 5–$15\,kW/m^2\,°C$ (1000–$3000\,Btu/h\,ft^2\,°F$).

The phenomenon of boiling and the determination of boiling film heat transfer coefficients have received increasing attention.[4]

These coefficients tend to be higher in forced circulation, as opposed to natural circulation systems (see Appendix II). However, as yet, general methods for calculating boiling film coefficients are unreliable. In a well-designed natural circulation evaporator, flows of 1–$2\,m/s$ of liquid through the heat exchanger are developed, while for forced circulation units, where the flow velocity is increased by means of some mechanical agency such as a circulation pump or an impeller, velocities of 3–$5\,m/s$ are commonly quoted. A number of workers have shown that the boiling film heat transfer coefficient, h, is critically dependent on the temperature difference, ΔT_s, between the submerged heating surface and the liquid. As the temperature difference increases, the heat transfer coefficient initially increases (Fig. 12.3). In this region of the curve, superheated liquid rises to the liquid–vapour interface by natural convection, where gentle boiling takes place. At somewhat higher values of ΔT_s, bubbles of vapour form at projections on the submerged surface. The bubbles break away, agitating the liquid as they rise to the surface. The number of these 'active nuclei' increases rapidly with increasing ΔT_s and an appreciable increase in heat transfer results. The promotion of this vigorous 'nucleate boiling' is important in industrial applications. At still higher values of ΔT_s, the heat flux passes through a maximum, corresponding to a 'critical temperature difference' and then starts to fall. This fall off in heat transfer is due to blanketing of the heating surface by vapour.

In industrial evaporation the aim is to achieve a value of ΔT_s just below the critical value. For many applications it appears that this corresponds to an overall temperature difference, $\Delta T,'$ of about 25–$30\,°C$.

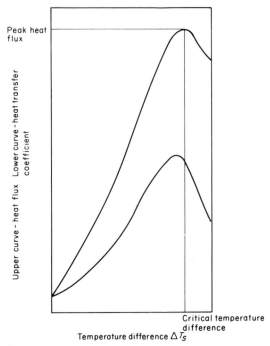

Fig. 12.3.   Heat flux and heat transfer coefficient—variation with temperature difference. For water boiling at 100 C on submerged surfaces.

In summary, it may be said that the calculation of U-values is difficult if not impossible. Pilot plant studies give valuable information, but the process engineer leans heavily on experience when selecting a value of U for use in design studies.

12.5.   THE INFLUENCE OF FEED LIQUOR PROPERTIES ON EVAPORATION

The choice of evaporator type for a given process duty is greatly influenced by the properties of the feed liquor.

12.5.1. VISCOSITY

Higher viscosities lead to reduced circulation rates and lower heat transfer coefficients. Since, in general, the viscosity of a solution undergoing evaporation increases with concentration, a fall-off in heat transfer rate is to be expected as evaporation proceeds.

12.5.2. FOULING—SCALING

Deposition of scale on heat transfer surfaces during evaporation lowers the U-value. This fouling may be due to adhesion of suspended solids present in the feed liquor. More usually the scale is deposited from solution on heating. Experience shows that fouling is less pronounced at high liquid velocities. This is possibly due to the scouring action of the fast-flowing liquid stream. For this reason, liquids likely to result in severe scaling are best processed in forced circulation evaporators.

The phenomenon of fouling on heat transfer surfaces is little understood. The design engineer incorporates a 'fouling factor' into the OHTC to take into account the additional resistance to heat transfer offered by a layer of scale but over-allowances can lead to large increases in capital cost. Recent work on fouling is discussed by Bott[5] and Mannheim and Passy.[6]

Magnetic scale prevention devices are said to be capable of reducing cleaning down-time very significantly in some evaporator applications. Passage of feed liquor through a strong magnetic field prior to entering the evaporator is said to lead to modifications in the physical characteristics of the deposited solids. Instead of a difficult to remove scale, solids are deposited in a form which is easy to remove. The scouring effect of the boiling liquid can then keep heat transfer surfaces cleaner for longer periods. According to Diamant,[7] the interval between 'shut-downs' for the descaling of sugar evaporators was increased from 6 days to 52 days after magnetic treatment had been introduced.

In order to reduce labour costs, scale-forming liquids should always be processed in evaporators affording easy access for cleaning. Food engineers are increasingly turning to 'chemical, in-place cleaning' as an answer to the clean-down problem (Chapter 17).

12.5.3. FOAMING

The formation of a stable foam during boiling is encountered with many liquids. This is particularly the case where boiling takes place under reduced pressure and the hydrostatic head is large. Foaming is thought to be related to the interfacial forces that arise between vapour, superheated liquid and suspended solids, the solids being capable of acting as nuclei for bubble formation. Surface active agents have been used to control foaming, and a number of mechanical devices for the breakdown of foams are in common use (see Section 12.7.3).

12.5.4. TEMPERATURE SENSITIVITY

To reduce the risk of damage to heat-sensitive materials during evaporation, boiling temperatures should be kept low and residence times of the liquors in the heating zone short.

Boiling temperatures are lowered by reducing the operating pressure of the evaporator. Satisfactory temperature differences can then be achieved with heating media at correspondingly lower temperatures.

It is now generally accepted that somewhat higher temperatures than those previously regarded as safe working maxima can be tolerated if residence times at these elevated temperatures are kept very short. For this reason mechanical 'thin-film' evaporators are finding increasing use in the concentration of heat-sensitive materials[8] (Section 12.6.6).

12.5.5. AROMA LOSS

The aroma and flavour components in many liquid foods, fruit juices, etc., are more volatile than water. When such liquids are evaporated these components can be removed with the water vapour causing a deterioration in the quality of the resulting concentrate. Volatile constituents are commonly recovered from the vapour as an 'essence' by fractional distillation. The 'stripped' liquor is then concentrated separately and re-blended with the essence.[9, 10]

12.5.6. CORROSION CHARACTERISTICS

In process design studies, the corrosive nature of the materials handled must be considered. Materials of construction compatible with the food material must be selected. With foodstuffs even traces of contamination due to very slight corrosion can lead to infringement of the regulations prescribing maximum levels of trace elements in foods.[11] Stainless steel construction is commonly used (Chapter 17). Corrosive liquors necessitating expensive materials of construction are often concentrated in forced circulation evaporators, where the higher U-value obtained permits a reduction in surface area required.

12.6. EVAPORATION EQUIPMENT

A number of evaporator types are available. The essential features of the more important types are discussed below.

12.6.1. NATURAL CIRCULATION EVAPORATORS

12.6.1.1. Open pan evaporator. These are the simplest commercial evaporators available and their cheapness makes them popular. The pans can be directly heated. More often they are fitted with either an outer jacket, or with internal coils through which a heat transfer medium passes. In these units evaporation rates are low and heat economy is poor. The pans may be closed to permit vacuum operation. Stirring increases the rate of heat transfer and reduces the risk of 'burn-on'. These simple evaporators are used in tomato pulp concentration, soup and sauce preparations and in jam and

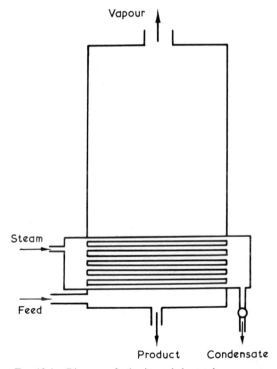

FIG. 12.4. Diagram of a horizontal short tube evaporator.

confectionery boilings. Small, jacketed pans are very useful, but with larger capacities the ratio of heat transfer surface to liquid volume falls and the heating becomes less effective. Internal heating coils fitted in larger units can interfere with the liquid circulation, so affecting the heat transfer rate. In general, when larger capacities are required, other types of evaporator offer greater advantages.

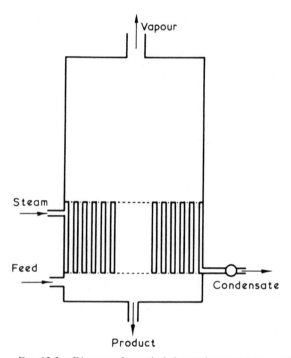

FIG. 12.5.   Diagram of a vertical short tube evaporator.

12.6.1.2. Horizontal short tube evaporator. The shell carries a bundle of internally steam heated, horizontal tubes (Fig. 12.4). The purpose of the disengagement space above the heater is to permit a gravity separation of liquid droplets carried off with the vapour from the bulk of the liquid. To reduce entrainment still further, impingement baffles are usually fitted. The horizontal tube bundle interferes with the circulation so the overall heat transfer coefficients are low.

This type of unit was originally intended for the evaporation of non-scaling, non-foaming, low viscosity liquids.

12.6.1.3. Vertical short tube evaporator. This type of unit (Fig. 12.5) is extensively used in the process industries and has become known as the 'standard evaporator'. Here steam condenses on the outside of tubes which are mounted vertically. The 'calandria'—the assembly of tubes built into a steam chest—often has a central downcomer which normally occupies at least 40 % of the flow area of the

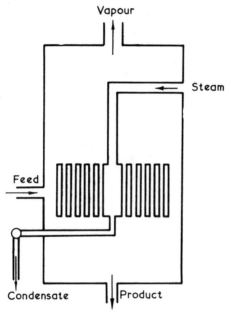

Fɪɢ. 12.6.   Diagram of a vertical short tube evaporator using a basket type calandria.

riser tubes. Since liquid in the downcomer is cooler than that in the heated risers, natural circulation currents are set up. Tube lengths are from 0·5 to 2 m (2–6 ft) and tube diameters 25–75 mm (1–3 in).

With scale-forming liquors, the tubes should be kept covered with liquor to minimise fouling. Units can be fitted with 'basket calandrias' (Fig. 12.6) which can be easily removed for maintenance.

This evaporator gives good rates of evaporation with non-corrosive, mildly scaling liquors of moderate viscosity. Typical applications include the concentration of solutions of cane sugar, beet sugar, glucose, malt extract, salt and fruit juices.

12.6.1.4. Natural circulation evaporator with external calandria. In this unit the calandria is outside the vapour disengagement space (Fig. 12.7). Construction is simple and permits easy access to the tube

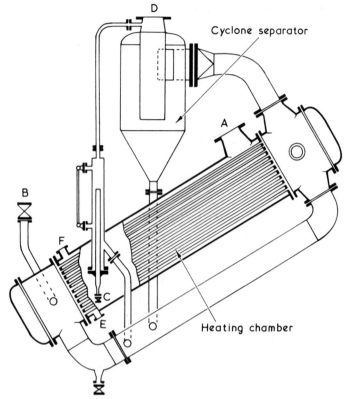

FIG. 12.7. Natural circulation evaporator with external calandria and a cyclone separator for vapour disengagement. A, steam inlet; B, feed inlet; C, extraction outlet; D, vapour outlet; E, condensate outlet; F, incondensable gas outlet. (By courtesy of Aiton and Co. Ltd., Derby.)

bundle. The tube and shell assembly is often replaced by a plate heat exchanger. This is particularly useful if scale formation or product degradation is likely, since the unit can be quickly opened for cleaning. Despite the recirculation of large volumes of liquid, evaporators of this type working at reduced pressures are extensively used for the concentration of heat sensitive food materials including milk, meat extracts and fruit juices.

12.6.2. FORCED CIRCULATION EVAPORATORS

Evaporators with external calandrias are often operated as forced circulation units (Fig. 12.8). Such units are capable of concentrating

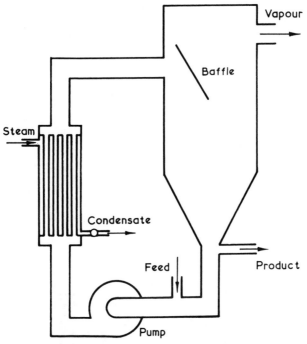

FIG. 12.8.   Diagram of a forced circulation evaporator with an external calandria.

viscous liquids, adequate circulation rates being maintained by use of a suitable pump. Centrifugal pumps are used with lower viscosity liquids. Positive displacement pumps—gear or lobe type—can be used with more viscous materials.

With some crystallising evaporators, the circulation is increased by means of an impeller mounted inside the central downcomer.

12.6.3. LONG TUBE EVAPORATORS

These evaporators may be regarded as vertical shell and tube heat exchangers. The heating medium is usually steam, condensing inside the shell.

12.6.3.1. Climbing film evaporator. Typical evaporators of this type (Fig. 12.9a) have tubes 3–12 m in length with diameters of 25–50 mm. Liquid, pre-heated to near boiling, is introduced at the bottom of the tube assembly. Boiling commences a short distance up the tubes. Expansion on vaporisation causes high velocity vapour bubbles and slugs of liquid to rise rapidly up the tubes. Evaporation proceeds as the liquid ascends. Under optimum conditions the vapour lifts a thin film of rapidly concentrating liquid up the walls of the tubes. The vapour–liquid mixture leaving, passes into a separator where vapour is removed. The concentrated liquid may be used directly, mixed with fresh feed and recirculated, or passed to a second

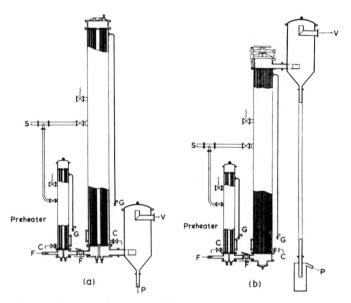

FIG. 12.9.   Long tube evaporators. (a) Climbing and falling film evaporator. (b) A climbing film evaporator with a barometric leg for product removal. (By courtesy of A.P.V.-Kestner Ltd., Greenhithe, Kent.)

evaporator for further concentration (see Section 12.8.1). Residence time in the heating zone is short and U-values high, making the climbing film evaporator useful for concentrating heat-sensitive materials.

12.6.3.2. Falling film evaporator. This is similar to the above, but pre-heated feed liquid enters at the top of the tube assembly. As evaporation proceeds the vapour passes down the tubes as a central, high velocity core, dragging a film of liquid with it. There is no hydrostatic liquid head in the tubes so a uniform, low boiling temperature may be maintained. Residence times are short so this unit is excellent for the concentration of heat-sensitive materials. It is widely used with citrus fruit juices where high rates of evaporation are obtained at temperatures as low as 10–16 °C under vacuum operation.

Falling film evaporators are becoming increasingly important in the food industry, particularly in the dairy field.[12, 13]

12.6.3.3. Climbing–falling film evaporator. A climbing film-falling film combination (Fig. 12.9a) is often used. The dilute feed is partially concentrated in the climbing film section and the more viscous material then encounters the falling film region. High rates of evaporation can be achieved in such combinations.

12.6.4. PLATE EVAPORATORS

Though the modern plate evaporator, so popular in the process industries, has only been commercially available since the 1950s, the first evaporator based on the principles used in the plate heat-exchanger was first installed for the concentration of a clear marmalade as long ago as 1928.[14]

The plate evaporator utilises the climbing–falling film principle within a plate heat exchanger. The plates are commonly arranged in units of four (Fig. 12.10). Steam condenses in plate spaces 4–1 and

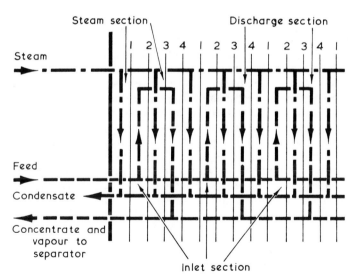

FIG. 12.10. Arrangements of plates in an APV plate evaporator showing how the steam, inlet climbing film and discharge falling film sections are repeated. (By courtesy of The A.P.V. Co. Ltd., Crawley, Sussex.)

2–3. Pre-heated liquid boils at the plate surfaces, rising as a film in plate space 1–2 and falling in 3–4. The number of such units can be varied to suit the plant capacity required. The vapour–liquid mixture leaving the plate assembly passes into a centrifugal separator. High liquid velocities lead to good heat transfer with short residence times, making this evaporator useful for the concentration of heat-sensitive materials. This, together with its facility for rapid dismantling and its small floor space requirement, makes the evaporator a very popular unit.

In a new type of plate evaporator recently introduced by the APV Co. Ltd., the climbing-film sections have been discarded. Liquid flows entirely in the form of a falling-film over plates larger than those in the conventional plate evaporator. Internal recirculation is said to be avoided and very short residence times are claimed for the new unit which is being used for citrus juice concentration.[6] In another type of evaporator, designed for larger evaporative capacities, the heating surface—in the form of a pack of vertical plates—is suspended inside a cylindrical vessel which acts as a vapour–liquid disengagement space. Pre-heated feed liquor is sprayed onto the top of the heated plate assembly again flowing downwards over the heating surface in the form of a thin film.

12.6.5. EXPANDING FLOW EVAPORATOR

In this device for the concentration of dairy products, fruit juices etc.,[15, 16] liquid and steam flow through alternate passages in a manner similar to that in the plate evaporator (Fig. 12.11). The plates, however, are replaced by thin, inverted stainless steel cones, gasketed to prevent leakage. Feed enters through a central spindle at the base of the cone assembly and is fed, via nozzles, to the heated cone spaces. Flowing upwards and outwards over the steam-heated surfaces, under vacuum operation, liquid rapidly attains boiling point. A high velocity vapour–liquid stream leaves the cone assembly tangentially, ensuring a good separation. Vapour passes upwards to leave via a concentric baffle separating the inner and outer shells. The high velocity in the cone spaces promotes thin, turbulent films of evaporating liquid giving high rates of heat transfer and short residence times. The unit has been designed for 'in-place cleaning'.

12.6.6. MECHANICAL THIN FILM EVAPORATORS

These evaporators[17, 18, 19] often consist of a jacketed shell containing a multi-bladed rotor and may be mounted vertically or horizontally. Horizontally mounted shells are often tapered (Fig. 12.12). With a cross-sectional area decreasing in the direction of flow, adequate wetting of the walls is possible even at low flow rates, thus minimising the risk of 'burn-on'.

'Thin-film' units have clearances between rotor-blade tips and heat transfer surfaces in the range 0·5–1·25 mm (0·02–0·05 in). 'Wiped-film' evaporators have lower clearances giving film thicknesses as

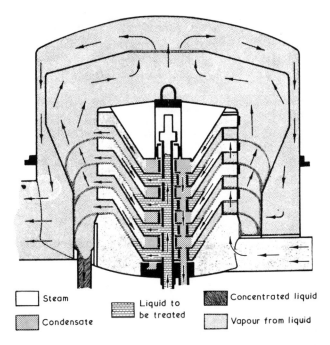

| | Steam | | Liquid to be treated | | Concentrated liquid |
| | Condensate | | | | Vapour from liquid |

FIG. 12.11. A cross-section of the Alfa-Laval expanding flow evaporator shows the method of operation in diagrammatic form. (By courtesy of Alfa-Laval Co. Ltd., Brentford, Middlesex.)

small as 0·25 mm (0·001 in.). These types of evaporator are finding increasing use in the concentration of heat-sensitive materials including tomato pastes, coffee, milk, whey, malt and sugar products. The main advantage of mechanical thin-film evaporators is their ability to handle highly viscous liquids of the order of 50–100 kg/ms (50 000–100 000 cP) while maintaining high rates of heat transfer. These advantages are, to some extent, offset by the relatively high capital costs and small capacities of most commercially available units. For this reason these evaporators are usually employed as 'finishers', where smaller capacities and higher viscosities are usually encountered.

Another mechanical thin-film evaporator developed for heat-sensitive materials is similar to the expanding-flow unit. The stack of cones rotates at high speed, and liquid droplets and steam condensate are thrown off the heating surfaces under the action of centrifugal

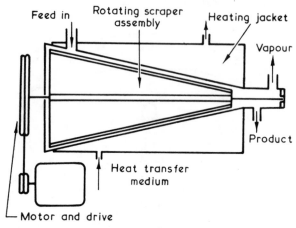

FIG. 12.12.   Horizontal scraped surface evaporator.

force. Good separations and high rates of heat transfer with extremely short residence times are reported with the 'Centritherm' evaporator.[15, 20]

12.6.7. LOW TEMPERATURE EVAPORATORS—HEAT PUMP OR REFRIGERATION CYCLE EVAPORATORS

For the vacuum concentration of highly heat-sensitive materials at low pressures, correspondingly low temperatures are required for vapour condensation. Evaporators using 'heat pumps' have therefore been developed (Fig. 12.13). A refrigerant gas condenses on the calandria tubes to supply heat and evaporates in the condenser to condense the vapour produced.[17]

In evaporators of this type boiling temperatures as low as 20 C are used to avoid heat damage, corresponding residence times being 20–35 min. More recent work has shown that a combination of temperature and contact time (temperature–time integral) is of great importance. It has been shown that some quite heat-sensitive materials, *e.g.* citrus fruit juices, can withstand much higher temperatures than had previously been thought possible provided that contact times are kept short.[6]

Since higher boiling temperatures have more favourable economies, the use of low temperature evaporators for the processing of heat-sensitive food-stuffs has declined in recent years.

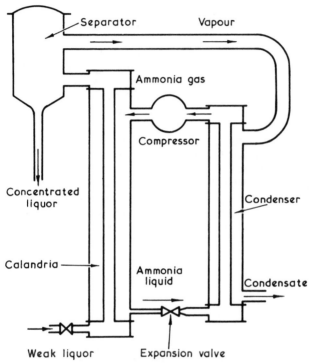

FIG. 12.13.   The working principle of the Kestner Coolcentrator. (By courtesy of A.P.V.-Kestner Ltd., Greenhithe, Kent.)

12.7.   EVAPORATOR ANCILLARY PLANT

Since most evaporator systems processing food materials operate below atmospheric pressure, vapour condensers and vacuum pumps or ejectors are usually required.

The atmosphere in an evaporator consists of:

(i)   Condensable vapour.
(ii)   Incondensable gases—air from leaks into the system and from degassing of the feed liquors.

In vacuum evaporation the partial pressure of the vapour is kept low by condensing the water vapour, and the incondensables are removed by pump or ejector.

12.7.1. CONDENSERS

Surface condensers (*e.g.* shell and tube condensers) are used when the condensed vapour cannot be mixed with cooling water. These units have both a high capital cost and cooling water requirement as compared to the jet condenser commonly used in food applications. In the latter unit the vapour mixes directly with a spray of cooling water. Jet condensers are simpler, smaller and cheaper than surface condensers. Condensate and the cooling water from the jet condensers are removed using either a condensate pump or a barometric leg. The latter is a vertical pipe about 11 m (34 ft) long. At the top it is connected to the discharge from the condenser while its lower end is immersed in a small seal pot (Fig. 12.9b).

The difference in head between the liquid level in the pipe and in the seal pot automatically adjusts so as to correspond to the difference in pressure between the evacuated equipment and that of the atmosphere. Under these conditions liquid can be removed without breaking the vacuum.

12.7.2. VACUUM PUMPS

Positive displacement pumps and steam jet-ejectors are commonly used. In the jet-ejector (Fig. 12.14) high-pressure steam is fed through a nozzle into a chamber where it entrains surrounding vapour or gases. The steam and entrained fluids pass, at high velocity, into a convergent-divergent nozzle where velocity energy is converted into pressure energy. A single-stage ejector will produce a vacuum of about $16\cdot7\,kN/m^2$ (25 in Hg), a two-stage unit one of about $3\cdot4\,kN/m^2$ (29 in), and a three-stage ejector a vacuum of less than $1\,kN/m^2$

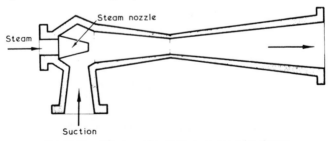

Fig. 12.14.   Diagram of a single stage steam jet-ejector.

(30 in). It is important to appreciate that the vacuum equipment is responsible for removing non-condensable gases from the system. It is not responsible for maintaining boiling at the desired temperature, this being the duty of the condenser. With either type of condenser overall performance is greatly influenced by both cooling water flow rate and temperature. Many operating difficulties in evaporator systems can arise through inadequate cooling water conditions.

12.7.3. ENTRAINMENT SEPARATORS

At higher evaporation rates liquid droplets are carried from the boiling liquid by the vapour. To reduce the loss of concentrated liquor entrained in the vapour, entrainment separators are used.

They may consist of a single baffle plate (Fig. 12.8) or an inclined plate assembly (louvre-baffle) positioned near the vapour off-take. Close-woven knitmesh packs of stainless steel or other material are becoming popular.[21]

The centrifugal separator is also popular. Here the vapour–liquid mixture is introduced tangentially into a cylindrical vessel (Fig. 12.7). Under the influence of centrifugal force the heavier, liquid droplets are thrown to the wall where, on collision, they lose kinetic energy and drain away, the vapour passing out of the unit at a separate take-off. In principle, these simple 'momentum separators' arrest the heavier liquid droplets but permit the passage of vapour. In practice, much depends on liquid level, boil-off rate and overall operator efficiency.

12.7.4. STEAM TRAPS AND VENTS

It must be stressed that for maximum steam economy and heat transfer, any equipment using steam as a process heating medium must be fitted with adequate condensate removal and inert gas-venting systems. Inadequately vented and partially water-logged heat exchangers are causes of a great deal of inefficiency in the operation of evaporation plant and should not be tolerated. For a comprehensive account of these important ancillary systems see Lyle.[2]

12.8. HEAT CONSERVATION IN EVAPORATOR SYSTEMS

Vapour removed from an evaporator contains heat. This is wasted if the vapour is discarded. The re-use of this heat reduces the operating costs of the plant. For this, several methods are available.

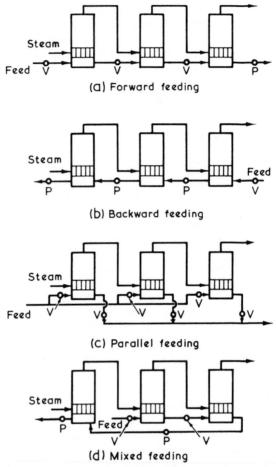

Fig. 12.15. Methods of feeding a triple effect evaporator. P, extraction pump; V, control valve.

12.8.1. MULTIPLE EFFECT EVAPORATION

The exhaust vapour can be used in the calandria of a second evaporator provided that the boiling temperature of the liquid in this evaporator is sufficiently low to maintain an adequate temperature difference. This is achieved by operating successive 'effects' under reducing pressures. The re-use of heat in this way can be extended to a number of effects and is called multiple effect evaporation. Triple effect systems are shown in Fig. 12.15.

It should be understood that multiple effect evaporation does not lead to larger throughputs than those obtainable with single-effect systems with comparable heat exchange surface. The object of multiple effect operation is an improvement in overall steam economy for the process, not to increase plant capacity. As a rough guide a single unit requires about 1·3 kg of steam to evaporate 1 kg of water, a double-effect unit about 0·6 kg of steam per 1 kg of water and a triple-effect unit about 0·4 kg of steam per 1 kg of water.

In general, the greater the number of effects, the better the steam economy. The price of the steam economy is an increase in capital cost of the installation as the number of effects increases. It can be shown that the area of each effect in a multiple system must be the same as that of a single effect if the overall operating conditions are the same. The cost of 'n' effects is approximately 'n' times the cost of a single effect, so the capital cost of the plant rises rapidly as the number of effects increases. To arrive at the optimum number of effects the decreasing operating costs must be balanced against the increased capital charges. No more than five or six effect units are normally encountered.

12.8.2. THE OPERATION OF MULTIPLE EFFECT EVAPORATOR SYSTEMS

12.8.2.1. Forward feeding (Fig. 12.15a). This is the simplest, hence most common method of feeding. Feed passes forward in the same direction as the vapours, namely from the first effect to the second, hence to the third effect, etc. An extraction pump only is required, the final effect being operated at low pressure. With this feed arrangement the viscosity of the process liquor increases during passage through the plant owing to both an increase in concentration and decrease in temperature in each effect. Thus the overall heat transfer coefficient is low in the later effects. However, the lower temperature in these effects is less likely to produce heat damage in the more viscous liquors. High quality raw steam condenses in the first effect calandria. If the initial feed is below its boiling point some of the heat transferred must be used for pre-heating the feedstock. Since less heat is available for vaporisation, less vapour condenses in the second effect and this pattern is repeated in later effects. The overall result is a loss in steam economy.

12.8.2.2. Backward feeding (Fig. 12.15b). Interstage pumps are required for this arrangement. Dilute, cooler feed liquor meets poorer quality steam since steam and liquor flows are counter-current. An improved steam economy results. The increase in viscosity on concentration is off-set by the higher temperatures experienced, since the more viscous material meets increasingly hotter surfaces in going from effect to effect. However, care must be taken to avoid localised overheating.

12.8.2.3. Parallel feeding (Fig. 12.15c). This is commonly used with crystallising evaporators. This mode of operation leads to better control over the crystallisation operation and also avoids the pumping of dense slurries—with all the attendant flow problems—between effects.

12.8.2.4. Mixed feeding (Fig. 12.15d). This method is common with a larger number of effects. It represents a compromise between the simplicity of 'forward feeding' and the greater economy of 'backward feeding'. The method is useful with very viscous liquids and is recommended when large increases in viscosity with concentration are likely.

12.8.3. FEED PRE-HEATING

A second method used for the conservation of heat is to use hot vapours from a single effect evaporator to pre-heat the incoming cold feed liquor. Steam temperatures are likely to be low, so large surface areas may be required.

12.8.4. VAPOUR RECOMPRESSION

Another method for heat conservation is that of vapour recompression. In this method, vapour from an evaporator is compressed and returned to the calandria. Increasing the pressure increases the condensing temperature of the steam.

Two methods of recompression are available:

(i)   Mechanical vapour recompression[22] in which a mechanical pump is used to compress the vapours and
(ii) Thermal vapour recompression where a steam jet compressor is employed.

The use of vapour recompression systems can, in certain cases,[23] result in considerable savings in overall energy requirements when compared with multiple effect evaporation. Mechanical vapour recompression is more suitable for the concentration of dilute solutions since the method is economically favourable when low temperature differences between heating medium and boiling liquid are acceptable.[24] This is the case when concentrating dilute, low viscosity solutions.

Multiple effect evaporation systems incorporating vapour recompression on one or more effects are finding increasing use as energy costs rise.

REFERENCES

1. Honig, P., 'Principles of Sugar Technology', Vol. 2. (Elsevier: 1959).
2. Lyle, O., 'Efficient Use of Steam'. (H.M.S.O.: 1947).
3. Perry, J. H. (Ed.) 'Chemical Engineers' Handbook', 5th ed. (McGraw-Hill: 1973).
4. Leppert, G., and Pitts, C. C., *in* Irvine, T. F., and Hartnett, J. P. (Eds.) 'Advances in Heat Transfer'. Vol. 1, 185 (Academic Press: 1964).
5. Bott, T. R., 'Understand Fouling and Keep Down Heat Exchanger Costs'. Heat Transfer Survey 75, Process Engng, 76–81, November (1975).
6. Mannheim, C. H., and Passy, N., 'Non-membrane Concentration'. *in* Spicer, A. (Ed.) 'Advances in Preconcentration and Dehydration of Foods'. 151–191 (Applied Science Publishers: 1974).
7. Diamant, R. M. E., 'The Use of Magnetic Water Treatment'. Chemical Processing, 31–35, November (1970).
8. Moore, J. G., and Hesler, W. E., 'Evaporation of Heat Sensitive Materials'. Chem. Engng Prog., 59(2), 87–92 (1963).
9. Robbins, R. H., and Greswell, D. M., 'The Evaporation of Fruit Juices'. J. Appl. Chem. Biotechnol., 21(12), 363–365 (1971).
10. Shore, D. T., 'Essence Recovery on Citrus Evaporators'. *in* Spicer, A. (Ed.) 'Advances in Preconcentration and Dehydration of Foods'. 95–99 (Applied Science Publishers: 1974).
11. Davis, M. S., 'UK Regulations on Trace Elements in Foods'. Fd Trade Rev., 36(3), 55–56 (1966).
12. Wiegand. J., 'Falling Film Evaporators and their Applications in the Food Industry'. J. Appl. Chem. Biotechnol., 21(12) (1971).
13. Gray, R. M., 'Recent Developments in the Evaporation of Milk and Milk Products'. J. Soc. Dairy Technol., 22(4) (1969).
14. Gray, R. M., 'The Plate Evaporator'. J. Appl. Chem. Biotechnol., 21(12), (1971).
15. Halstrom, B., 'The Use of Centri-Therm, Expanding Flow and Forced Circulation Plate Evaporators in the Food and Biochemical Industries'. Food Industry Studies No. 1, UNIDO, Vienna. (United Nations: 1969).
16. Shinn, B. E., 'Evaporators Utilising Stationary or Rotating Conical Heating Surfaces'. Fd. Process. Mkt., 434–437, November (1965).
17. Armerding, G. D., *in* Chichester, C. O., Mrak, E. M., and Stewart, G. F. (Eds.) 'Advances in Food Research'. Vol. 15, 303–358 (Academic Press: 1966).
18. Skocylas, A., 'Thin Film Evaporator Construction and Performance'. Brit. Chem. Engng, 12(8), 415–419 (1967).
19. Guttridge, D., and Anderson, B., 'Will Thin-Film Technology Spread in the Process Industries'. Process Engng, 49–51, January (1975).
20. Shinn, B. E., 'The Centri-Therm Evaporator and its Application to Heat Sensitive Foods'. J. Appl. Chem. Biotechnol., 21(12), 366–371 (1971).

21. Pryce Bayley, D., and Davies, G. A., 'Process Applications of Knitted Mesh Mist Eliminators'. Chemical Processing, 33–39, May (1973).
22. Cole, T. W., 'Mechanical Vapour Recompression for Evaporators'. The Chemical Engineer, No. 294, February (1975).
23. Gray, R. M., 'Cut Evaporation Costs'. Chemical Processing, 35–41, September (1974).
24. Dinnage, D. F., 'How to Design for Economic Evaporation'. Fd Engng, **47**(12), 51–54 (1975).

CHAPTER 13

DEHYDRATION

13.1. INTRODUCTION

In this chapter the terms 'food dehydration' and 'food drying' are used interchangeably to describe the unit operation in which nearly all the water normally present in a foodstuff is removed by evaporation or sublimation, as a result of the application of heat under controlled conditions. By this definition, therefore, these terms do not include alternative methods of moisture removal such as Filtration and Membrane Separation (Chapter 6), Centrifugation (Chapter 7), Solid–Liquid Extraction and Expression (Chapter 8). Sun-drying is also excluded because of the lack of control over the drying conditions. Evaporation or concentration of liquid foods is dealt with elsewhere in the text (Chapter 12) and is omitted by definition from this chapter because the extent to which moisture is removed is usually much less than during drying.

Dehydration of foods results in savings in weight and, usually, bulk to be carried, per unit food value, and in products with extended shelf lives as compared with fresh material. The advantages and limitations of dehydration as a means of preservation are discussed elsewhere.[1, 3−6, 7a]

The methods used for the drying of foodstuffs may be conveniently classified as follows:

(i) *Drying by heated air:* The food is placed in contact with a moving stream of heated air. Heat is supplied to the product mainly by convection.

(ii) *Drying by direct contact with a heated surface:* Heat is supplied to the product mainly by conduction.

(iii) *Drying by the application of energy* from a *radiating, microwave* or *dielectric source.*

(iv) *Freeze-drying:* The moisture in the food is frozen and then sublimed to vapour, usually by the application of heat under very low-pressure conditions.

13.2. THEORETICAL CONSIDERATIONS

Here the intention is to consider some of the theoretical aspects of the drying of solid foods mainly by method (i), *i.e.* by means of heated air.

13.2.1. TERMINOLOGY

The following are explanations of some of the terms used in connection with drying.

13.2.1.1. Moisture content. The moisture content of a material may be expressed on a *wet-weight basis, i.e.* mass of water per unit mass of wet material, or on a *dry-weight basis, i.e.* mass of water per unit mass of dry solids. The latter method is more commonly used in connection with drying calculations.[8]

13.2.1.2. Equilibrium moisture content. In general if a moist organic material is kept in contact with air at a constant temperature and humidity, until equilibrium is reached, it will attain a definite moisture content. This moisture content is termed the equilibrium moisture content of the material under the specified conditions. It is possible to measure the equilibrium moisture content of a material

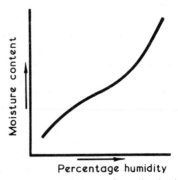

FIG. 13.1.   Typical shape of sorption isotherm.

under different conditions of temperature and humidity and to construct curves relating the moisture content of the material and the humidity of the atmosphere with which it is in equilibrium, at different temperatures. Such *sorption isotherms*, as they are called, are reported in the literature.[1, 5, 10d] Many have a characteristic sigmoid shape as illustrated in Fig. 13.1. A knowledge of the sorption characteristics of foods to be dried is important as, in fact, the equilibrium moisture content is the lowest moisture content that can be achieved under a given set of conditions of temperature and humidity. An understanding of the sorption behaviour is also important in the study of the mechanisms of drying and the stability of the dried food during storage.[7a]

13.2.1.3. Free moisture. The free moisture in a material is that moisture present in excess of the equilibrium moisture content at any given temperature and humidity.[1, 10a]

13.2.2. GENERAL THEORY

During the drying of a wet solid in heated air, the air supplies the necessary sensible and latent heat of evaporation to the moisture and also acts as a carrier gas for the removal of the water vapour formed from the vicinity of the evaporating surface.

Consider the situation where an inert solid, wetted with pure water, is being dried in a current of heated air flowing parallel to the drying surface. Assume that the temperature and humidity of the air above the drying surface remain constant throughout the drying cycle and that all the necessary heat is supplied to the material by convection. If the change in moisture content of the material is recorded throughout drying, the data can be presented in the form of curves as shown in Fig. 13.2. A study of these curves shows that the drying cycle can be considered to consist of a number of stages.

Stage A–B. This stage represents a 'settling down' period during which the solid surface conditions come into equilibrium with the drying air. It is often a negligible proportion of the overall drying cycle but in some cases it may be significant.

Stage B–C. This stage is known as the *constant rate period* of drying. During this period the surface of the solid remains saturated with liquid water by virtue of the fact that movement of water within the solid to the surface takes place at a rate as great as the rate of evaporation from the surface. Drying takes place by movement of water vapour from the saturated surface through a stagnant air film into the main stream of the drying air. The rate of drying is dependent on the rate of heat transfer to the drying surface. The rate of mass transfer balances the rate of heat transfer, and so the temperature of the drying surface remains constant. The surface of the solid can be compared to the wick of a wet-bulb thermometer (*see* Appendix III) and, under the conditions specified, the constant surface temperature will correspond to the wet-bulb temperature of the drying air. The

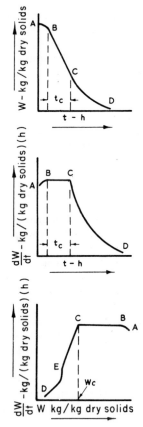

Fig. 13.2.   Drying curves for a wet solid in heated air at constant temperature and humidity.

'driving-force' causing vapour movement through the stagnant air film is the water vapour pressure gradient between the drying surface and the main stream of the drying air. The rate of mass transfer can be expressed in the form of an equation as follows:

$$\left(\frac{dw}{dt}\right)_c = -K_g A (p_s - p_a) \qquad (13.1)$$

where $-(dw/dt)_c$ = drying rate; K_g = mass transfer coefficient; A = drying surface area; p_s = water vapour pressure at surface (*i.e.* vapour pressure of water at surface temperature); p_a = partial pressure of water vapour in air.

Equation (13.1) may also be written in the form:

$$\left(\frac{dw}{dt}\right)_c = -K_g^1 A(H_s - H_a) \tag{13.2}$$

where K_g^1 = mass transfer coefficient; H_s = humidity at surface (*i.e.* saturation humidity of the air at surface temperature); H_a = humidity of air.

The rate of heat transfer to the drying surface may be expressed thus:

$$\left(\frac{dQ}{dt}\right)_c = h_c A(\theta_a - \theta_s) \tag{13.3}$$

where $(dQ/dt)_c$ = rate of heat transfer; h_c = heat transfer coefficient for convection heating; A = area for heat transfer (*i.e.* drying surface area); θ_a = dry-bulb temperature of air; θ_s = temperature of drying surface.

In the situation being considered here, *i.e.* convection heating only, θ_s is the wet-bulb temperature of the air.

Since a state of equilibrium exists between the rate of heat transfer to the body and the rate of mass transfer from it these two rates may be related simply as follows:

$$\left(\frac{dw}{dt}\right)_c L = -\left(\frac{dQ}{dt}\right)_c \tag{13.4}$$

where L = latent heat of evaporation at θ_s.

Combining equations (13.3) and (13.4)

$$\left(\frac{dw}{dt}\right)_c = -\frac{h_c A}{L}(\theta_a - \theta_s) \tag{13.5}$$

If the drying rate is expressed in terms of the rate of change of moisture content W (dry-weight basis), equation (13.5) may be written:

$$\left(\frac{dW}{dt}\right)_c = -\frac{h_c A^1}{L}(\theta_a - \theta_s) \tag{13.6}$$

where $-(dW/dt)_c$ = drying rate; A^1 = effective drying surface per unit mass of dry solids.

For a tray of wet material of depth d, evaporating only from its upper surface, assuming no shrinkage during drying:

$$\left(\frac{dW}{dt}\right)_c = -\frac{h_c}{\rho_s L d}(\theta_a - \theta_s) \tag{13.7}$$

where ρ_s = bulk density of the dry material. The drying time in the constant rate period can be obtained by the integration of equation (13.7) thus:

$$t_c = \frac{(W_o - W_c)\rho_s Ld}{h_c(\theta_a - \theta_s)} \tag{13.8}$$

where t_c = constant rate drying time; W_o = initial moisture content of solid; W_c = moisture content at end of constant rate period.

The rate controlling factors during the constant rate period are, therefore: (1) the drying surface area, (2) the difference in temperature or humidity between the air and the drying surface, (3) the heat or mass transfer coefficients.

Perry and Chilton[8] state that in estimating drying rates, the use of heat transfer coefficients is more reliable than mass transfer coefficients and suggest that for many cases the heat transfer coefficient can be expressed as:

$$h_c = \frac{aG^n}{D_c^m} \tag{13.9}$$

where G = mass velocity of air; D_c = characteristic dimension of the system; a, n and m are empirical constants.

Thus the air velocity and system dimensions influence drying rates in the constant rate period.

Alternative expressions for h_c are used where the air flow is not parallel to the drying surface or for through-flow situations.[8]

Where heat is supplied to the material by radiation and/or conduction, in addition to convection, then an overall heat-transfer coefficient, taking this into account, must be substituted for h_c in equation (13.7). Under these circumstances the surface temperature during the constant rate period of drying remains constant, but at some value above the wet-bulb temperature of the air and below the boiling point of water.

Stage C–D (Fig. 13.2). As drying proceeds, a point is reached at which the rate of movement of moisture within the material to the surface is reduced to the extent that the surface begins to dry out. At this point, C, the rate of drying begins to fall and the *falling rate period* commences. The moisture content of the material at point C is known as the *critical moisture content* (W_c). From point C onwards the surface temperature begins to rise and continues to do so as drying proceeds, approaching the dry-bulb temperature of the air as the material approaches dryness. Often the falling rate period consists of two parts known as the first and second falling rate periods, *C–E* and *E–D* respectively. In the first falling rate period the surface is drying out and the drying rate falls. At point E the plane of evaporation moves into the solid and the drying rate falls further. In the falling rate periods the rate of drying is mainly influenced by the rate of movement of moisture within the solid and the effects of external factors, in particular air velocity, are reduced, especially in the latter stage. Usually the falling rate periods represent the major proportion of the overall drying time.

The nature of the mechanism of moisture movement within the solid has received much attention in the literature.[1, 8, 9] There appear to be four probable major modes of transfer: liquid movement caused by capillary forces, liquid diffusion resulting from concentration gradients, vapour diffusion due to partial pressure gradients, and diffusion in liquid layers adsorbed at solid interfaces. The mechanisms of capillarity and liquid diffusion have received the most detailed treatment. In general the former is most applicable to coarse granular materials and the latter to single-phase solids with colloidal or gel-like structures. In many cases it appears that the two mechanisms may be applicable to a single drying operation, *i.e.* capillarity accounting for the moisture movement in the early stages of drying while a diffusional mechanism applies at lower moisture contents.

Perry and Chilton[8] suggest that for systems where a capillary flow mechanism applies, the rate of drying can often be expressed with reasonable accuracy by an equation of the type:

$$\left(\frac{dW}{dt}\right)_f = -K(W - W_e) \tag{13.10}$$

where $-(dW/dt)_f$ = rate of drying at time t from the start of the falling rate period; W = moisture content of the material at time t; W_e = equilibrium moisture content of material at air temperature and humidity.

$$K = \frac{-\left(\dfrac{dW}{dt}\right)_c}{W_c - W_e} \tag{13.11}$$

Combining equations (13.7), (13.10), and (13.11):

$$\left(\frac{dW}{dt}\right)_f = \frac{-h_c(\theta_a - \theta_s)}{\rho_s L d} \frac{(W - W_e)}{(W_c - W_e)} \tag{13.12}$$

Integration of this expression within limits $t = 0$, $W = W_c$; $t = t$, $W = W$, gives the drying time in the falling rate period thus:

$$t = \frac{\rho_s L d(W_c - W_e)}{h_c(\theta_a - \theta_s)} \ln \frac{(W_c - W_e)}{(W - W_e)} \tag{13.13}$$

For slab-shaped solids, drying from one large face only, where liquid diffusion controls the internal movement of moisture, Perry and Chilton[8] suggest the following type of expression:

$$\frac{W - W_e}{W_c - W_e} = \frac{8}{\pi^2}\left\{\exp\left[-Dt\left(\frac{\pi}{2d}\right)^2\right] + \frac{1}{9}\exp\left[-9Dt\left(\frac{\pi}{2d}\right)^2\right] + \cdots\right\}$$

(13.14)

where W = average moisture content, at time t, of an infinite slab of thickness d; W_c = initial moisture content, assumed to be uniform throughout the slab; D = liquid diffusivity.

For large values of t, equation (13.14) may be reduced to:

$$\frac{W - W_e}{W_c - W_e} \simeq \frac{8}{\pi^2}\left\{\exp\left[-Dt\left(\frac{\pi}{2d}\right)^2\right]\right\}$$

or

$$t = -\frac{4d^2}{\pi^2 D}\left(\ln\frac{W - W_e}{W_c - W_e} - \ln\frac{8}{\pi^2}\right)$$

(13.15)

Equation (13.15) holds for values of $(W - W_e)/(W_c - W_e) < 0.6$.

By differentiating equation (13.15) a rate equation similar in form to equation (13.12) is obtained:

$$\left(\frac{dW}{dt}\right)_f = -\frac{D\pi^2}{4d^2}(W - W_e)$$

(13.16)

The rate equations (13.7), (13.8), (13.12) and (13.16) apply when drying takes place from one side only. For situations where drying occurs from both large faces, then d = half the thickness of the slab.

To establish whether or not a simple relationship exists during the falling rate period, $(W - W_e)/(W_c - W_e)$ may be plotted against t on semi-logarithmic paper. If a uniform straight line results (13.12) applies and the slope of the curve should relate to the drying rate during the constant rate period as in equation (13.11). If the plot becomes asymptotic to a straight line as t increases, equation (13.16) may apply and D can be calculated from the slope of the asymptote. The effect of thickness d on the drying rate may be determined experimentally and used to distinguish between the two mechanisms.[8, 9]

Some data is available on the critical moisture content of non-food materials[8] but very little relating to foodstuffs.[11] The critical moisture content generally depends on the drying rate, dimensions of the material and moisture movement mechanisms. Normally it increases with drying rate and material thickness.

13.2.3. DRYING OF FOODSTUFFS

The theoretical considerations given in Section 13.2.2 apply only to the simple system defined therein. Foodstuffs, however, are far more complex and heterogeneous than this system. The components of foods include proteins, fats, carbohydrates, vitamins, enzymes and inorganic salts, many of which are strongly hydrated. The water present is not pure but may be in the form of a solution of solids, a gel, an emulsion or bound in various ways with the solid constituents. In addition, both plant and animal tissue are cellular. This further affects their drying behaviour.[1, 7a, 10a]

13.2.3.1. Movement of solubles. One particular feature of the drying of foodstuffs that is of interest is the movement of soluble solids which occurs during drying. If there is a flow of liquid water to the surface during drying, the water carries with it various soluble materials. The movement of some soluble compounds may be hindered by cell walls acting as semi-permeable membranes. Shrinkage of the material, setting up pressures in the interior of the pieces, may also contribute to the migration of solids. The net result may be a build-up of such soluble materials at the surface as the water evaporates.

As Van Arsdel[1] points out, migration of soluble solids in the opposite direction, towards the centre of the pieces, can also occur. As the surface dries out, a concentration gradient is set up between it and the wet centre of the piece which could result in the diffusion of soluble material to the centre. Which of these two phenomena predominates depends on the characteristics of the material and the drying conditions. Both mechanisms have been demonstrated as occurring in foods during drying.

13.2.3.2. Shrinkage. Animal and vegetable tissue undergo some degree of shrinkage during drying by all the drying methods, with the possible exception of freeze-drying. Colloidal materials also shrink. In the early stages of drying, at low rates, the amount of shrinkage bears a simple relationship to the amount of moisture removed. Towards the end of drying, shrinkage is reduced so that the final size and shape of the material is fixed before drying is completed.

The bulk density and porosity of dried vegetable pieces depends to a large extent on the drying conditions. At high initial drying rates the outer layers of the pieces become rigid and their final volume is fixed early in the drying. As drying proceeds, the tissues split and rupture internally forming an open structure. The product in this case has a low bulk density and good rehydration characteristics. At low initial drying rates the pieces will shrink inwards to give a product of high bulk density. Shrinkage of foodstuffs during drying may influence their drying rates because of the changes in drying surface area and the setting up of pressure gradients within the material.[1, 9, 10c] Some work done indicates that shrinkage does not affect drying behaviour.[10c]

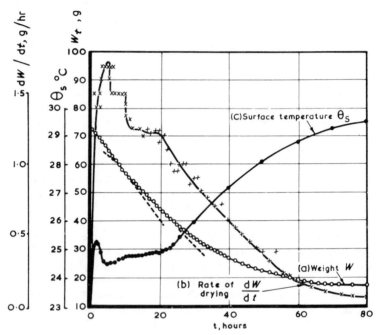

FIG. 13.3.   Initial drying behaviour of single fillet piece 10 × 5 × 1·5 cm exposed to air stream of velocity 30 cm/s parallel to 10 cm edges. Dry-bulb temperature 30 C; wet-bulb temperature 18 C. Curve A: weight as a function of time; Curve B: rate of drying as a function of time; Curve C: temperature at centre of surface as a function of time.
(From Jason,[10c] by courtesy of the Society of Chemical Industry.)

13.2.3.3. Case hardening. It has been observed that during the drying of some fruits, meat and fish, a hard impermeable skin often forms at the surface. This usually results in a reduction in drying rate, and the phenomenon is usually known as case hardening. The exact mechanism of case hardening is far from fully understood but is probably influenced by a number of factors, including migration of soluble solids to the surface and high surface temperature towards the end of drying resulting in complex physical and chemical changes in the surface layer.[1, 10b]

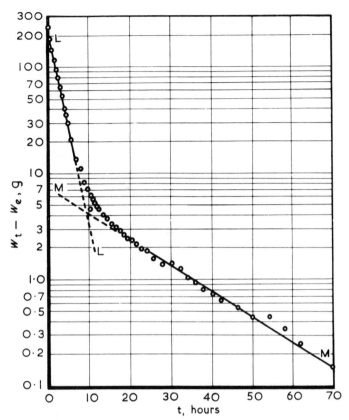

FIG. 13.4.   Amount of free water remaining in fillet piece 10 × 5 × 0·60 cm as function of time. Dry-bulb temperature 35 C; wet-bulb temperature 20·3 C; air velocity 366 cm/s. (From Jason,[10e] by courtesy of the Society of Chemical Industry.)

13.2.4. STUDIES OF DRYING MECHANISMS

Following are some examples of studies made of the drying behaviour of foodstuffs. These indicate the complexity of food dehydration as compared with the simple model system for which the theory in Section 13.2.2 was developed.

13.2.4.1. Jason[10e] studied the drying of fish muscle under carefully controlled conditions. Figure 13.3 is a typical example of the behaviour of a cod fillet dried in heated air flowing parallel to the longest edge. He concludes that there are at least two periods during the initial stages of drying during which the drying rates remain relatively constant. The end of the first period occurs when the surface near the leading edge of the piece has dried out. The second period ends when the rest of the surface begins to dry out. Otherwise he concludes that in the early stages of drying the cod muscle behaves as though the surface was saturated with water. Jason presented the falling rate period results in the form of the curve shown in Fig. 13.4.

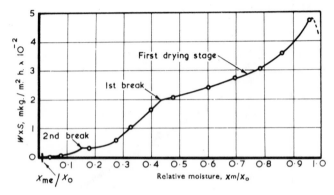

FIG. 13.5. Complete drying-rate curve for one-sided drying of potato slices in an air current at 60 °C. (From Gorling,[10c] by courtesy of the Society of Chemical Industry.)

Here the difference between the equilibrium weight (W_e) and the weight (W_t) at time t after the commencement of drying is plotted on a logarithmic scale as a function of time. The results may be seen to fall on two straight lines LL and MM over most of the curve. The drying behaviour in the first of these falling rate phases can be explained by the solution of a diffusion equation based on Fick's Law. The results indicate that the diffusion coefficient is constant and that its effective value is not dependent on the shrinkage of the muscle. In the second phase a similar explanation applies, but the effective diffusion constant assumes a value less than that of the first phase.

13.2.4.2. Gorling[10c] presented in the form of a curve, as shown in Fig. 13.5, the results obtained by one-sided drying of a potato slice. The ratio X_m/X_o, where X_o = initial moisture content and X_m = average moisture content at any given time, is plotted against the product of the drying rate and sample thickness (to allow for shrinkage). There are three stages evident in the drying. From the results of systematic tests Gorling concluded that, with vegetable products, moisture is transferred to the surface during the first stage

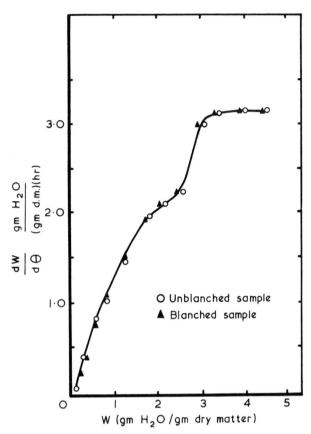

FIG. 13.6. Effect of blanching on the drying rate of potato. Drying conditions: potato dice, $\frac{1}{2} \times \frac{1}{2} \times \frac{1}{4}$ in; air velocity, 400 fpm; dbt, 150°F; wbt, 92°F. (From Saravacos and Charm.[11])

only by a capillary mechanism. Due to shrinkage, the rate of drying is not constant.

13.2.4.3. Saravacos and Charm[11] studied the drying of fruits and vegetables in single layers. Constant rate periods were found with most materials, followed by falling rate periods of a sigmoid form. Fig. 13.6 shows a typical drying curve. The drying of potato was studied in detail and, when tests of the type referred to in Section 13.2.2 were applied to the data, *i.e.* when $(W - W_e)/(W_c - W_e)$ was plotted on semi-logarithmic paper against time, a straight line was obtained in the moisture content range 1·0–0·1 g/g dry solids (Fig.

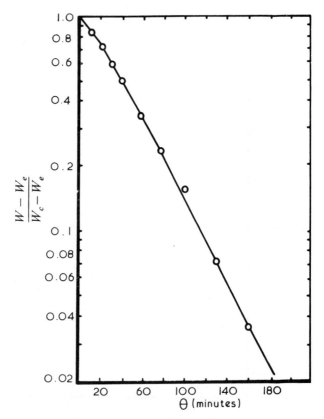

$\dfrac{W - W_e}{W_c - W_e}$

θ (minutes)

Fig. 13.7. Falling-rate period of blanched potato dice. Drying conditions; air
velocity, 400 fpm; dbt, 150 °F; wbt, 90 °F. (From Saravacos and Charm.[11])

13.7). The drying time in the falling rate period was found to be
proportional to the square of the sample thickness. It was concluded
from this work that moisture is transferred by a diffusion-type
mechanism. No evidence of a capillary mechanism was found.

The application of simple theoretical expressions, such as those
discussed in Section 13.2.2, to the drying of foodstuffs, suffers from
serious limitations due to the complexity of such materials. More
sophisticated mathematical expressions have been proposed for this
purpose.[7a, 12] However, the lack of data on the drying characteristics
of specific foods, *e.g.* critical and equilibrium moisture contents,
diffusivities and thermal properties, limits the application of such
relationships in practice. Where simple relationships are found to be
valid and data is available drying times may be estimated by

calculation. Alternatively accumulated data obtained by workers in this field and/or data obtained by pilot scale experimentation may be used to estimate drying times.[1]

13.3 DRYING EQUIPMENT—PRINCIPLES, DESIGN FEATURES AND APPLICATIONS

13.3.1. HOT-AIR DRYING

13.3.1.1. Kiln drier. This consists basically of a two-storey building with a furnace or burner located on the ground floor. The heated air and the products of combustion rise, by natural or forced convection, through the slatted floor of the second storey, on which the wet material is spread in an even layer, usually $0 \cdot 1$–$0 \cdot 2$ m deep. The humidified air is exhausted through a flue in the upper storey. Regular raking or turning of the product is necessary to promote uniform drying. The most obvious limitations of this type of equipment are long drying times and lack of control of drying conditions.

The applications of this type of equipment are mainly in the drying of hops, apple rings and malt.

13.3.1.2. Cabinet, tray or compartment drier. This consists essentially of an insulated cabinet containing an air circulating fan which moves the air through a heater and then through adjustable baffles which direct it either horizontally between the trays of food material or vertically through the trays and food. Dampers are provided to control the rate of fresh air intake and the amount of air recirculation as required. Air heaters may be direct gas burners, steam coil exchangers or electrical resistance heaters in smaller models. In cross-flow systems, air velocities of the order of 2–5 m/s are used while through-flow systems require $0 \cdot 5$–$1 \cdot 25$ m^3/(s) (m^2 of tray area). Cabinet driers are relatively cheap to build and maintain, and are very flexible. They are used singly or in groups, mainly for drying fruits and vegetables at throughputs of 1–20 tons/day (1000–20 000 kg/day). They are also useful for pilot scale work.

13.3.1.3. Tunnel drier. This type of equipment provides a means of drying fruits and vegetables in piece form on a semi-continuous basis at high throughputs. It consists of a tunnel, which may be up to 24 m long with a square or rectangular cross-section of the order of 2 m by 2 m. The wet food material is spread in even layers on trays of slatted wood or metal mesh. The trays are assembled in stacks on trucks, clear spaces being provided between the trays to permit passage of the drying air. The loaded trucks are fed one by one, at suitable intervals, into the tunnel. As one truck enters the 'wet end' of the tunnel a truck of dry product is removed from the other, 'dry end'. Air is moved by fans through heaters and horizontally between the trays, although some through-flow does occur. Air velocities of the order of 2·5–6·0 m/s are normally employed.

Tunnel driers are usually classified in terms of the relative direction of movement of the material and the air. In one class of tunnel drier a

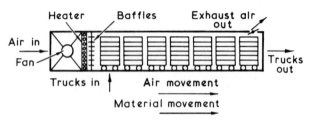

FIG. 13.8.   Principle of concurrent drier.

concurrent system of material/air flow is employed as illustrated in Fig. 13.8. The characteristic features of this class of tunnel are:

(i)   High rates of evaporation are achieved at the 'wet end' of the tunnel as relatively high air temperatures can be used without the dangers of overheating the material. The surface temperature of material in this portion of the tunnel is usually well below the dry bulb temperature of the air due to evaporative cooling. This high initial drying rate results in a product of low bulk density as little shrinkage occurs (Section 13.2.3.2).

(ii)   As the product moves down the tunnel it comes into contact with cooler moister air. The drying rate falls off and heat damage to product is minimised.

(iii)   Very low moisture contents are difficult to achieve due to poor drying conditions at the 'dry end' of the tunnel.

In another class of tunnel drier a *countercurrent system* of material/air flow is maintained as illustrated in Fig. 13.9.

The characteristic features of this class are:

(i)   Relatively low initial rates of drying occur at the 'wet end' of the tunnel because of the relatively poor drying characteristics of the air. This causes severe shrinkage of cellular material giving a product of high bulk density (*see* Section 13.2.3.2).

Overloading of the drier with wet feed can result in long exposure of the food to a warm moist atmosphere and lead to spoilage.
(ii)   The conditions at the 'dry end' of the tunnel, *i.e.* hot dry air, are such that low moisture contents are attainable but the risks of overheating the product are high.
(iii) This system is usually more economical in the use of heat than the concurrent system.

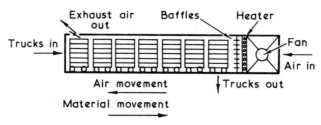

Fig. 13.9.   Principle of countercurrent tunnel drier.

Two or more tunnels may be used in series in order to give more flexibility of control of the drying conditions at various stages of the cycle. The most common combination, however, consists of a concurrent primary tunnel followed by a countercurrent secondary tunnel. In this system advantage may be taken of the characteristic high initial drying rate in the concurrent tunnel while the good drying conditions in the secondary countercurrent tunnel permit more rapid finishing and lower final moisture contents in the product.

Single tunnels are also in use which provide for two-stage drying in one unit. One type employs a movable partition separating the stages while another, often known as the *centre-exhaust* tunnel, has a single fan near the centre of the tunnel. This draws heated air into the system from both ends and the air, after contacting the food, is partly exhausted from the centre or recirculated as required. Figure 13.10 illustrates the principle of the two-stage tunnel.

In some two-stage units stages of equal length are used, but in many cases the primary part of the tunnel is shorter than the secondary to compensate for the low drying rates in the latter section. Relatively high air temperatures and flow rates are used in the concurrent section while fresh, dry but cooler air is used in the countercurrent section. The main features of such systems are:

(i)   Shorter drying times and thus increased throughput are attainable as compared with single stage units of similar size.

(ii) Better control can be exercised generally over drying conditions although achieving good uniform air flow particularly near the tunnel centre is difficult.

(iii) They incur higher capital cost as compared with single stage tunnels.

In yet another class of tunnel drier a *cross-flow system* of air/product movement may be employed. The principle of such a unit

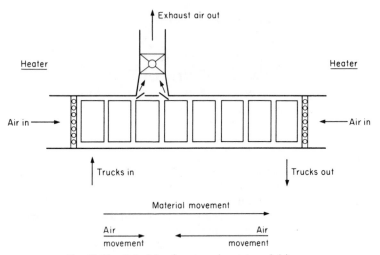

FIG. 13.10.   Principle of centre-exhaust tunnel drier.

is illustrated in Fig. 13.11. The characteristic features of such a system are:

(i) Flexibility of control is attainable due to air heating facilities between stages.

(ii) Uniform moisture content in the product results from the frequent change in direction of the air.

(iii) Such units are rather complex and expensive to purchase and maintain as compared with simpler systems.

From the point of view of economy of heat usage and control of air humidity, recirculation of part of the exhaust air from tunnel driers would appear beneficial. However, as Van Arsdel *et al.*[1] point out each drying operation should be evaluated for overall cost as recirculation inevitably results in a decrease in throughput of wet material. Up to 75% of the exhaust air can be recirculated under certain circumstances but there are situations where little or no recirculation may be the most economic procedure. Many modern commercial tunnel driers are constructed on simple lines with straight-through air flow.

13.3.1.4. Conveyor drier. This type of drier is similar in principle to a tunnel drier, but the wet material is conveyed through the system on a moving belt rather than on trucks. Any of the systems of material/air

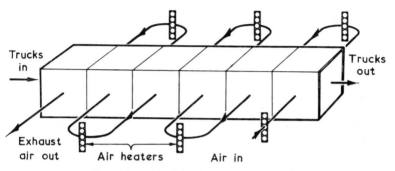

FIG. 13.11.   Principle of cross-flow tunnel drier.

movement referred to in Section 13.3.1.3 may be used, but the most common system used in practice is a *through-flow* one in which the air is directed through the belt and layer of material. Often upward air movement is employed in the first sections, *i.e.* at the 'wet end' of the tunnel, and downward air movement at the 'dry end' to avoid lifting of the low density dry material. Some models consist of two or more belts working in series.

The characteristic features of this type of drier are:

(i)   The wet material must be prepared in a suitable state of subdivision to permit good flow of air through the layer on the belt. Materials which tend to mat together are difficult to dry on this equipment.

(ii)   High drying rates occur due to the relatively large surface area exposed to the drying air, the relatively short travel path for internal moisture and the intimate contacting of air and product.

(iii)   The equipment is relatively expensive, and to ensure its efficient use products are usually dried to 10–15 % moisture in such driers and finished in bin driers.

Such driers find application in the drying of fruits and vegetables of various kinds, mainly in diced form.

Foam mat drying is a technique involving the production of a porous structure. The liquid material has mixed with it a small quantity (1 %) of edible foaming agent and air or inert gas is whipped in by mechanical means or by injection. The foam is spread on a coated belt and passed through a heated air drier. Usually a tunnel system involving a concurrent and countercurrent stage is used. Special techniques may be employed to increase drying rates, such as extruding the foam on to the belt in strips or blowing craters in the foam layer with compressed air. Again rapid drying and good product quality are the features and it has been applied on an experimental scale to fruit juices, potato slurries and baby foods.[1, 9, 13]

13.3.1.5. Bin drier. In its simple form this type of drier consists of a box with a false bottom or wire mesh base. A fan moves air over a heater and up through the material at relatively low speed, not greater than $0.5 \, m^3/(s)(m^2)$. Stationary bins of large capacity are fitted with their own fans and heaters. Portable bins are fitted with wheels and can be 'plugged in' to a stationary air supply system.

The characteristic features of bin driers are:

(i)   Low rates of drying, resulting in extended drying time, and
(ii)   Capital and running costs are low compared with most other forms of hot air drier.

The main application for this type of drier is in 'finishing' vegetable products dried in other types of drier from moisture contents of about 15 % down to about 3 %.

13.3.1.6. Fluidised bed drier. The principle of this type of drier is that heated air is forced up through a bed of solids under such conditions that the solids are suspended in the air. The heated air acts both as the fluidising and drying medium. Detailed treatment of the principles of solids fluidisation may be found elsewhere (Appendix I).[9, 14, 15]

Fluidised bed driers may be operated as batch units, or on a continuous basis. Figure 13.12 illustrates a simple continuous unit. The grid supporting the bed may be a simple perforated plate, but very complex designs incorporating jets, bubble caps, etc., are also employed. Some units have vibrating bases to assist movement of the product. Dust separators, usually cyclones, are included in the exhaust air line to remove fines. Driers may be operated under applied overhead pressure or reduced pressure by suitable siting of the fans.

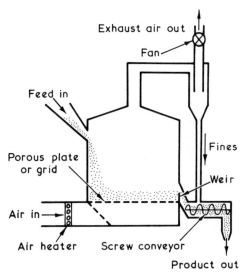

FIG. 13.12.   Principle of continuous fluidised bed drier.

The characteristic features of fluidised bed driers are:

(i)   They are limited in application mainly by the suitability of the
        feed for fluidisation. Some food materials, *e.g.* cereals, fluidise
        readily over a wide range of moisture contents. Other foods
        will only fluidise at low moisture contents. In the latter cases
        the wet product can often be handled by dispersing it in a bed
        of already dried material. Some materials are too fragile to be
        fluidised without suffering excessive mechanical damage.
(ii)   Fluidised drying occurs at relatively high rates and is readily
        controlled.
(iii)   Good mixing of the solids leads to uniform drying on a batch
        scale. However, in continuous systems, this mixing can lead to
        some undried product being discharged from the drier.

Fluidised bed drying has been applied on either a commercial or
experimental scale to a wide variety of products with varying success.
These include peas, beans, carrots, onions, potato granules, meat
cubes, flour, cocoa, coffee, salt and sugar. Beds are also used for
agglomeration and coating of dried powders.

13.3.1.7. Pneumatic drier. In this type of drier the wet material is
suspended in a moving stream of heated air which conveys it through

the drying system. It can be looked on as an extension of fluidised bed drying where higher air velocities are used. The principles of pneumatic conveying are dealt with in Chapter 19.

In a simple drier of this type the feed material is introduced into the moving stream of heated air. The solids are then carried in the air stream through ducts of sufficient length to give the required residence time. The air is exhausted from the system through a solids/gas separator, usually a cyclone, and the dried product collected.

The drying ducts may be arranged vertically, as in 'Air Lift Driers', or horizontally. In single pass systems relatively high air temperatures need to be used to avoid excessively long lengths of ducting. Better control of air temperatures at different stages can be exercised by introducing expansion chambers into the system. Alternatively, two or more such driers may be used in series with fresh air supplies to each.

In a pneumatic ring drier the ducting is in the form of an endless ring. The material can be directed around this ring continuously for several minutes while the drying air is constantly renewed, fresh material introduced and dried product removed continuously.[16] In such units drying times can be varied over a wide range.

The characteristic features of pneumatic driers are very similar to those of fluidised bed driers:

(i)   The application of such driers is limited by the types of foods it will handle, as are fluidised bed driers.
(ii) High drying rates are attainable.
(iii) The unit acts both as a drier and conveyor, which is useful in certain circumstances.

Pneumatic driers have been used for handling many food products, including grains and flour, granulated potato, meat cubes and as secondary driers for spray dried milk and egg products.

13.3.1.8. Rotary drier. In this type of drier the wet material is rotated in a cylindrical shell and heated air passed through as the material is agitated. In some cases the shell wall is also heated or heated tubes are located in the cylinder. The cylindrical steel shell is mounted on rollers at a small angle to the horizontal. The inside surface of the shell is fitted with flights which lift the material up as the shell rotates and cause it to shower down through the current of heated air passing through the cylinder. The wet feed is introduced continuously at the elevated end of the cylinder, and the dry product removed *via* a weir from the lower end. Air may flow concurrently or countercurrently to the direction of solids movement. In some designs through-flow air movement occurs.

The characteristic features of rotary driers are:

(i)   Application is limited to particulate material with reasonably free flowing characteristics.
(ii) High evaporation rates and good uniform drying, due to mixing, are attainable.

This type of drier has had only limited application to food, for example in the drying of meat pellets, granulated sugar and the treatment of cocoa beans.

13.3.1.9. Spray drier. This type of drier is used extensively in the food industry for drying solutions and slurries. The food material is introduced into the drying chamber in the form of a fine spray where it is brought into intimate contact with a stream of heated air. Thus very rapid drying occurs and a dry powder is produced. The very short drying times, of the order of 1–10 s, and the relatively low product temperatures are the main features of this type of drying. The droplets of the spray usually have diameters of the order of 10–200 μm thus presenting a very large surface area per unit volume of material to the drying air, resulting in rapid drying. Most of the drying occurs under conditions which promote constant rate drying so that the solids temperature does not rise much above the wet-bulb temperature of the drying air until drying nears completion. If operating conditions are correct and equipment design is good, the residence time of the particles in the drying chamber can be controlled so that the time the dry particles remain in contact with the heated air is kept to a minimum, thus their temperature is kept low.

The theory of evaporation from droplets in spray drying is treated elsewhere in the literature.[7c, 17–19]

The essential components of a spray drier include:

(i)   An air heating and circulating system.
(ii)   A spray-forming device.
(iii) A drying chamber.
(iv)   A product recovery system.

A typical spray drier is illustrated in Fig. 13.13.

(*i*) *Air heating and circulating systems.* Direct use of fuel gases is not common in spray driers. Steam heaters are commonly used on

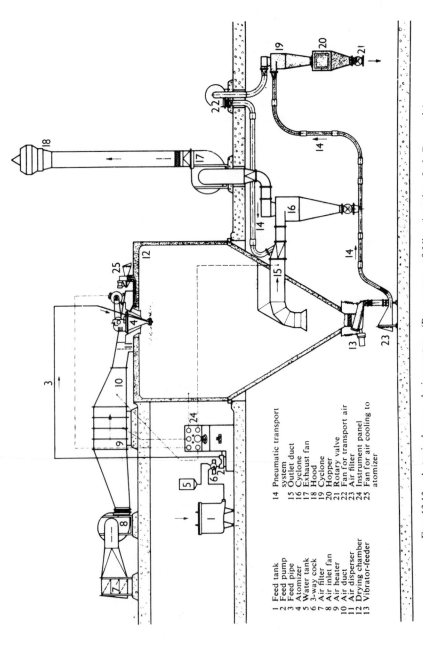

1 Feed tank
2 Feed pump
3 Feed pipe
4 Atomizer
5 Water tank
6 3-way cock
7 Air filter
8 Air inlet fan
9 Air heater
10 Air duct
11 Air disperser
12 Drying chamber
13 Vibrator-feeder
14 Pneumatic transport
   system
15 Outlet duct
16 Cyclone
17 Exhaust fan
18 Hood
19 Cyclone
20 Hopper
21 Rotary valve
22 Fan for transport air
23 Air filter
24 Instrument panel
25 Fan for air cooling to
   atomizer

FIG. 13.13. A typical spray drying system. (By courtesy of Niro Atomizer Ltd, Denmark.)

their own or to supplement indirect fuel gas heating. Electric heaters are seldom used except in pilot scale plant.

Centrifugal fans or blowers are usually used for moving the air through the system. Some spray driers have a single exhaust fan while others employ both an inlet and outlet fan. Thus many drying chambers operate under a very slight negative pressure. Dampers are normally provided in air inlet and outlet ducts to control air flow. Filters are also provided to clean the inlet air.

(*ii*) *Spray forming devices.* The formation of a spray of the feed material, with uniform droplets of the desired dimensions, and the distribution of this spray throughout the heated air is of utmost importance for successful spray drying. The term usually employed to describe the formation of the spray is atomisation. There are three main types of atomising devices used in spray driers, namely: *Pressure nozzles, centrifugal atomisers* and *two-fluid nozzles.*

The principle of the *pressure nozzle* is that the feed material is pumped at relatively high pressure, usually in the range 500–7000 psig (3.6–48.4 MN/m^2), through a small orifice. Thus the energy in the high pressure liquid is used to form the spray. A grooved core insert, sited before the orifice, imparts a spinning motion to the liquid and a cone of spray is formed. Hollow cone sprays are commonly employed in food spray driers. A typical nozzle is shown in Fig. 13.14. Various other designs are available. Pressure nozzles, if fed at a uniform pressure, recommended for the particular design, can produce fine,

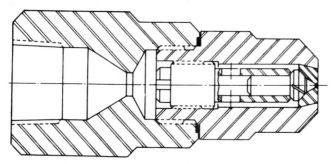

Fig. 13.14. A pressure nozzle. (By courtesy of Niro Atomizer Ltd, Denmark.)

uniform sprays. Blockage of the orifice by particulate matter and widening of the orifice, particularly if the feed contains abrasive solid, are limitations.

A *centrifugal atomiser* usually consists of a disc or bowl rotating on the end of a shaft. The liquid feed is introduced near the centre of rotation of the atomiser, accelerated to the linear velocity of the periphery of the head and spun off in the form of a spray into the drying chamber. The rotating head can take various forms including: inverted bowls, rimless wheels with hollow spokes, discs with holes at the periphery and turbine type impellers. A typical design is shown in Fig. 13.15. Sizes and speeds vary from say a 2 in (5·08 cm) disc rotating at 50 000 rev/min to a 30 in (76·2 cm) spoked wheel rotating at

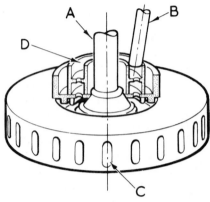

Fig. 13.15.   A centrifugal atomiser head. A, shaft; B, feed pipe; C, radial channel; D, dispenser. (By courtesy of Niro Atomizer Ltd, Denmark.)

3450 rev/min. Provided they are correctly operated, centrifugal atomisers can produce fine uniform sprays. They are not very subject to blockage or abrasion due to solids in the feed and can handle viscous materials at relatively low pumping pressures. Special wear-resistant designs are available and also some suited to the production of relatively large particles, 0·5–1·0 mm diameter. The latter are applicable to spray congealing of melted products.[7b]

The *two-fluid nozzle* depends on the energy in a high velocity stream of gas to atomise the feed material. The principle of this type of nozzle is shown in Fig. 13.16. The feed pressures used are less than those necessary for pressure nozzles. They suffer from orifice widening and blockage as do the latter type. They are generally of comparatively low capacity and a wide variation in droplet size very often occurs. Mainly for these latter reasons they are seldom used for the spray drying of foods.

(*iii*) *Drying chambers.* The drying chamber is that part of the spray drier where hot air and feed meet and drying occurs. The many types of chamber available were classified by Seltzer and Settelmeyer.[20] The general principle of each of these classes is shown diagrammatically in

Fig. 13.17. Pilot plant experimentation or trial runs on industrial scale plant are the only reliable methods for selecting a drier for a particular duty. Due to the dangers of damaging heat-sensitive materials, countercurrent spray driers are seldom used for food drying.

Recent advances in chamber design include the *W-chamber* in which the cone tip is built into the chamber and the *spray-fluidiser*

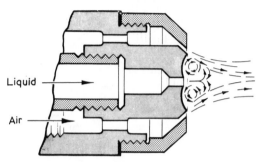

Liquid

Air

FIG. 13.16.   The principle of the two-fluid nozzle. (By courtesy of Niro Atomizer Ltd, Denmark.)

which incorporates both a spray drier, with a nozzle atomiser, and a fluidised bed drier.[7b]

(*iv*) *Product recovery systems.* In some spray driers the major proportion of the dry product falls to the bottom of the chamber and is removed with the aid of rakes, screw conveyors and rotary valves. When the dried product is thermoplastic and/or hygroscopic, special chamber designs involving cooled walls, air brooms and similar features may be necessary to facilitate product discharge.[19]

In other driers all the dried product leaves the drying chamber in the outgoing air. In all driers it is necessary to clean the outgoing air and recover the product therein. The three methods commonly employed for this purpose are *Dry Cyclone Separators, Wet Scrubbers* and *Bag Filters.*

The principle of the *cyclone separator* is the same as that of the centrifugal entrainment separator (Section 12.7.3, Fig. 12.7). Large cyclones, *e.g.* 10 ft (3·05 m) in diameter, are often used singly, or in pairs in series. Alternatively, banks of smaller cyclones in parallel may be employed. The latter tend to be more effective in removing light products of small particle size, *e.g.* less than 50 μm in diameter. Cyclones generally give recoveries of the order of 90–97 %. They are simple to operate and maintain.

The principle of the *wet scrubber* is to draw the exhaust air from the drying chamber through a vessel where it is washed with a liquid,

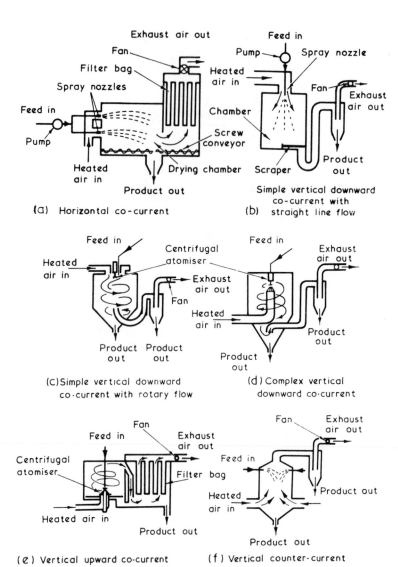

FIG. 13.17. Schematic drawings of various spray drying systems.

usually the incoming feed to the atomiser. In some plants this system is employed not only to scrub the exhaust air but also to preheat or preconcentrate the incoming feed, thus improving the overall efficiency of the system. Growth of micro-organisms in wet scrubbers can be difficult to control and recirculation of some of the product can lead to heat damage. Recovery is usually of the order of 95–98 %.

Drawing the exhaust air from the chamber through *cloth filters* is another technique employed for air cleaning and product recovery. Filters may be tubular or flat screen types. Such filters need to be mechanically shaken at intervals to loosen the product. Unless the temperature and humidity in the bag house is carefully controlled during shut-down, plugging can occur. Recovery is of the same order as wet scrubbers.

In some driers a combination of methods is employed for product recovery, *e.g.* cyclones followed by bag filters.

Systems are also available which enable spray drying to be carried out under aseptic conditions. These are mainly in use in the pharmaceutical industry. Closed cycle driers are also in use, mainly in the chemical industry.

Spray driers are used extensively in the food industry. Examples of food products which are spray dried are: milk (skim and whole), whey, ice cream mix, butter, cheese, milk based baby foods, coffee and tea whiteners, eggs (whole, yolk and white), coffee, tea, fruit and vegetable juices, edible proteins, meat and yeast extracts, wheat and corn products.

13.3.2. DRYING BY CONTACT WITH A HEATED SURFACE

As an alternative to the use of hot air as a drying medium, water may be removed by placing the wet material in contact with a heated surface. In such systems the necessary sensible and latent heat of evaporation is supplied to the material by conduction. The drying pattern is similar to that of hot air drying to the extent that drying occurs mainly in two stages. During the initial constant rate period the material temperature approximates its boiling point at the prevailing pressure. The drying rates during this period are higher than those attained by drying in air at the same temperature as the heated surface. When the rate of movement of liquid to the evaporating surface falls below the rate of evaporation, the falling rate period commences and the material temperature rises and approaches that of the heated surface. If drying is carried out at atmospheric pressure, the material temperature, during the initial drying stage, is in excess of 100 C. In order to achieve reasonable drying times and to dry to low moisture contents, the heated surface temperature needs to be appreciably higher than this and, therefore, as drying nears completion the material temperature rises quite high. Thus the danger of heat damage to sensitive food materials is comparatively high. To reduce this hazard, drying by contact is often carried out under reduced pressure so that lower surface and material temperatures may be employed.

13.3.2.1. Drum drier (film drier, roller drier). This type of drier consists essentially of one or more hollow metal cylinders, revolving on horizontal axes and heated internally by steam, water or other liquid heating medium. A film of the wet material, of uniform thickness, is applied to the drum surface. As the drum rotates drying takes place and the dried material is removed from the drum surface by a scraping device located usually $\frac{1}{2}-\frac{3}{4}$ of a revolution from the point of application of the feed. Drum driers are often classified into three types namely: *single drum*, *double drum* and *twin drum*. These are illustrated in Fig. 13.18. Drums have to be carefully machined to true cylindrical forms. Scraper knives need to be very sharp and to touch the drum surface uniformly, along its length. Adjusting screws are provided for this purpose.

It is essential, to ensure good performance, that the film of feed material applied to the drum surface should be as uniform as possible in depth. Single drums are fed by the use of feed vessels into which the drum dips, by the use of rotating devices to spray or splash the feed on and spreading knives or rollers to even out the film, or by the use of unheated feed rollers. The feed to the double drum drier is introduced into the trough between the drums.

For handling heat-sensitive materials, drums enclosed in a vacuum-tight chamber may be employed so that drying can be carried out at pressures less than atmospheric. Such a drier is also shown in Fig. 13.18. Vacuum steam or heated water is usually used as a heating medium. The product is discharged into receivers, and adjustments to feeders, scrapers, etc., are made from outside the chamber. Such driers have relatively high capital cost and are normally used only for very heat-sensitive materials.

The factors affecting the drying rate and final moisture content of a particular material on a drum drier are: speed of rotation of drum (controlling dwell time), steam pressure or heating medium temperature and film thickness. The latter parameter depends on the feeding mechanism used and the solids content, rheological and surface tension properties of the feed.[21]

The advantages of drum drying are high rates of drying and economic use of heat. The main limitations are that it can only be

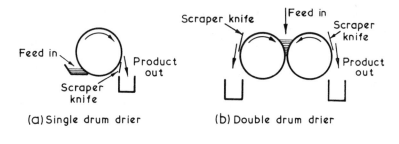

(a) Single drum drier   (b) Double drum drier

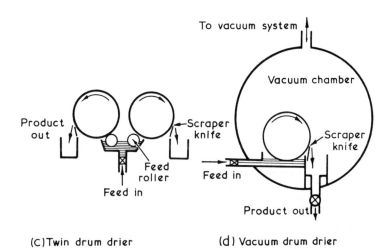

(C) Twin drum drier   (d) Vacuum drum drier

FIG. 13.18.   Schematic drawings of various types of drum drier.

applied to foods in a liquid or slurry form and which can withstand relatively high temperatures for short times (of the order of 2–30 s). Drum driers have been applied to drying of milk, soup mixes, baby foods, mashed potato and many other foods.

13.3.2.2. Vacuum shelf drier. This is another method for drying heat-sensitive foods in the solid or liquid state by the application of heat by conduction. Such a drier consists of a vacuum tight chamber of heavy construction, with one or more access doors and an outlet for vapours and gases. Hollow shelves, through which the heating medium is circulated, are fitted inside the chamber. The feed material is spread in fairly thin layers on metal trays which rest on these hollow shelves. A vacuum is drawn on the chamber *via* the vapour outlet, and drying proceeds at pressures of the order of 1–70 torr

(0·135–9·45 kN/m^2). Shelves and trays need to be as flat as possible to ensure good thermal contact. Initial drying rates are high but as the food dries and shrinks, contact with the tray becomes less effective and heat transfer declines. The shelf temperature requires very careful control to avoid overheating the dried portions of the food in contact with the trays. Vacuum shelf driers and their ancillaries incur high capital cost, and are normally only used for very heat-sensitive foods, for example fruit juice concentrates.

13.3.2.3. The vacuum band drier. This is mainly applicable to the drying of liquids and slurries. The principle of one such drier is shown in Fig. 13.19. It consists of a continuous stainless steel belt which passes over a heating and cooling drum inside a vacuum chamber. The feed is applied to the underside of this belt and heat is supplied both *via* the heated drum and radiant heaters. The dried product is cooled as the belt passes over the cooled drum and is removed by means of a scraper blade. Other band driers of this type have belts made up of stainless steel plates. Other heat sources may be used, such as steam

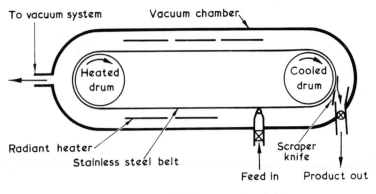

FIG. 13.19.   Principle of the vacuum band drier.

coils and heated platens. Applications include drying of fruit juice concentrates, tomato concentrates and coffee extracts.[2]

Puff drying is a form of vacuum drying applied to heat-sensitive material such as fruit juice concentrate. Generally drying is carried out in vacuum shelf or band driers, the vacuum being drawn in such a way that the material puffs up due to the evolution of gases and vapours. The porous structure thus formed promotes rapid drying and the product is of good quality and reconstitutability.[1, 6, 7f, 9]

13.3.3. DRYING BY THE APPLICATION OF ENERGY FROM A RADIATING, MICROWAVE OR DIELECTRIC SOURCE

13.3.3.1. Radiant heating. This has been applied to a limited extent to food dehydration. The characteristics of radiant heating and the methods of generating such radiation are dealt with in Chapter 10, Section 10.4.3.1. The basic equations governing heat transfer by radiation are given in Appendix II.

It must be realised that radiant heat plays a part in supplying the necessary sensible and latent heat of evaporation in both hot air drying and direct contact drying. Taking the cabinet drier as an example, the walls of the cabinet, the trays and other metal parts of the cabinet will radiate heat to the food.

The application of radiant heat as the major source of heat for food dehydration is limited because of its limited penetration into foods except at certain wavelengths. The heterogeneous nature of foods both in surface and absorptive characteristics can lead to uneven heating and hence non-uniform drying. Careful control of high temperature sources is necessary to avoid overheating. On the other hand, radiant heaters do not suffer from the disadvantages of poor contact and sluggish response to changes in temperature, experienced with most conduction sources.

13.3.3.2. The continuous infra-red drier. This has found some application to food dehydration. In this type of equipment the food material is carried on a conveyor belt or vibrating deck beneath infra-red sources for the required drying times. The sources used for heat sensitive food materials are usually short-wave lamps while long-wave bar generators may be used for less sensitive materials. Some applications quoted by the manufacturers include drying of bread crumbs, starches, custard powders, cake mixtures, tea, almonds and spices.

The vacuum band drier discussed in 13.3.2.3 also employs radiant heating.

13.3.3.3. Microwave and dielectric heating. This has so far had little commercial application to food dehydration. The characteristics of this type of heating and the types of generating equipment are dealt with in Chapter 10, Sections 10.4.3.2 and 10.4.3.3. While at this stage of its development this type of heating appears to be uneconomic for removing moisture in bulk, some of the duties to which it is put are essentially dehydration processes. The drying of starch-reduced rolls in dielectric ovens at 35 MHz and the finishing of biscuits are examples. To date, dielectric heating seems to have wider commercial application than microwave mainly due to the comparative simplicity of the equipment available. Microwave systems would appear potentially better because of the greater dissipation of heat in foods and the higher power potential of the generators. Some encouraging results have been obtained recently in work on the application of microwave heating in vacuum drying.[7f]

13.3.4. FREEZE DRYING (SUBLIMATION-DRYING; LYOPHILISATION)

This method of drying involves freezing the material followed by sublimation of the ice from the frozen state to produce a dried product. Sublimation is brought about by maintaining a water vapour pressure gradient between the immediate surroundings of the material and the ice front within the material. Complete drying could be said to take place in three stages. Initially, by freezing, water is withdrawn from the hydrated components of the food by the formation of crystals of ice or eutectic mixtures. By subsequent sublimation of these crystals, water is removed from the body of the material. When all the ice has been removed the solid remaining will still have a small amount of water absorbed within the structure of its components. This may be removed by evaporation in the freeze-drying equipment, usually by raising the material temperature, or alternatively the 'finishing' of the material may be carried out in another form of drier, such as a bin drier.

The removal of the major portion of the water by sublimation results in a product with a light porous structure, retaining the shape and size of the original material. Many of the disadvantages associated with other drying methods as discussed in Section 13.2.3 are avoided or minimised. Shrinkage is almost negligible, movement of soluble solids is limited and heat damage is minimised. The reconstitution characteristics of the product are good both in terms of rate and extent of reconstitution. The retention of volatile odour and flavour compounds is also high. On the other hand cell structure may be damaged during freezing, giving poor texture in the reconstituted product, and the dried product itself is very brittle and susceptible to mechanical damage.

In most conventional freeze-drying systems the vapour pressure gradient necessary for sublimation is attained by maintaining the total pressure in the drying chamber at a low level of the order of 0·1–2·0 torr (13·5–270·0 N/m^2). A condensing system is provided to remove the water vapour formed and a heating system to supply the necessary latent heat of sublimation to the frozen material. Such a system is shown schematically in Fig. 13.20. In such a system the two main factors affecting the rate of drying are the rate of movement of water vapour from the ice surface through the porous layer of dry material and the rate of transfer of heat to the ice front.

The movement of water vapour through the porous layer of dried material has been discussed by various authors.[1, 7a, 22a, 23, 24g] Except in the very initial stages of drying, such movement must occur. In some early work Harper and Tappel[23] studied the movement of vapours and gases through freeze-dried beef and found that the mechanism of

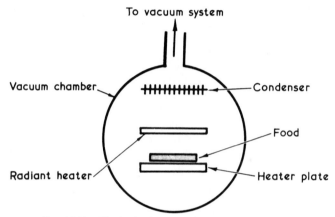

FIG. 13.20. The basic elements of a freeze-drying system.

vapour flow was different at different total pressures in the system. By considering the flow of vapour through the dried meat as being analogous to flow through a bundle of capillary tubes, with slip flow conditions prevailing (*i.e.* when the rate of flow exceeds that calculated from Poiseuille's law, due to movement at the capillary walls) the mass flow rate of gas, m, at constant temperature is given by an expression of the form:

$$m = \frac{a}{l} A \, \Delta P (P_m + b) \qquad (13.17)$$

where ΔP = pressure drop across the dried layer, P_m = arithmetic average of pressures at both faces of the dried layer, l = length of flow path, A = area normal to the direction of flow of gas, a, b = constants.

Such an expression applies at pressures below 10 torr ($1\cdot35\,\text{kN/m}^2$). These same workers also found that vapour flow rate was approximately proportional to the ice vapour pressure and that the best level for the total chamber pressure is of the order of $\frac{1}{4}-\frac{1}{3}$ of the ice vapour pressure. Other workers suggest that this ratio should be of the order of $\frac{1}{2}$.[1, 24g]

More recent work on vapour movement through dry layers is summarised by Karel.[7a] He uses a more general equation to represent the rate of flow of vapour through the solid layer:

$$\frac{dw}{dt} = \frac{Ab(p_i - p_D)}{l} \qquad (13.18)$$

where dw/dt = mass flow rate of vapour through dry layer, b = permeability of the dry layer, p_i = vapour pressure of ice at specified temperature, p_D = partial pressure of water vapour at surface of dry layer, l = thickness of dry layer.

In order to achieve the maximum rate of drying, the ice temperature should be as high as possible consistent with product quality. Unless the heat of sublimation is supplied to the ice at a sufficient rate, the ice temperature will fall and, consequently, so will the drying rate. In a system where the heat is transferred to the ice through the dried layer only and where drying takes place only from the heated surface (as would happen, theoretically, if the heat supply to the lower plate in Fig. 13.20 were cut off), then the rate of heat input, dQ/dt, is given by the equation:

$$\frac{dQ}{dt} = \frac{k_D A(\theta_D - \theta_i)}{l} \qquad (13.19)$$

where k_D = thermal conductivity of dried layer, θ_D = temperature of dried surface, θ_i = temperature of ice surface.

An energy balance combining equations (13.18) and (13.19) gives:

$$\frac{k_D A(\theta_D - \theta_i)}{l} = -\frac{L_s Ab(p_i - p_D)}{l} \qquad (13.20)$$

where L_s = latent heat of sublimation at θ_i.

Note that l cancels out so that the relationship is independent of the extent of drying. If the dried surface temperature and chamber pressure are fixed then the ice surface temperature is also fixed (since θ_i and p_i are thermodynamically related).

If a slab-shaped solid is being freeze-dried from one or both large faces, *i.e.* end effects are ignored, if the moisture content of the dry layer formed is W_e, *dry-weight basis*, and if the ice front recedes in a uniform plane then the rate of drying, dw/dt, may be described by an equation thus:

$$\frac{dw}{dt} = A\rho_m(W_0 - W_e)\frac{dl}{dt} \qquad (13.21)$$

where ρ_m = the density of the dried solid, W_0 = initial moisture content of the material, *dry-weight basis*.

From (13.20) and (13.21) one can deduce the relationship:

$$\frac{dw}{dt} = -\frac{Ak_D(\theta_D - \theta_i)}{L_s l} = \frac{Ab(p_i - p_D)}{l} = A\rho_m(W_0 - W_e)\frac{dl}{dt}$$

(13.22)

Integrating within the limits: $t = 0,\ l = 0; t = t_t,\ l = l_t$:

$$t_t = \frac{\rho_m(W_0 - W_e)}{b(p_i - p_D)}\frac{l_t^2}{2} = \frac{L_s\rho_m(W_0 - W_e)}{k_D(\theta_D - \theta_i)}\frac{l_t^2}{2}$$

(13.23)

where t_t = total drying time to W_e, l_t = total thickness of slab for one-sided drying, = half the slab thickness for two-sided drying. Note that t_t is proportional to l_t^2, hence the drying of thick slabs is prolonged.

Harper and Tappel[23] and Rolfe[24g] found good agreement between calculated drying times and those obtained experimentally. Both the permeability and thermal conductivity of the dry layer are dependent on pressure and the nature of the gases in the pores. Some values of these properties for meat, fish, coffee and apple are reported by Karel.[7a] This author also presents expressions relating heater plate temperature to dry surface temperature and discusses the situation when heat is conducted through the ice layer to the subliming surface.

13.3.4.1. Freezing. Ideally, to carry out the freeze drying process correctly, all the liquid present in the food should be frozen. However, in practice this is not feasible, and provided the amount of unfrozen liquid remaining is small the product quality is not seriously affected.[23]

The optimum rate of freezing for freeze drying depends largely on the nature of the product. Variation in rate of freezing affects ice crystal size and hence pore size in the dried product, and so can be expected to influence the rate of drying and the characteristics of the product, particularly its reconstitutability. Optimum rates of freezing should be determined experimentally. Freezing may be carried out by any of the methods discussed in Chapter 14.

13.3.4.2. Batch freeze driers. The essential components of a batch freeze drier are a vacuum cabinet, a vacuum system and a heating system. Freeze drier cabinets are essentially similar to the vacuum shelf driers described in 13.2.2.2. Parts in direct contact with the food are usually of stainless steel and other internal surfaces are suitably coated.[24h, i, j, k]

The *vacuum system* must be capable of pumping down the cabinet initially in a short time to prevent melting of the frozen product. In practice this usually entails lowering the cabinet pressure to between 5 and 1 torr (675 and 135 N/m^2) within 10 min. The cabinet pressure then needs to be lowered to the required level for drying, usually well below 1 torr (135 N/m^2), and held at that pressure during the drying. The vacuum system has to cope with the vapour produced during drying, gases evolved from the food and leakage into the chamber. It is usual to provide 'roughing pumps' for the initial pump down and smaller capacity, holding pumps for use during drying.

Refrigerated condensers, backed by a mechanical pumping system, are commonly used, commercially, for producing and maintaining chamber vacuum. Most of the water vapour is condensed as ice onto the refrigerated plates or coils and the pumps remove the non-condensable gases and residual vapour. Location of two or more condensers in separate chambers (traps), connected to the drying chamber through sliding gates or valves, facilitates deicing during operation of the drier. Multistage steam ejector systems may be used instead of the condenser-pump systems but are less effective at very low chamber pressures. The features of various vacuum systems are discussed elsewhere.[7d, 24a, b, f]

The use of scraped surface condensers to remove the ice formed or adsorption systems in which the water vapour is absorbed by a material such as glycerol or glycol have also been investigated but, as far as is known, such methods have not been employed commercially. Cyclic-pressure freeze drying involves subjecting the product to repeated cyclic changes in pressure, in the range 20–0·2 torr (2·7 kN/m^2 to 27 N/m^2) and is said to improve rates of drying in some circumstances.[7e]

Heat may be supplied to the frozen material by conduction or radiation or from a microwave source. The former two methods are used commercially, often in combination. The simplest method for supplying heat by *conduction* is to place the food material in a metal tray and place this tray on a heated shelf as in vacuum-shelf drying. Some drying inevitably occurs from the heated surface resulting in the formation of a dried layer, thus reducing heat transfer. Also a low plate temperature must be used, particularly in the early stages of drying, to avoid melting the ice. The application of conducted heat from both sides using hydraulically operated heating plates to maintain good thermal contact, reduces drying times somewhat but the escape of water vapour from the surface may be impaired, necessitating reduction of the plate temperature and slower drying. To overcome this problem the Accelerated Freeze-Drying Method (AFD) was developed.[24c] In this method a layer of expanded metal mesh is inserted on each side of the food. By this technique good thermal contact is maintained throughout drying while an adequate path of escape for the vapour is provided.

Radiant heating from one or both sides should theoretically provide uniform heating and a constant temperature. However, as previously mentioned in Section 13.3.3.1, variation in the surface characteristics of foods can lead to non-uniform heating, and careful control of the source temperature is required to avoid scorching the dried surface, even when the ice surface temperature is quite low. A common method is direct contact conduction heating from the bottom and radiant heating from the top, *e.g.* by placing the trays of food between heated plates with a fixed spacing. Under certain circumstances this can promote quicker drying than pure radiant heating.[24f] The use of ribbed aluminium trays with compartments about 2 in (5·04 cm) wide and deep, instead of flat metal trays, is said to increase the rate of transfer of both radiant and conducted heat and promote quicker drying in certain products, particularly those with a granular structure.

Microwave heating on first consideration appears to offer an ideal form of heating for freeze drying. The loss factors (Chapter 10, Section 10.4.3.2) for ice and water are considerably higher than for dry tissue, so the ice core should absorb energy preferentially. Difficulties arise, however, in controlling the heat input as the loss factor increases with temperature so as the ice core heats up it will absorb more energy. This, combined with the problems associated with the heterogeneous nature of foods, can lead to thawing. Thawing would be a serious problem because the loss factor for liquid water is much greater than for ice and rapid evaporation would occur which could cause the product to explode. Ionisation of the rarefied gases in the freeze drier is another problem but this can be reduced by the use of high frequency sources, *e.g.* 2450 MHz, and low chamber pressures. As far as is known, microwave energy has not, as yet, been applied commercially to the freeze drying of foods but it has promise particularly for the 'finishing' of freeze dried materials.

Many other techniques for applying heat during freeze drying have been investigated experimentally. These include the use of heated plates fitted with hollow spikes to penetrate into the food and the use of radiant heat applied to the surface of a bed of granular material with provision for removing the dried layer as it forms. None of these techniques have as yet been applied commercially.[7a, 24a, d, e, f]

A typical batch freeze drier would have a capacity of 900 lb (408·6 kg) of prepared food and a drying cycle of the order of 7–8 h, with most materials.

13.3.4.3. Multicabinet units. These are widely used for freeze drying of foods at larger throughputs of the order of 5 tons/day (5080 kg/day) material. A typical unit consists of four batch cabinets each fitted with its own heater plates but all four connected to two vacuum manifolds. One manifold is used for pump down and roughing duties and the other for maintaining the appropriate pressure during drying. The cabinets are loaded sequentially at appropriate intervals, depending on the food, but usually 2–3 h, and the vacuum system controlled to maintain appropriate pressures in each cabinet at all times.

13.3.4.4. Tunnel freeze-driers. These are available for very high throughput operations. Such a unit consists of a cylindrical tunnel 6–8 ft (1·8–2·4 m) in diameter fitted with heater plates with fixed spacing. The food material in trays or ribbed dishes is carried, either on a trolley running on ground rails or suspended from an overhead rail, so that the trays fit between the heater plates in the tunnel (Fig. 13.21). In some units the trays can be lowered as required into direct contact with the heater shelves. The tunnel has a length dependent largely on the throughput required and is generally made up of a

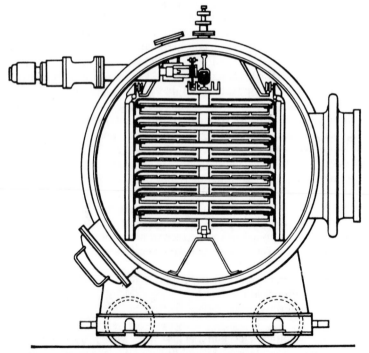

FIG. 13.21. Typical cross-section through the tunnel. (Reproduced from *Freeze-drying of Foodstuffs*[24] by courtesy of Columbine Press (Publishers) Ltd.)

number of standard sections. The complete tunnel is fitted with entry and delivery locks at the ends. The batches of food are fed into the tunnel at suitable intervals through the entry lock, the latter being pumped down rapidly after each entry. As the batch passes from the lock into the tunnel proper a sliding pressure gate closes off the lock, the vacuum therein is broken and it is ready to receive the next batch. Dried product is removed similarly from the exit lock and here the vacuum may be broken by the introduction of inert gas.

For efficient operation the vacuum system and heating system should be designed to suit the load at the various stages in the tunnel. Both the vapour load and the heat load decrease as the drying proceeds.[7d, 24h, i, j, k]

13.3.4.5. Other systems for freeze-drying of foods have been investigated and are reported on in the literature. These include atmospheric freeze-drying in which sublimation is brought about by exposing the food to a stream of cold dry air at atmospheric pressure. Other systems involve the application of tumbler driers, fluidised-bed driers, spray driers and many other forms of drying equipment to freeze drying. Treatment of such widely diverse methods is not practicable here and as far as is known none of these methods has as yet been applied commercially on any large scale.[1, 9, 22, 24]

Because of the high capital and operating costs involved in freeze drying and the stringent packaging requirements of the product, this method of preservation remains very expensive.

Applications for freeze drying include: coffee, tea, meat and fish (*e.g.* shrimp and prawn), and some vegetable and fruit products.

13.4.   DEHYDRO FREEZING

This has been applied mainly in the USA to fruits and vegetables. It involves partial drying of the material, usually down to below 50 % of the original fresh weight, by heated air methods and then freezing the partially dried material and holding it in frozen storage. Thus advantage is taken of the savings in weight and bulk resulting from the partial drying while the disadvantages associated with the latter stages of drying, such as heat damage, are reduced. One problem in the drying stage is to obtain a uniform moisture content in the partially dried material. To this end drying equipment involving movement of the solid during drying, such as crossflow tunnels, conveyor driers, rotary driers and possibly fluidised bed and pneumatic driers, is preferable. Freezing can be by any of the conventional techniques. As far as is known dehydro freezing has so far been mainly applied to fruits and vegetables for institutional use and for remanufacture.[25, 26]

13.5.   RECONSTITUTABILITY OF DRIED FOODS

Reconstitutability, as applied to dehydrated foods, is the term used to describe the rate at and extent to which dried foods pick up, absorb water and revert to a condition resembling the undried material, when put in contact with a surplus of water.

13.5.1. FACTORS INFLUENCING RECONSTITUTION

In the case of dried foods in piece form such as sliced or diced vegetables or diced meat products, the reconstitutability largely depends on the structure of the dried pieces and the extent to which the water holding components, mainly proteins and starch, have been affected by the drying operation. For example, the rate at which air dried vegetables reconstitute can depend on the initial rates of drying (*see* Section 13.2.3.2). Freeze dried foods often reconstitute rapidly because of the porous structure, which is a feature of this method of drying (*see* Section 13.3.4). On the other hand, excessive heat damage during drying, or freezing damage in the case of freeze dried foods, can result in a reduction in the water holding capacity of the reconstituted material and hence a poor appearance and texture.

In the case of dried powders a number of properties may influence the overall reconstitution characteristics of the material. These include:

Wettability. This term describes the ability of the powder particle to adsorb water on its surface, thus initiating reconstitution. This property largely depends on particle size. Small particles, representing a large surface area:mass ratio, may not be wetted individually, but clump together, sharing a wetted surface layer. This layer reduces the rate at which water penetrates into the clump of particles. Increasing the particle size and/or agglomerating particles can reduce the incidence of clumping. The nature of the surface of the particles can also affect wettability. For example the presence of free fat at the surface reduces wettability. The selective use of surface active agents such as lecithin can sometimes improve wettability in dried powders containing fat.

Sinkability. This term describes the ability of the powder particles to sink quickly into the water. It depends mainly on the size and density of the particles. Larger, more dense particles sink more rapidly than fine, lighter particles. Particles with a high content of occluded air may be relatively large but exhibit poor sinkability because of their low density.

Dispersability. This term describes the ease with which the powder may be distributed, as single particles, over the surface and throughout the bulk of the reconstituting water. Dispersability is reduced by clump formation and is improved when the sinkability is high.

Solubility. This term describes the rate and extent to which the components of the powder particles dissolve in the water. It depends mainly on the chemical composition of the powder and its physical state, *e.g.* degree and type of crystallinity.

For a powder to exhibit good reconstitution characteristics, *i.e.* a so-called 'instant' powder, there needs to be a correct balance between the individual properties discussed above. In many cases alteration of one or two of these properties can markedly change the behaviour of the powder on reconstitution. In addition to their influence on the reconstitution of dried powders, properties such as particle size, density and bulk density can affect the handling characteristics and appearance of such products.

13.5.2. PROCEDURES FOR IMPROVING RECONSTITUTABILITY

13.5.2.1. Adjustment of drying conditions. Variations in the feed (solids content, viscosity, temperature), atomisation (type of atomiser and operating pressure or speed) and drying air (inlet and outlet temperatures) can result in changes in the particle size, density and bulk density of the product. Adjustment of conditions can sometimes lead to an improvement in reconstitution characteristics. The introduction of additional steps in the process may also help. An example of the latter remedy is the inclusion of crystallisation stages in the spray drying of whey.

13.5.2.2. Recycling of fines. The fine particles produced in a spray drier may be recycled to the wet zone of the drying chamber, near the atomiser. A typical plant layout, featuring the recycling of fines, is shown in Fig. 13.22. Dried particles from the chamber are cooled on a vibrating, fluidised-bed cooler. The fines from this cooler together with those in the exhaust air from the drying chamber are recycled and

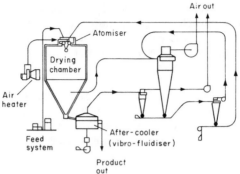

FIG. 13.22. Plant layout featuring recycling of fines. (Reproduced from 'Spray Drying'[19] by courtesy of the author.)

form agglomerates with the spray. Thus the very fine particles are eliminated from the product and the reconstitutability, mainly in terms of wettability and dispersability, may be improved.

13.5.2.3. Straight-through instantiser. A typical layout for this type of plant is shown in Fig. 13.23. Again fines are recycled to the wet zone of the drier. The product leaving the drying chamber is maintained at a relatively high moisture content, 6–8% *wet-weight basis*. In this condition the particles may be thermoplastic and tacky at the surface and further agglomeration occurs. On leaving the chamber the agglomerates, now 300–400 μm in diameter, are dried further and cooled in a two-stage vibrating, fluidised-bed unit.

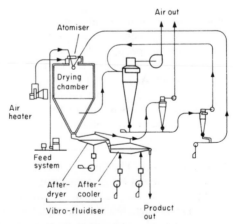

FIG. 13.23. Straight-through instantiser. (Reproduced from 'Spray Drying'[19] by courtesy of the author.)

13.5.2.4. Rewetting. This is probably the most effective and widely used method of improving the reconstitution characteristics of dried powders. Spray dried powder, produced in a conventional plant, is treated with steam or warm, humid air such that condensation occurs on the surface of the particles. Inter-particle contact is promoted, often by swirling the wetted powder in a vortex. Agglomerates are formed. The agglomerates are dried in a chamber, then cooled on a

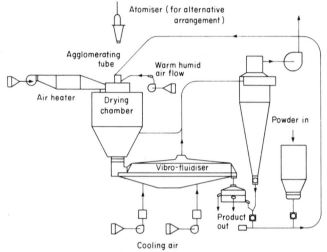

FIG. 13.24. Rewet instantiser. (Reproduced from 'Spray Drying'[19] by courtesy of the author.)

vibrating fluidised-bed. Fines from the bed and chamber are recycled to the agglomeration zone. This procedure is known as surface agglomeration. An alternative procedure, known as droplet agglomeration, involves contacting the dried powder with a fine mist or spray of water or a solution of some or all of the components of the powder. The mist may be formed by spray jets or an atomiser wheel (*see* Fig. 13.24). The agglomerates formed are dried and cooled as in surface agglomeration.

Agglomeration results in an increase in interstitial air between the particles. On reconstitution this air is replaced rapidly by water and rapid wetting and dispersion of the particles occurs.[19, 27-29]

REFERENCES

1. Van Arsdel, W. B., Copley, M. J., and Morgan, Jr, A. I. (Eds), 'Food Dehydration', 2nd ed., Volume I, Drying methods and phenomena. (AVI: 1973.)

2. Van Arsdel, W. B., Copley, M. J., and Morgan, Jr, A. I. (Eds), 'Food Dehydration'. 2nd ed., Volume II, Practices and applications. (AVI: 1973.)
3. Von Loesecke, H. B., 'Drying and Dehydration of Foods', 2nd ed. (Reinhold: 1955).
4. Morris, T. N., 'The Dehydration of Food'. (Chapman & Hall: 1947.)
5. Desrosier, N. W., 'The Technology of Food Preservation'. (AVI: 1959.)
6. Heid, J. L., and Joslyn, M. A., 'Food Processing Operations', Volume II. (AVI: 1963.)
7. Spicer, A. (Ed.), 'Advances in Preconcentration and Dehydration of Foods'. (Applied Science Publishers Ltd: 1974.)
   Particular papers referred to:
   (a) Karel, M., 'Fundamentals of dehydration processes'.
   (b) Kjaergaard, O. G., 'Effects of the latest developments on design and practice of spray drying'.
   (c) Kerkhof, P. J. A. M., and Schoeber, W. J. A. H., 'Theoretical modelling of the drying behaviour of droplets in spray dryers'.
   (d) Lorentzen, J., 'New directions in freeze-drying'.
   (e) Mellor, J. D., 'Cyclic-pressure freeze-drying in practice'.
   (f) Meisel, N., 'Microwave heating in vacuum drying'.
8. Perry, R. H., and Chilton, C. H. (Eds), 'Chemical Engineers Handbook', 5th ed. (McGraw-Hill: 1973).
9. Charm, S. E., 'The Fundamentals of Food Engineering', 2nd ed. (AVI: 1971).
10. 'Conference on the fundamental aspects of the dehydration of foodstuffs', (SCI: 1958).
    Particular papers referred to:
    (a) Kuprianoff, J., 'Bound water in foods'.
    (b) Crank, J., 'Some mathematical diffusion studies relevant to dehydration'.
    (c) Gorling, P., 'Physical phenomena during the drying of foodstuffs'.
    (d) Stitt, F., 'Moisture equilibrium and the determination of water content of dehydrated foods'.
    (e) Jason, A. C., 'A study of evaporation and diffusion processes in the drying of fish muscle'.
11. Saravacos, G. D., and Charm, S. E., 'A study of the mechanism of fruit and vegetable dehydration'. Fd Technol., Champaign, **16**(1), 78–81 (1962).
12. King, C. J., 'Rates of moisture sorption and desorption in porous dried foodstuffs'. Fd Technol., Champaign, **22**(4), 509–515 (1968).
13. Morgan, Jr, A. I., 'Foam-mat drying' *in* 'Encyclopedia of Food Technology', Johnson, A. H. and Peterson, M. S. (Eds), (AVI: 1974).
14. Brown, G. G. (Ed.), 'Unit Operations'. (John Wiley: 1955.)
15. Vojtěch Vaněcěk, Miroslav Markvart and Radek Drbohlav, 'Fluidised Bed Drying'. (Leonard Hill: 1966.)
16. Slade, F. H., 'Automation in food processing—16—Drying'. Fd Process. Packag., **32**(378), 95–98 (1963).
17. Ranz, W. E., and Marshall Jr, W. R., 'Evaporation from drops'. Chem. Engng Prog., **48**(3), 141–146 (1952) and **48**(4), 173–180 (1952).
18. Marshall Jr., W. R., 'Atomization and spray drying', Chem. Engng Prog., Monog. Ser., **50**(2) (1954).
19. Masters, K., 'Spray Drying'. (Leonard Hill: 1972.)
20. Seltzer, E., and Settelmeyer, J. T., 'Spray drying of foods', Advances in Food Research, Volume II, 399–520. (Academic Press: 1949.)
21. Spadaro, J. J., Wadsworth, J. I., and Vix, H. L. E., 'Drum drying of foods'. ASHRAE Jl., 55–63 (1966).
22. Rey, L. (Ed.), 'Researches and development in freeze-drying'. (Hermann: 1964.)
    Particular papers referred to:

    (a) Rowe, T. W. G., 'Energy, mass transfer and economy in large scale freeze drying'.

    (b) Greaves, R. I. N., 'High vacuum spray freeze drying'.

23. Harper, J. C., and Tappel, A. L., 'Freeze drying of food products'. Advances in Food Research, Volume VII, 172–232 (Academic Press: 1957).

24. Cotson, S., and Smith, D. B. (Eds), 'Freeze drying of foodstuffs—a Symposium'. (Columbine Press: 1963.)

    Particular papers referred to:

    (a) Greaves, R. I. N., 'General principles of freeze drying'.

    (b) Rowe, T. W. G., 'Vacuum systems for freeze drying'.

    (c) Forrest, J. C., 'Development of the accelerated freeze drying process'.

    (d) Walker, B. C., 'Problems of heat transfer in the freeze drying process'.

    (e) Decareau, R. V., 'Microwave freeze drying'.

    (f) Rowe, T. W. G., Achucarro, J. L., and Drummond Smith, B., 'Factors affecting the economy of the freeze drying process'.

    (g) Rolfe, E., 'The freeze-drying of fish and meat'.

    (h) Petersen, E. E., 'The Atlas AFD equipment'.

    (i) Woodward, E. A., and Mason, P. B., 'The Mitchell freeze drying plant'.

    (j) Ward, K., and Thompson, H. F., 'Vickers AFD plant and equipment'.

    (k) Dalgleish, J. M., 'Leybold continuous plant and equipment'.

    (l) Smith, D. B.. 'Commercial equipment in the United States'.

25. Tressler, D. K., and Evers, C. F., 'The Freezing Preservation of Food'. (AVI: 1957.)

26. Powers, M. J., and Miller, W. J., 'Frozen concentrated apple segments'. CSIRO Food Research Quarterly, **31**, 76–78 (1971).

27. Knipschildt, M. E., 'Recent developments in milk drying techniques'. J. Soc. Dairy Tech., **22**(4), 201–216 (1969).

28. Jensen, J. D., 'Methods of instantizing powders for the preparation of food drinks'. Mfg. Confect., **53**(10), 47–56 (1973).

29. Jensen, J. D., 'Agglomerating, instantizing, and spray drying'. Fd Technol., Champaign, **29**(6), 60–71 (1975).

CHAPTER 14

FREEZING

14.1. INTRODUCTION AND DEFINITIONS

From time immemorial food has been preserved by freezing in localities which have a sufficiently low ambient temperature (weather freezing). Iced confections, produced from naturally occurring snow and ice, have been available from antiquity and in the Andes of South America, potato tubers were weather frozen as a preparatory operation in the traditional manufacture of a dried potato product. The second half of the nineteenth century saw the development of reliable mechanical refrigeration equipment and the foundation of the present day cold storage and frozen food industries. The increasing impact of the freezing industry on United Kingdom eating habits can be clearly seen in Table 14.1.

The earliest freezing processes, known as 'sharp freezing', involved placing food in refrigerated rooms, usually with natural air circulation. Fish, meat, poultry, eggs and fruit for jam manufacture were frozen in this way. Vegetable freezing developed after 1930,

TABLE 14.1.
Quick-frozen white fish: Production and imports by UK producers[1, 2]

Year	Estimated whole weight of fish used in production (1000 tonnes)	Percentage of total landings
1963	131	16·0
1964	139	16·3
1965	162	17·6
1966	184	20·6
1967	192	21·2
1968	196	20·7
1969	210	22·8
1970	243	26·2
1971	220	24·7
1972	242	28·1
1973	253	27·6
1974	240	27·0

360

following the work of, among others, Clarence Birdseye. This indicated that the rate of freezing influenced the quality of the thawed product and led to rapid freezing to attain a high quality product and to the use of the term 'quick freezing'. More recent work has indicated that food quality is not always improved by an increase in freezing rate;[3] indeed very rapid freezing (say by immersion in liquefied gases at about $-200\,°C$) can set up disruptive stresses in the frozen material, leading even to shattering. Nevertheless, the prediction and control of freezing time remain matters of importance, not only because of quality considerations, but also because the freezing time controls the throughput possible with a given freezing plant and therefore the economics of the freezing process.

The definition of the term 'freezing time' presents some difficulty. Two instants need to be defined, the instant that the freezing time starts and the instant that it stops. Unfortunately freezing will occur at different rates at different points in the piece or package of food. Freezing will be faster at some point on the surface. In the body of the piece or package will be located a point which cools the slowest. This is known as the thermal centre and measurements of temperature histories during freezing are normally made at this point. The highest temperature at which ice crystals have a stable existence in a food material is conventionally known as the 'freezing point' of that material and the formation of the first ice crystals at the surface of the body being frozen can be utilised as signalling the start of the 'freezing time'. However, because of the nature of foodstuffs and the presence of water-soluble constituents, all of the water present does not solidify at this temperature. Under equilibrium conditions and at a temperature just below the freezing point, a certain fraction of the water present remains in a fluid phase. This fraction falls when the temperature is lowered and eutectic mixtures may separate from the unfrozen fluid, but unfrozen water is still present even at comparatively low temperatures. Thus it is not possible to define a clear endpoint to the freezing process. There are two approaches to a practical definition of freezing time, one relevant to the quality of the product and the other to the throughput of the freezing plant.

First, the freezing time may be defined as that time during which the majority of the ice is formed in the body. Thus the International Institute of Refrigeration[4] defines the 'nominal freezing time' to be the time elapsing from the instant the surface of a body reaches $0\,°C$ to the instant that the thermal centre reaches a temperature $10\,°C$ colder than the temperature of initial ice formation at that point. While it might be objected that ice formation will not occur until the surface temperature of the body has fallen below $0\,°C$, the difference in time involved is probably too small to be of importance. The significance of taking the end point of the freezing process as the achievement of a temperature ten degrees below the freezing point at the thermal centre is clear from Fig. 14.1, which shows that for a typical food product, virtually the whole of the ice formation will have occurred by that time. Because we are considering here the time during which the majority of the ice is formed, this definition may be used in circumstances where the influence of freezing rate on quality is under consideration.

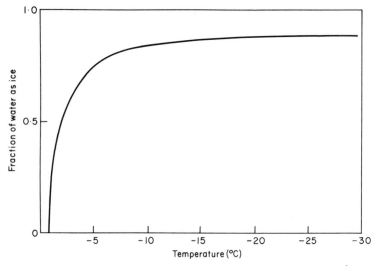

FIG. 14.1.   The ice content of beef muscle (74·5 % water) after Riedel.[5]

On the other hand, the processor will require to know the total time that an item will remain in the freezing plant. For this reason the 'effective freezing time' (t_e) has been defined[4] as the time to lower the temperature of the product from its initial average value to a given value at the thermal centre. The final centre temperature taken will, of course, be that at which it is desired to remove the product from the freezer and statements of the effective freezing time are meaningless unless the initial and final conditions are clearly specified.

There are alternative, though unsatisfactory, definitions of freezing time. If a temperature history is measured at the thermal centre of a body cooling from above its freezing point to below, a curve as in Fig. 14.2 results. There is quite a sharp 'knee' in the vicinity of the freezing point (θ_1) of the body and while before this point the temperature changes slowly, afterwards there is a rapid fall. Many workers have taken two arbitrary temperatures, one slightly above and the other below the freezing point, and treated the time to cool through this temperature range at the thermal centre as a measure of the freezing time of the body. The term 'period of thermal arrest' has been used for this time, since the temperature changes only slowly with time during the period. Such a definition is unsatisfactory for a number of reasons. First the temperature limits are specified arbitrarily and a wide variety of intervals have been chosen by different workers.[6] Secondly, as Long[7] has shown, the period of thermal arrest, in any

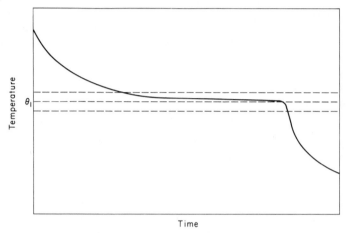

FIG. 14.2.   Typical temperature history at the thermal centre during the freezing of a food body (diagrammatic).

instance, is a function of the initial temperature of the body, reducing with rise of initial temperature. And finally, as may be seen by reference to Fig. 14.12, by the time the temperature at the thermal centre approaches anywhere near the freezing point, ice formation can have advanced well into the body.

14.2.   THE ESTIMATION OF FREEZING TIMES

Calculations involving unsteady state conduction heat transfer with change of phase are not easy. However, if it is desired to estimate a freezing time from physical data, rather than determine it experimentally, two approaches are possible. In the first case, a very crude and simple mathematical model is assumed and an equation derived which, while highly approximate, can be used to estimate freezing times in a wide variety of situations. Alternatively, with the advent of modern computer technology, a much more realistic—and consequently complicated—model may be adopted and the differential equations for heat flow solved by numerical, rather than analytical, methods. While such an approach can be more accurate, the results obtained relate only to the data included in the calculation and so will be of specific, rather than general, applicability.

Formulae for estimating freezing times are usually based on the assumption that the body to be frozen is initially at a uniform temperature and is cooled by a constant temperature medium, there being a uniform and constant heat transfer coefficient between the surface of the body and the cooling medium. It is also assumed that the material of the body has a constant thermal conductivity and specific heat (different for the frozen and unfrozen states), a density which does not vary with temperature or alter during the freezing process and a definite freezing point at which all the latent heat of fusion is liberated. This last assumption enables freezing to be divided into three processes: *precooling* of the unfrozen material, *freezing* proper and cooling the frozen material to its final state (*tempering*). If the body to be frozen is initially at its freezing point there is no pre-cooling period, hence no heat flow in the unfrozen material, and calculation of its freezing time is comparatively simple. Further simplification occurs if the material at the thermal centre at the end of the freezing process is assumed to be frozen, but still at its freezing point. The freezing time calculated on these assumptions may be termed the 'calculated freezing time' (t_f). The effective freezing time can be estimated from the calculated freezing time by applying corrections to allow for the precooling and tempering periods.

Formulae for the calculated freezing time can be simplified by making use of three dimensionless groups. Two of these, the Biot (Bi) and Fourier (Fo) Numbers, are commonly used for unsteady state heat transfer involving thermal conduction (see Appendix II). The third group is:

$$\frac{L}{c\Delta\theta}$$

where L = the latent heat of fusion of the material, c = its specific heat in the frozen state, $\Delta\theta$ = the difference between the freezing point of the material and the temperature of the cooling medium.

Russian workers have called this group the 'Kossovitch Number' (Ko). This terminology will be adopted here.

In calculating the Biot and Fourier numbers, in this instance, the characteristic dimension (l) is the shortest distance from the thermal centre to the surface of the body being frozen, the time is the calculated freezing time and the thermal constants used are those for the frozen material.

The freezing of an infinite slab of material initially at its freezing point (*i.e.* a block of infinite length, breadth and uniform thickness $2l$) by cooling its exposed surfaces, there being an infinite surface heat transfer coefficient, is one of the few cases for which, making the assumptions outlined above, an exact formal closed solution to the equation of conduction of heat has been obtained. This solution, due to Stefan,[8] yields the relationship:

$$\left(\frac{\pi}{4Fo}\right)^{1/2} \exp\left\{\frac{1}{4Fo}\right\} \mathrm{erf}\left\{\frac{1}{(4Fo)^{1/2}}\right\} = \frac{1}{Ko} \qquad (14.1)$$

where $\mathrm{erf}\,(x) = \dfrac{2}{(\pi)^{1/2}} \displaystyle\int_0^x \exp\,(-x^2)\,\mathrm{d}x$ and is known as the error function.

Expanding the reciprocal of the left hand side of equation (14.1) as a power series:

$$2Fo\left\{1 - \frac{1}{6Fo} + \frac{1}{90Fo^2} - \ldots\right\} = Ko \qquad (14.2)$$

so for large values of Fo

$$2Fo = Ko \qquad (14.3)$$

This approximation is often acceptable, having regard to the simplifying assumptions previously made. For instance, the values of the Fourier numbers calculated from equations (14.1) and (14.3) for peas frozen by a medium at $-32\,^\circ\mathrm{C}$ differ by 7%. If the cooling medium temperature or the moisture content of the food (on which the value of the ratio L/c largely depends) is lower, the error in this approximation will be larger, and *vice versa*.

Equation (14.3) can also be deduced by making an interesting physical approximation. Let the freezing point of the material be θ_1 and the temperature of the cooling medium θ_2. At time t, let the thickness of frozen material at each face of the slab be x (see Fig. 14.3). Assume the heat transfer through the frozen material to be the same as would occur if the frozen material were conducting heat in the steady state between static plane surfaces at temperatures θ_1 and θ_2 separated by a distance x. This assumption, known as the quasistatic assumption, should be noted carefully. It implies that the dynamic process of freezing can be approximated by a sequence of instantaneous thermal equilibrium states. With this assumption it is obvious that the heat transferred, per unit area, to one face of the slab in time $\mathrm{d}t$ at time t

$$= \frac{k\,(\theta_1 - \theta_2)\,\mathrm{d}t}{x}$$

where k is the thermal conductivity of the frozen material.

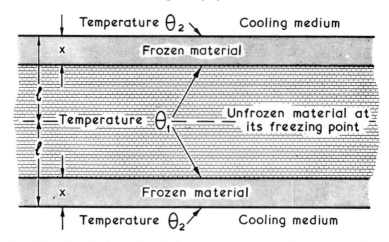

FIG. 14.3.   The infinite slab with infinite surface heat transfer coefficient at time *t* after
the commencement of freezing.

This abstraction of heat will freeze a thickness d*x* of the material
given by:

$$\frac{k\,(\theta_1 - \theta_2)\,\mathrm{d}t}{x} = L\rho\mathrm{d}x \qquad (14.4)$$

where L is the latent heat of the material and ρ its density.

Integrating equation (14.4) and substituting the boundary
conditions:

$$x = 0 \quad \text{at} \quad t = 0$$
$$x = l \quad \text{at} \quad t = t_f$$

one obtains:

$$k\,(\theta_1 - \theta_2)\,t_f = \frac{L\rho l^2}{2} \qquad (14.5)$$

When equation (14.5) is expressed in dimensionless form it reduces at
once to equation (14.3).

The above discussion shows that, in the particular case investigated,
the quasistatic assumption leads to a simple and reasonably accurate
formula for the calculated freezing time. The quasistatic assumption
has been used by Plank[9-11] to obtain similar approximate formulae
in the case of freezing infinite slabs, infinite cylinders and spheres
when there is a finite surface heat transfer coefficient (h) and, making
still further approximations, infinite rods of rectangular cross-section
and rectangular parallelepipeds ('bricks') have been treated. Formal
solutions, similar to equation (14.1), are not available in any of these
cases.

Plank's work may be summarised in the formula

$$t_f = \frac{DL\rho}{\Delta\theta}\left\{\frac{l}{h} + \frac{Gl^2}{k}\right\} \qquad (14.6)$$

or in the dimensionless form:

$$\frac{Fo}{Ko} = D\left\{\frac{1}{Bi} + G\right\} \qquad (14.7)$$

where the constants D and G are determined by the geometry of the body being frozen and the other symbols are as previously defined. G takes the value $\frac{1}{2}$ for the infinite slab, infinite cylinder and sphere. The values of G calculated from Plank's expressions for an infinite rod of

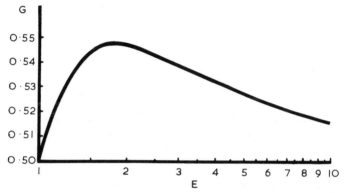

FIG. 14.4. The values of the constant G for a rod of infinite length with rectangular cross-section $2l \times 2El$.[12]

rectangular section and a brick can be read from Figs. 14.4 and 14.5 respectively. In view of the crudity of Plank's assumptions it is questionable if these values differ significantly from $\frac{1}{2}$.

The constant D is given by

$$D = \frac{v}{al}$$

where v = the volume of the body, and a = the area of its cooled surface.

For the infinite slab, infinite cylinder and sphere respectively, D takes the values 1, $\frac{1}{2}$ and $\frac{1}{3}$.

In the practical application of equation (14.6) it is often difficult to decide on an appropriate value for the heat transfer coefficient h. An indication of the size of this coefficient may be obtained from Fig. 14.6

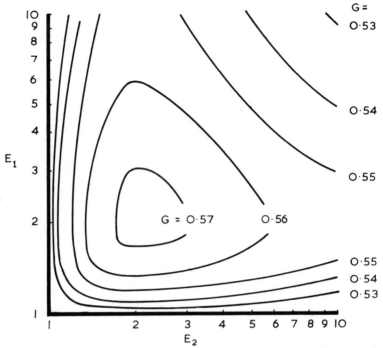

FIG. 14.5.   The values of the constant G for a brick-shaped body $2l \times 2E_1l \times 2E_2l$.[12]

but few measurements of this quantity are reported in the literature and, unfortunately, most of those are derived from measured freezing times by arbitrarily assuming the validity of an expression relating freezing time and heat transfer coefficient. For the blast freezing of unpackaged food, heat transfer coefficients can be calculated from standard formulae (see Appendix II).

It is also necessary to select average values of the specific heat and thermal conductivity of the frozen material, as well as adopting a value for the latent heat of fusion to be used in equation (14.6). While data for the enthalpy of foods in the freezing zone is available (*e.g.* Riedel[5]), the simple model assumed here for calculation divides the enthalpy change experienced by a food in cooling from marginally above its freezing point to some arbitrary lower temperature into a latent heat of fusion given out at the freezing point and a loss of sensible heat proportional to the temperature drop thereafter. This division, and the latent and specific heats that result from it, must be somewhat arbitrary. For rough work, a latent heat equal to

$$3 \cdot 3\, M\, \text{kJ/kg}$$

and a specific heat capacity equal to

$$\frac{M}{80} + 0.84 \, \text{kJ/kg}$$

may be adopted, where M is the percentage by weight of water in the foodstuff (wet weight basis).

Only scattered information is available concerning ways of allowing for the precooling and tempering stages when estimating the

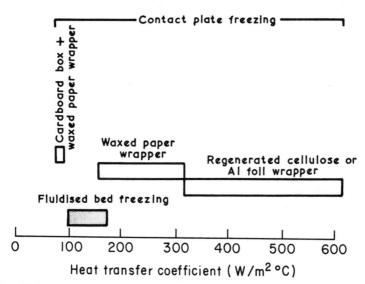

FIG. 14.6. Chart indicating the magnitude of the heat transfer coefficients in contact plate and fluidised bed freezing and the effect of the packaging material.[15, 16]

effective freezing time. One suggested method[13, 14] is to modify equation (14.6) by replacing the latent heat, L, by the enthalpy change at the thermal centre over the entire process. A time t'_f is then calculated from this modified equation and the effective freezing time estimated by:

$$t_e = t'_f \, (1 + 0.0081 \, \Delta\theta_p)$$

where $\Delta\theta_p$ °C is the temperature difference between the initial temperature and the freezing point of the food.

While the above method may be suitable for cases where the tempering period is comparatively short it is likely to underestimate the duration of a process where the food is cooled considerably below its freezing point. If the food body is in the form of an infinite slab,

Rutov[17] estimates the duration (t_t) of the tempering process to be given by:

$$\frac{Kt_t}{l^2} = \frac{8n}{\pi^2}\left\{\ln\left(\frac{\Delta\theta}{\Delta\theta_t}\right) - 0.21\right\}\left\{\frac{1}{Bi} + \frac{1}{2}\right\} \qquad (14.8)$$

where $\Delta\theta_t$ = the difference between the temperature at the thermal centre at the end of the process and the temperature of the cooling medium and $n = 1.03$–1.06 for quick freezing and 1.16 for slow freezing. K is the thermal diffusivity of the frozen material, therefore the expression on the left hand side of equation (14.8) is the Fourier Number for the tempering period.

14.3. FREEZING EQUIPMENT

14.3.1. FREEZING BY CONTACT WITH A COOLED SOLID

The plate contact freezer invented by Birdseye is, with some modification, still used extensively today. Freezers of this type consist of a series of flat hollow refrigerated metal plates. The plates are mounted parallel to each other and may be either horizontal or vertical. The spaces between the plates are variable, the plates being opened out for loading and, prior to the freezing operation, closed so that the surface of the plates is in intimate contact with the packaged or unpackaged food. Clearly the frozen product is in the form of parallel sided blocks and, during the freezing process, heat flow is perpendicular to the faces of the plates. Thus freezing times can be calculated assuming that the material between the plates forms part of an infinite slab with cooled faces.

Freezers with horizontal plates may be used for processing foods in rectangular cartons (see Fig. 14.7). To facilitate batch loading, these packs are normally placed in aluminium freezing trays dimensioned to utilise the plate area efficiently. After loading, the plates are closed by an hydraulic ram operating either on the top (as shown) or on the base of the stack of plates. A moderate pressure (of the order of 10–$30\,\text{kN/m}^2$) is maintained between the plates and the package surfaces during freezing to promote good face to face contact. Spacers, fractionally thinner than the cartons, are often set between the plates to prevent packages being crushed should the plates close unevenly.

Units such as this may also be adapted to continuous operation. In this case the entire plate stack is indexed, layer by layer, past loading and unloading devices which accept packages off a conveyor from a continuous filling line and reject them, when frozen, to an output conveyor. Only two plates are separated at a time, while the packages between them are level with the loading/unloading devices. Machines of this type are used, for instance, in the hardening of ice cream blocks. Ice cream is initially frozen in a scraped surface heat exchanger (see Fig. 9·9), which itself constitutes another class of continuous freezer where heat is transferred by contact with a cooled solid (the heat

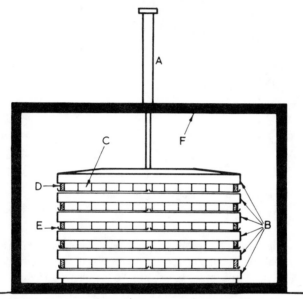

FIG. 14.7. Diagrammatic view of a horizontal plate freezer. A, ram for raising and lowering the freezer plates; B, hollow refrigerated freezer plates; C, food packages; D, spacer bar; E, freezing tray; F, insulated enclosure.

transfer tube). The vigorous mixing of the fluid being frozen allows a rapid heat removal, but the final product must be sufficiently plastic to flow from the machine and be formed into the required product shapes. Freezing then continues to harden these products, either in a plate freezer as described above or in an air blast freezer (see Section 14.3.3).

Vertical plate freezers are well suited to freezing unpackaged deformable materials such as fish, meat and offal and have been used principally for freezing whole fish at sea. The product is fed directly between the vertical plates (see Fig. 14.8) to form blocks which may be compacted further by closing the plates a little on to limit stops prior to freezing. At the end of the freezing process the plates are heated

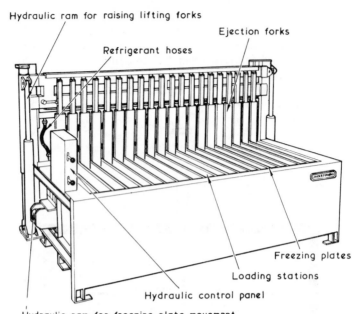

Hydraulic ram for raising lifting forks

Ejection forks

Refrigerant hoses

Freezing plates

Loading stations

Hydraulic control panel

Hydraulic ram, for freezing plate movement

FIG. 14.8.   A 'Jackstone' vertical plate-contact freezer. (Courtesy of Jackstone Froster Ltd.)

both to release the frozen block and to defrost and clean the plate surfaces before the next freezing cycle. It is important that the refrigeration circuit be designed to give a quick defrost, say within $1\frac{1}{2}$ min, to minimise reheating of the frozen product.

For efficient operation, the heat transfer coefficient between the surface of the food and the cooling medium in a plate freezer must be both high and uniform. These conditions will be achieved if packages are completely filled with food (so that the latter is in good contact with the inner faces of the packaging material), if the packages are in uniform contact with plates which are free from any ice or other deposit and if the plates themselves are designed for a rapid and uniform exchange of heat. The introduction of plates made from aluminium alloy extrusions has considerably improved the performance of plate contact freezers.

14.3.2. FREEZING BY CONTACT WITH A COOLED LIQUID

In theory, the freezing of solid foods by immersion in a cooled liquid has three advantages over plate contact freezing. High heat transfer coefficients can be developed between the solid and liquid, bodies of irregular shape can be frozen as easily as rectangular blocks and individual food items can be frozen separately rather than compacted together in a block. The production of individually quick frozen (IQF) food materials is advantageous since it enables individual items or portions of food to be dispensed from a pack, the remaining material being retained in the package and stored until required. If unpackaged foods are to be frozen by immersion, the heat transfer fluid must be edible and acceptable as a contaminant to the product.

In the early days of freezing, salt brines and syrups were used for immersion freezing, or such materials were sprayed directly on to the foods to freeze them. The difficulties encountered, however, led to the virtual abandonment of the process. However, with the recent development of a much wider range of packaging materials, there has been a re-awakened interest in the method, since the problems of cross contamination of food and coolant are overcome and also both solid and liquid foods can be processed. Of course, there is the problem of coolant remaining on the package after the process is over (unless the coolant is volatile—alcohol was used in one process), but this can usually be overcome satisfactorily by rinsing the package with water.

Today canned citrus juice concentrate is frozen by immersion. Also large poultry carcasses are closely wrapped in plastic film and frozen in brine or glycol to achieve rapid freezing of their surface flesh. This produces a crust of small, highly reflective ice crystals (see Section 9.6) which give that whiter appearance to the frozen carcase which is desired by the consumer. After this process the remainder of the freezing process is usually conducted in a blast freezer. In New Zealand an immersion freezing system has been developed for packaged edible offal.[18]

14.3.3. FREEZING BY CONTACT WITH A COOLED GAS

Freezing food in cold air, a technique practised from the earliest days of food freezing, has many of the advantages of immersion freezing. Foods of irregular shape can be frozen and IQF products produced. In addition the problem of transfer of material between the fluid cooling medium and the food is limited to the evaporation of moisture from unpackaged products. However, the heat transfer coefficients developed at the surface of foods in forced air circulation freezers ('blast freezers') are lower than can be obtained in liquid immersion freezing. Nevertheless, because of their other advantages, blast freezers are extensively used in the food freezing industry.

Blast freezers may either operate batchwise or continuously. Air temperatures are generally in the region -20 to $-40\,^{\circ}$C and air velocities from 0·5 to 18 m/s have been reported.[3] A velocity of 6 m/s has been recommended as suitable for freezing unpackaged whole fish.[19] The higher the air velocity, of course, the greater is the heat transfer coefficient between the moving air and the solid body (see Appendix II). However, a reduction in this heat transfer coefficient does not result in a proportional decrease in freezing time owing to the thermal resistance of any packaging materials and the effect of heat transfer by conduction within the freezing food. Additionally, at the higher velocities, the energy dissipation of the fans moving the air provides a not inconsiderable fraction of the load on the refrigerator. Therefore the cost of providing air circulation above a certain velocity in any given instance will not be economically justifiable.

Batch blast freezers are only used where the throughput of material is low. Such a unit would consist of a well-insulated chamber equipped with an air cooler and suitable fans. The product is usually loaded by hand on to trolley mounted trays, and guide rails are provided within the chamber to locate the trolley in the air stream and facilitate loading the chamber. To obtain uniform cooling, the air is ducted so that it flows evenly over all the food items. It is therefore most undesirable to load a partially filled trolley into the freezer, since this could lead to a redistribution of the air flow, with air bypassing the material to be frozen by flowing preferentially through the empty spaces in the trolley. Similarly, if the trolley used is too small and does not fill the space available in the chamber, air will again bypass the load, this time by flowing round the trolley.

Continuous air blast freezers are either (a) built on the principle of a tunnel through which the food is transported, either on trolleys, by conveyor or, in the case of carcase meat, on hooks suspended from a track, or (b) utilise the fluidised bed principle. The air in tunnel freezers using trolleys can either flow parallel to the direction of product movement or perpendicular to it ('cross flow'). The second system is perhaps more frequently used today. In this system a series of unit coolers, comprising refrigerated air coolers, fans and associated duct-work, are mounted side-by-side along the length of the tunnel. The unit coolers provide a blast of cold air through adjacent sections of the tunnel and perpendicular to the direction of product movement. This arrangement has a number of advantages. For instance, to load and unload the tunnel, openings must be provided at either end. The cross flow system allows the pressures to be balanced at these points to minimise air exchange between inside and outside the tunnel. Again, the thermal conditions can be controlled in each zone to maintain a high humidity in the circulating air to minimise evaporation from the product. Such evaporation, if excessive, can lead to a condition of surface dehydration known as 'freezer burn'.

Clearly, if food is to be frozen on a travelling conveyor belt, rather than on trays stacked in trolleys, a considerable length of conveyor must be accommodated within the insulated enclosure. Figure 14.9 shows a unit where a very economical use of factory floor-space is achieved by employing a flexible stainless steel link conveyor belt wound in vertical helices.

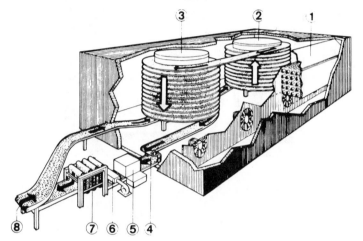

Fig. 14.9. Diagram of the Frigoscandia GyroFreeze system showing the main features: (1) cooling coil with cover in open position with fans below; (2) first drum where the belt runs upwards; (3) second drum with belt running downwards; (4) discharge; (5) automatic belt washing station; (6) dryer fan; (7) belt tension control and take-up; (8) turn roller. Products are loaded onto the belt on the free run after this roller.

Indeed, the design of continuous air-blast freezers largely reduces to a problem of materials handling, *i.e.* packing the product-supporting conveyors or trays in such a way that a high product throughput can be achieved for a modest utilisation of factory floor space. Plant designers continually offer more elegant solutions to this practical problem. Another problem in blast freezers where, for instance, unpackaged sliced vegetables are being frozen on a moving conveyor is that items will freeze both to each other and to the conveyor. They must be broken apart to produce an IQF product and the conveyor must be cleaned before reloading, as in Fig. 14.9. This difficulty is overcome in the fluidised bed freezer.

Fluidised bed freezers consist of a trough with a perforated bottom through which refrigerated air is blown vertically upwards (see Fig. 14.10). The air velocity is such that when small particulate food bodies of fairly uniform size, *e.g.* peas, Brussels sprouts, berry fruits or even chips (French fried potatoes), are fed into the trough they form a fluidised bed (see Section 13.3.1.6). Froude numbers (see Appendix I) between about 65 and 180 are developed in commercial units, though

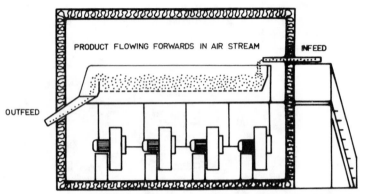

FIG. 14.10.   Diagrammatic longitudinal section of a fluidised bed freezer. (By courtesy of Frigoscandia Ltd.)

100–120 is the normal range. The feed is at one end of the trough and the product is discharged over a weir at the other end to give a bed depth of the order of 15 cm. The feed rate is adjusted so that the dwell time of individual pieces in the fluidised bed is sufficient to allow proper freezing. In cases where the product to be frozen is not of ideal shape for fluidisation, *i.e.* deviates widely from that of a small sphere, the bed may be operated at the state of incipient fluidisation with only slight bed expansion (see Appendix I.2) and in place of a stationary perforated base to the fluidising trough, a travelling perforated belt is used, thus imparting forward motion to the product above.

One of the major advantages of fluidised bed freezers is their compact size. This compactness is possible since the surface heat transfer coefficient developed in them is comparatively high and a large total surface of particles exists in the bed. For instance, in a fluidised bed of peas 14 cm deep, the product surface is 60–70 times the superficial area of the freezing trough. Since the food items are in constant motion and are surrounded and supported by air, they freeze separately to give a free-flowing product. In addition, any water remaining on the items from earlier preparative and cleaning processes is spread over their surfaces by the air stream and gives a glazing of ice, protecting the food itself from 'freezer burn'.

In continuous blast freezers, since water will evaporate from unpackaged food and deposit as frost on the refrigeration units, the latter must be defrosted periodically if their efficiency is to be maintained. Three methods are currently in use. Firstly the unit may be designed to accommodate the frost build-up in the course of one shift of operation and be defrosted in the cleaning period between shifts. Secondly, since the cooling/air circulating system is frequently split into a number of parallel units (see Fig. 14.10), these may be so sized that one unit can be taken out of operation and defrosted while the cooling duty is shared between the others. Thus sequential defrosting permits the cooling efficiency to be maintained indefinitely. Of course, in fluidised bed freezers, the fluidising air supply must be maintained during this process. With either method of defrosting, the frost-loaded cooling surface may be heated (a) electrically, (b) by water sprays or (c) in the case of those units cooled by direct expansion of liquid refrigerant, by discharging the hot refrigerant gases from the refrigeration compressor through the cooling coils. An alternative procedure, used in some other fluidised bed freezers, is to spray the evaporator coils of the refrigerator continuously with propylene or ethylene glycol. The water condensed at the evaporator dissolves in the glycol and the water-diluted glycol runs off the coils to a sump from where a pump recirculates it to the sprays. To maintain the glycol solution at the strength necessary to prevent it freezing, a small amount of the solution is bled from the tank and circulated through a concentration system where it is stripped of dissolved water.

14.3.4. TWO-PHASE FREEZING SYSTEMS

A variety of freezing systems have been designed in which the cooling medium is a subliming solid (*e.g.* solid carbon dioxide) or a boiling liquid (*e.g.* liquid nitrogen). In the majority of such systems the refrigerating effect is not provided by an on-site refrigerator, but by the heat transfer agent itself as a consequence of its phase change. The gases resulting from this phase change are vented to the atmosphere. These systems are known as cryogenic freezers and the materials providing the refrigeration as cryogens.

Carbon dioxide is most conveniently handled as a liquid under pressure. Sprayed through nozzles to atmospheric pressure it gives a mixture of cold gaseous carbon dioxide and carbon dioxide snow (solid) which can be contacted with the food to be frozen. The system can either be used to boost the capacity of conventional blast freezing lines at peak processing periods or provide the sole cooling for a freezing plant.[20]

The boiling point of liquid nitrogen ($-196\,°C$ at atmospheric pressure) is such that food may be frozen at very high rates. This in turn has made possible improvements in the quality of products which did not freeze well by conventional methods (*e.g.* mushrooms and many sea-foods) and, coupled with the low water holding capacity of the very cold gas, to a reduction in loss of product weight by evaporation of water during freezing. The cost of liquid nitrogen freezing is very dependent on the cost of the gas itself, since the capital cost of the equipment used is comparatively low. The price paid for liquid nitrogen is in turn dependent on the quantity used and the expense of bringing it from the liquefaction plant to the food factory. At present the process is more expensive than conventional freezing but some of the increased cost can be set against the better price obtainable for products of high quality. In the case of expensive products, some of the cost of liquid nitrogen freezing can be justified by the resulting reduction in evaporation losses during freezing.

The use of liquid nitrogen simply as an immersion medium is disadvantageous from two points of view. The rate of cooling of a body plunged into the liquid cannot be controlled, and efficient use is not made of the refrigerating capacity of the medium. The latent heat of evaporation of liquid nitrogen at $-196\,°C$ is $200\,kJ/kg$. Gaseous nitrogen warming at constant pressure from this temperature to $-18\,°C$ absorbs a further $209\,kJ/kg$. Commercial plant, as shown diagrammatically in Fig. 14.11, therefore makes extensive use of the refrigerating capacity of the nitrogen gas. The liquid nitrogen, if applied directly to the food, is sprayed on at a controlled rate to control the rate of freezing.

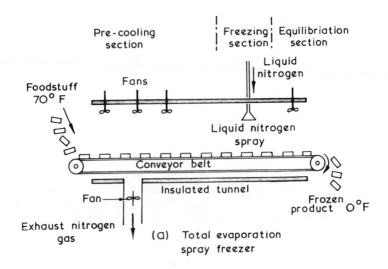

(a) Total evaporation spray freezer

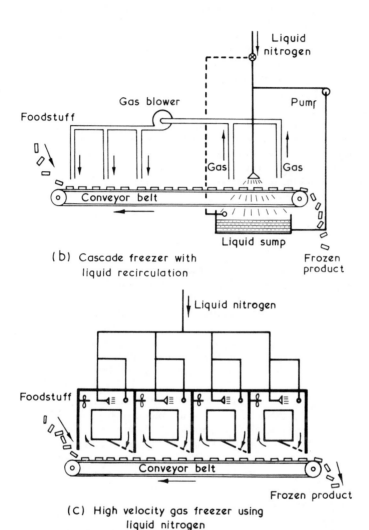

(b) Cascade freezer with liquid recirculation

(C) High velocity gas freezer using liquid nitrogen

FIG. 14.11. Three methods of efficiently using the refrigerating power of liquid nitrogen. In method (a) liquid nitrogen is sprayed directly onto the food and evaporates completely, the resultant cold gas moving to left and right to effect further cooling. Method (b) is similar, but an excess of liquid nitrogen is sprayed over the food and recirculated. Method (c) uses the liquid nitrogen to cool down one or more chambers in which the temperature is thermostatically controlled, but does not contact the food. (By courtesy of B.O.C.)

The Du Pont company have developed a freezing technique based on 'Freon 12' (dichlorodifluoromethane). This material boils at $-30\,°C$ at atmospheric pressure and is an excellent heat transfer medium. Food may be frozen by immersion in the liquid or by having the liquid sprayed onto its surface. Since the gas is expensive, it must be recovered. It is therefore recondensed on a refrigerated surface below its boiling point and re-cycled. Because the gas has a high density, the input conveyor, which has closed sides, is angled steeply down into the enclosed freezing zone and the output conveyor, similarly, mounts upwards. Thus the heavy Freon vapours are retained in the unit and Freon losses are reduced to a few percent of the product weight. Because the Freon contacts the food, however, questions of consumer safety arise and the use of this system is not universally approved.

14.4   THAWING

While the process of thawing is the converse of that of freezing, there are important differences. If a body is to be thawed as a piece, the heat of fusion must be conducted in through a layer of unfrozen material, whilst in freezing it was conducted out through a frozen layer. The thermal conductivity of water is about a quarter that of ice, the thermal diffusivity as low as one eighth. Again the temperature difference between the heating medium and product freezing point is much restricted in thawing because of the requirement not to heat damage the product.

In Fig. 14.12, computed temperature profiles are compared for the freezing and thawing of a 5 cm thick block of fish fillets. Not only should the considerable difference in processing time be observed but also that during freezing the bulk of the material spends about a quarter of an hour in the region of $-5\,°C$ to $-1\,°C$ (where the material is most at risk from damage by freeze-concentrated solutes) while in thawing this time extends to something over 2 h. Thus thawing presents its special problems.

Thawing on an industrial scale is necessary where bulk-frozen foods (*e.g.* cartons of boneless beef or frozen eviscerated whole fish) are to be thawed for subsequent manufacturing operations. Sometimes complete thawing is unnecessary, since all that is required is to soften the frozen material so that it can be cut with a guillotine. In this case the problems encountered are less severe since the process can be conducted in a temperature range where there is sufficient ice remaining in the material to give it a comparatively high thermal diffusivity. Thawing is also of interest in the field of catering, where the

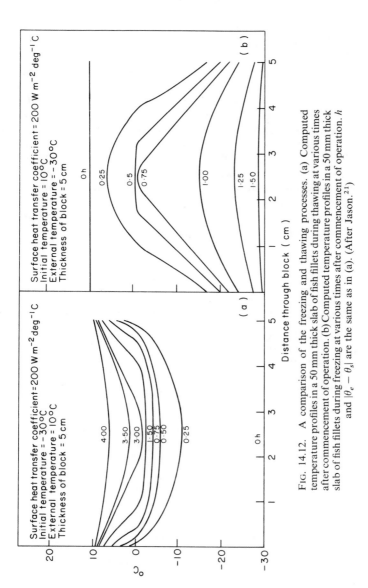

FIG. 14.12. A comparison of the freezing and thawing processes. (a) Computed temperature profiles in a 50 mm thick slab of fish fillets during thawing at various times after commencement of operation. (b) Computed temperature profiles in a 50 mm thick slab of fish fillets during freezing at various times after commencement of operation. h and $|\theta_e - \theta_s|$ are the same as in (a). (After Jason.[21])

freezing of cooked meals and meal components and their thawing and reheating for serving is being developed. This system is particularly suitable for institutional or hospital use and differs from industrial thawing in that small scale rapid versatile units are required which will raise the temperature of the food to that required for serving.

Thawing equipment has been constructed using warm air blasts, immersion of the frozen product in water or treatment of its surface with vacuum steam (a saturated steam treatment carried out in a vacuum chamber maintained at, say, $3 \, kN/m^2$ so that the saturation temperature of the steam is only $20 \, °C$). Dielectric, microwave and resistance heating (see Chapter 10) have also been investigated. The first of these is expensive, but has found application in the thawing of bread. The second has limited applicability, due to the limited depth of penetration of microwaves into foods between $-5°C$ and $-1°C$ (only a few millimetres) and the last method, which depends on the overlapping of high product thermal diffusivity below $-10°C$ and steadily increasing electrical conductivity above this temperature, has not yet achieved commercial exploitation.[21]

REFERENCES

1. Anon., 20th Annual Report of The White Fish Authority. (H.M.S.O.: 1971).
2. Anon., 24th Annual Report of The White Fish Authority. (H.M.S.O.: 1975).
3. Fennema, O., and Powrie, W. D., 'Fundamentals of Low Temperature Food Preservation', Advances in Food Research, 13, 220 (1964).
4. Anon., Recommendations for the Processing and Handling of Frozen Foods, 2nd ed. 14–16. (I.I.R. Paris: 1972).
5. Riedel, K., Kältetechnik, 9(2), 38 DKV Arbeitsblatt 8–11 (1957).
6. Cowell, N. D., in Cutting, C. L. (Ed.) Meat Freezing—Why and How? M.R.I. Symposium No. 3, 14.1. (M.R.I., Bristol: 1974).
7. Long, R. A. K., J. Sci. Fd Agric., 6, 621 (1955).
8. Stefan, J., Ann. Phys. u. Chem., 42, 269 (1891).
9. Plank, R., Zeitschrift für die gesamte Kälte-Industrie, H6, 109 (1913).
10. Plank, R., Zeitschrift für die gesamte Kälte-Industrie, H4, 39 (1932).
11. Plank, R., Zeitschrift für die gesamte Kälte-Industrie, R3, H10 (1941).
12. Cowell, N. D., Proc. 12th Int. Cong. Refrig., 2, 677 (1969).
13. Nagaoka, J., Takaji, S., and Hotani, S., Proc. 9th Int. Cong. Refrig., 2, 4–105 (1955).
14. Levy, F. L., Journal of Refrigeration, 1, 55 (1958).
15. Persson, P. O., ASHRAE Journal, 9(6), 42 (1967).
16. Watzinger, A., Kältetechnik, 1, 189 (1949).
17. Rutov, D. G., Actes du VII Congrès International du Froid, 4, 211 (1936).
18. Frazerhurst, L. F., Haughey, D. P., and Wyborn, L. G., Meat Industry Research Institute of New Zealand, Report No. 231 (1971).
19. Anon., 'Quick Freezing of Fish'. Torry Advisory Note No. 27 (H.M.S.O.: undated).
20. Anon., Food Engineering, 43(1), 110 (1971).
21. Jason, A. C., Proceedings of the I.F.S.T., 7(3), 146 (1974). Reprinted as Torry Memoir No. 482.

CHAPTER 15

IRRADIATION

15.1. INTRODUCTION

In 1896, a year after Röntgen discovered X-rays and the same year that Becquerel discovered radioactivity, a paper was published 'On the Question of the Effect of Röntgen Rays on Bacteria and the Possibility of their Eventual Application'.[1] However, early work in this field was handicapped by the low-intensity sources available and it was not until the mid-1940s that high-energy, high-intensity irradiation sources were sufficiently developed to make the irradiation of foods for preservation a feasible process. A considerable literature on food irradiation has accumulated since then, but there is as yet little or no commercialisation of the process—even though irradiation sterilisation of medical supplies is well established.

Most of the irradiation processes suggested for foods can be classed under one of five headings:

(i) Radappertisation—in which a 'commercially sterile' product is produced (*see* Section 11.1).

(ii) Radicidation—in which the treatment is intended to destroy organisms of public health significance—say salmonellas—while not achieving radappertisation.

(iii) Radurisation—in which the treatment is aimed simply at the prolongation of storage life by a general reduction in the level of vegetative bacteria.

(iv) Radiation disinfestation—where the targets are insect pests.

(v) Sprout inhibition in stored vegetables and growth inhibition in mushrooms.

While feasible processes have been developed in all these categories and equipment has been designed for their execution, before such processes can be commercially exploited they must be approved by the government of the manufacturer's country, and preferably by governments internationally, as not rendering the food unwholesome (*see* Section 15.3). Finally they must present a commercially attractive prospect to any intending processor.

To date, a number of irradiated products have been cleared for human consumption in a variety of countries. However, the industrial developments are largely only at the pilot plant stage. A potato irradiation plant was built and operated in Canada after government clearance was given in 1963—but the company went bankrupt in a year. However, potato irradiation on a fairly large scale is being undertaken in Russia[2] and Japan.[3] The radappertisation of feedingstuffs for specified-pathogen-free (SPF) laboratory animals is practised commercially in the UK.[4] Radappertised meat and bread were used by astronauts on the Apollo–Soyuz space flights[5] and in the near future it is to be expected that a number of commercial processes using irradiation treatments, either alone or in combination with other preservation methods, will be in operation.

15.2. ENERGY OF RADIATION

It is a prerequisite of food irradiation that it should in no way affect the fitness of the food for human consumption. This means, at the very least, that the radioactivity of the foodstuff should not be increased appreciably above its natural level. For this reason, the radiations investigated have been confined to electromagnetic waves (X-rays and γ-rays) of limited frequency and beams of electrons (cathode rays and β-rays) of limited energy. High frequency electromagnetic waves, high energy electrons and beams of the heavier atomic particles (such as neutrons) are capable of inducing nuclear transformations in the atoms of the target food, rendering them radioactive.

The energy associated with electrons is measured in electron volts. An electron volt (eV) is the energy acquired by an electron in falling through a potential difference of one volt and

$$1\,\mathrm{eV} \simeq 1{\cdot}6 \times 10^{-19}\,\mathrm{J}$$

The electron volt is small and in practice multiples of the unit are used:

$$1\,\mathrm{keV} = 10^3\,\mathrm{eV}$$
$$1\,\mathrm{MeV} = 10^6\,\mathrm{eV}$$
$$1\,\mathrm{GeV} = 10^9\,\mathrm{eV}$$

The energy of the quantum of electromagnetic energy, *i.e.* a photon, is a function of its frequency. It is also measured in electron volts and is given by the equation

$$E = h\nu$$

where E = photon energy (eV), h = Planck's constant = $4\cdot13\,\mathrm{eV\,s}$, v = frequency (Hertz).

15.3. EFFECTS OF RADIATION

The interactions between an electron and an atom of the target material can differ, depending on the energy exchanged in the event. In low energy encounters, the electron may become captured in the orbital electron shell of the atom, giving a negative ion. Alternatively it may impart some of its energy to the orbital electrons, leaving them in higher energy orbits; the atom is then said to be in an excited state. With higher energy exchange an orbital electron may be ejected from the atom. With higher energies still, the interactions may involve the nucleus and result in the conversion of energy supplied by the electrons into photons (bremsstrahlung).

Photons interact with the target material with similar results. Photons of ultraviolet light are only sufficiently energetic to excite the molecules of foodstuffs. Somewhat higher frequency radiation, with its higher energy photons, can cause ionisation. Photons can be absorbed by an atom, almost all the energy reappearing in the kinetic energy of an ejected electron (the photoelectric effect). With photons of higher energy still the interaction results in both an ejected electron and a photon of lower energy (the Compton effect). Finally, with the highest energies, interactions may take place with the nucleus. Such interactions can take three forms:

(i) A proton or neutron can be ejected from the nucleus, normally giving rise to induced radioactivity in the target material.

(ii) The photon is absorbed and an electron-positron pair created. The positron member of this pair is short lived and rapidly interacts with an electron, both particles disappearing and a further photon, or photons, being emitted.

(iii) The nucleus remains in an excited state after the interaction, subsequently releasing its excess energy by the emission of further photons. This type of interaction does not occur with the atoms forming the common constituents of foods.

From the above discussion it can be seen that irradiation with electrons, *or* photons, sufficiently energetic to cause ionisation but not induced radioactivity, gives rise to a chain of interactions resulting in the creation of chemically reactive ions, excited molecules and free radicals in the target food. The extra energy possessed by the food by virtue of the irradiation can therefore either be absorbed in chemical changes, lost in subsequent radiation from the system or appear as heat energy when the ions are neutralised and excited molecules decay to their ground states.

It is the chemical activity resulting from the irradiation that gives rise to the effects of importance in food technology. Such effects may be advantageous to the preservation of the material; vital processes leading to deterioration in the food itself may be inhibited, contaminating organisms such as bacteria or insects may either be destroyed, or have their reproductive systems impaired. At the same time disadvantageous changes may result. Vitamins may be destroyed or off-flavours develop. When such a broad spectrum of chemical change is induced in a material as complex as a food, there is no certainty that its wholesomeness has not been impaired. Carcinogenic compounds, for instance, could have been formed. For this reason a very substantial international programme of feeding trials on laboratory animals has been initiated and processes are only approved by government agencies when there is good reason to assume that the wholesomeness of the food has not been impaired by irradiation processing.

Although 10 MeV radiation does not produce induced radio-activity in the common atoms present in food, trace elements and rare isotopes can be affected by such radiation. Some of this induced radioactivity is short lived, and it has been calculated[6] that 24 h after such irradiation the increase in radioactivity would not be more than 30 % of the natural radioactivity of the food. With 5 MeV radiation the induced radioactivity is only about one hundredth of this value, and it is considered that the consumption of food irradiated with particles no more energetic than this involves no health hazard.

15.4. DOSIMETRY

The biological effects of ionising radiation depend not only on the energy of the incident radiation but also on the quantity which interacts with unit mass, or volume, of the target material. A unit of quantity, or 'dose', is thus required. The unit currently used for this is the 'rad'. When one rad of radiation has fallen on a body, that body has absorbed energy from the radiation amounting to 10^{-2} J/kg. For food irradiation purposes multiples, such as the Kilorad (krad) and Megarad (Mrad), are employed.

The following show roughly the range of dose requirements: for radappertisation, around 2·5 Mrad; for radicidation, 0·8–1 Mrad; for radurisation, 50–800 krad; for radiation disinfestation, 20–100 krad;

and for sprout inhibition, 5–15 krad. These may be compared with the dose of 500 rad which is sufficient to kill a man. Enzyme systems are even more resistant to radiation than bacterial spores, so enzyme preparations can be irradiation sterilised (*i.e.* radappertised) without being rendered inactive.

Before the introduction of the rad, other units such as the 'röntgen' and 'rep' were in use for specifying the doses given to foods. Doses expressed in these units may be taken to be roughly equal to doses of the same number of rads.

Dose measurements can be made directly in terms of the definition of the rad by calorimetric methods. Such calorimetric methods, however, must be highly sensitive because of the small thermal energies involved (1 Mrad raises the temperature of water only about 2 °C—the low heat dissipation during processing is one of the attractive features of irradiation processing since thermal damage to the foods is avoided). Therefore calorimetric methods are suitable only as primary standards. Secondary standards, normally involving measurements of some chemical change brought about by irradiation, are more simple to operate. The oxidation of ferrous sulphate solution under defined conditions (the Fricke dosimeter) is widely used, the yield being proportional to the dose up to about 40 krad. For higher doses ceric or ceric-cupric sulphate systems may be used.[7] Routine industrial measurements require even simpler devices, and colorimetric methods have been developed to fill this need. Certain dye solutions, coloured plastics and glasses change colour on irradiation. Dyed plastic sheet* has been used as the basis of a routine dosimeter by the UK Atomic Energy Authority. Dyed self-adhesive PVC film labels have been marketed as a 'go/no-go' device for checking that containers have been irradiated, the film changing colour after a certain dose has been received due to the release of hydrochloric acid from the plastic base. For monitoring the radiation received by personnel, a 'film badge' may be used. This uses the fogging of a photographic emulsion in a light-proof package as a measure of the dose of background radiation received. Currently, in the UK, film badges are being replaced by devices incorporating small bags of lithium fluoride. This material exhibits thermoluminescence. That is, irradiation of the material with X- or γ-rays stores energy in the crystal lattice which can subsequently be released as visible light by heating the material, the light emission being a measure of the dose received.

A beam of ionising radiation is attenuated in its passage through material so the dose given to the irradiated food will differ from point

---

* ICI Perspex Red 400.

to point. Measurements of the spatial distribution of radiation dose
are simple if the food irradiated is a fluid or a particulate assembly,
but dosimetry in a solid body, such as a joint of meat, presents greater
problems. In such cases a model may be made in the form of a hollow
shell filled with a fluid, the whole designed to have absorption
characteristics equivalent to those of the original body, and
measurements are carried out within the fluid in this replica.

Using the techniques of dosimetry outlined above, the relative
penetrating power of various radiations can be investigated. This, of

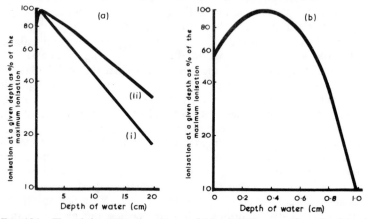

FIG. 15.1. The relative penetrating powers of (a) cobalt-60 γ-rays (from the data of
Jones *et al.*, Brit. J. Radiol., **25**, 302) and (b) 2 MeV electrons (from the data of Trump *et
al.*, J. appl. Phys., **21**, 345).

course, increases with increasing particle energy, but as may be seen in
Fig. 15.1, compared with photons, electrons dissipate their energy in a
thin layer of the target material. Thus electron irradiation is only
suitable for treating small objects or the surface layers of larger ones.
It is also clear that the dose-rate is not strictly exponentially
attenuated. It rises from its surface value to a maximum before
starting to fall. This maximum is the result both of the incident
radiation being scattered through its interaction with the target
material and of the production of secondary radiation in these
interactions. The curve (i) in Fig. 15.1(a) is drawn from data on the
variation in dose along the path of a narrow pencil of radiation. A
broad beam of radiation may be regarded as a bundle of such pencils,
in which case radiation scattered from one pencil reinforces the
ionisation in those which lie near by. This gives rise to the rather less
rapid attenuation in dose rate observed in broad beam irradiation, as
shown by curve (ii) in Fig. 15.1(a).

15.5. IRRADIATION PLANT

In the design of a food irradiation plant, it is necessary to ensure that:

(i)   suitable radiation will be produced at the lowest cost,
(ii) economic use is made of this radiation in treating the food so that a suitable dose distribution and total dose is given to each food item, and
(iii) operating personnel will not be subjected to harmful radiation either during normal operation of the plant or in the event of accidents and breakdowns.

15.5.1. RADIATION SOURCES

Sources suitable for irradiating foods are either made of radioactive materials which in decay emit suitable radiation or they take the form of electron accelerating machines. The accelerated electrons may be used directly or can interact with a suitable target to produce a beam of high-energy photons. Such photons are generally termed X-rays to distinguish them from the photon radiation of radioactive decay (γ-rays). An essential difference between radioactive and machine sources is that a machine can be switched off when not required, while the process of radioactive decay cannot be so arrested. Continuous operation of a radioactive source radiation facility is therefore indicated if the process is to be carried out relatively cheaply.

15.5.1.1. Radioactive sources. The activity of a radioactive source is measured in curies. In a source having a strength of 1 curie (1 Ci), $3 \cdot 7 \times 10^{10}$ atomic disintegrations occur per second. This number is specified since it is, approximately, the number of disintegrations occurring per second in one gram of pure radium. Clearly the effectiveness of a radioactive source in food irradiation depends not only on the number of disintegrations occurring but also on the energy and nature of the particles produced; nevertheless the curie does offer a means of comparing the size of sources constructed using the same radioactive nuclide (*e.g.* ^{60}Co). Sources for experimental work range from a few thousand to a few tens of thousands of curies while for production plants sources in the mega-curie (MCi) range are required.

The instability of the radioactive nucleus results in a steady decline in source activity. It is convenient to specify the rate of decay of a nuclide (that is of a single atom species characterised by specific atomic and mass numbers) by its 'half-life', *i.e.* the period during which one half of the atoms in a given amount of the nuclide undergo radioactive disintegration. Clearly, when a radioactive source is used in irradiation equipment, the source must be progressively renewed if its activity is to be maintained at a reasonably constant level. This renewal is simplified if the source is subdivided into a number of self-contained interchangeable units and if those nuclides in the source which emit useful radiation have reasonably long half-lives. Spent fuel rods removed from power reactors have provided the radiation source for experimental work, but their limited availability and the instability of their activity, due to many of the nuclides present having short half-lives, limits their usefulness.

Cobalt-60 (^{60}Co), which is more generally used, is an artificial isotope produced in relatively large amounts by neutron irradiation of natural cobalt in power reactors. ^{60}Co has a half-life of 5·3 years; sources constructed from this material lose activity at the rate of 1 % per month. In its decay, 1·17 and 1·33 MeV γ-rays and electrons of up to 0·31 MeV are emitted. The latter do not penetrate the protective stainless steel sheath enclosing the material. The γ-rays only, which are little attenuated by the sheath, are thus available for irradiation. ^{60}Co has provided the source of radiation for almost all the large irradiation plants constructed to date. Another radioactive source material, occasionally used, is caesium-137 (^{137}Cs). This can be separated from the fission products of power reactor fuel rods and has a half-life of 30 years, emitting γ-rays of 0·66 MeV.

15.5.1.2. Machine sources. As mentioned earlier, electron accelerating machines can be used as sources of ionising radiation. Such machines consist of two major components, an evacuated accelerating tube and a suitable source of electrical power. There are two main classes of machine. In one a high voltage electrostatic field applied to the accelerating tube accelerates to high energy the low energy electrons from a heated cathode. A variety of methods have been used for producing the accelerating voltage[8] and these devices are under continuous development to reduce costs. In the second class of machine, linear accelerators, the accelerating tube forms a waveguide along which radio frequency electromagnetic radiation (of, say, 10 cm wavelength) passes. By suitably designing the waveguide, it is possible to accelerate the electrons from a cathode axially along the tube in the direction of motion of the travelling waves.

The accelerated electrons may either be used directly for irradiation or converted to the more penetrating X-radiation by interaction with a suitable target. In X-ray machines of a conventional design only a small fraction of energy incident in the electron beam is converted into X-ray energy. The efficiency of conversion rises with the energy of the incident electrons. The German fisheries research vessel—formerly the 'Walther Herwig' (now refitted and re-named the 'Anton Dohrn')—is equipped with a 200 kV X-ray machine for the irradiation of cylindrical containers of fish. The X-ray generator is shown diagrammatically in Fig. 15.2. A cylindrical cathode surrounds a cylindrical water cooled anode and the fish passes along the axis of the system while being irradiated.

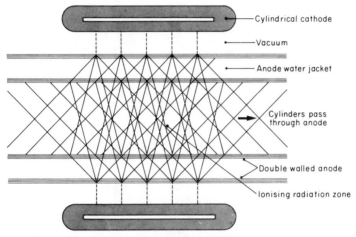

Fig. 15.2. Diagrammatic layout of the cylindrical X-ray tube irradiation source installed in the 'Anton Dohrn'. (From Electronics Today International, January 1973, 66, with permission.)

15.5.2. APPLICATION OF THE RADIATION

Electron beams are only capable of limited penetration into foods, so the material must be presented to the beam in a thin layer if it is to be treated in bulk, or all surfaces must be presented if a surface treatment is desired. Since electrons are charged particles, an electron beam can be deflected by an oscillating magnetic field to scan the material in a direction perpendicular to the direction of motion of the conveyor.

Because of the more penetrating nature of X- or γ-radiation and its progressive absorption throughout items or packages of the target material it is necessary to present this material in different orientations at various stages of the irradiation process to give a reasonably uniform dose distribution throughout the package. Alternatively the material may be surrounded by the radiation source

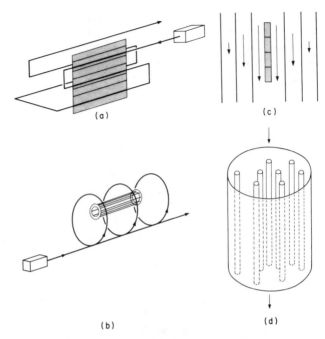

FIG. 15.3.   Source disposition and product movement patterns. (a) A plate source with
packages passing on both sides. A second layer of packages may be used to absorb the
radiation which has penetrated through the inner layer. This second layer may either
form a separate circuit or be an extension of the one flow path. (b) A cage source with
containers moving about it on a 'Ferris Wheel' system. (c) A rod source with particulate
or fluid material flowing past it in annular channels. The rate of flow in each channel is
controlled to regulate the dose given to the material passing through. (d) An array of
rod sources through which particulate or fluid material flows. The strength and
disposition of each rod is so fixed that the dose rate over the cross-section is reasonably
uniform.

as in Fig. 15.2. In order to make the maximum use of the continuous
emission from radioactive sources, it is necessary to box the source in
with target material. Figure 15.3 shows possible product movement
and source disposition patterns.

Another consequence of the continuous activity of radioactive
sources is that input and output storage facilities may have to be
provided so that irradiation can continue when the production and
distribution lines serving the plant are idle (overnight for instance).
Thus to satisfy the technical requirements of the process an elaborate
materials handling system is required, the reliability of which will
largely control the reliability of the whole plant. With machine
sources, the need for input and output storage is eliminated since the

source can be switched off and so a simpler conveying system is adequate.

Finally, if a plant is not completely loaded the distribution of radiation, and therefore the local dose rate, will differ from that in normal operation. Higher intensities of radiation falling on the walls of the plant will result in a greater leakage of radiation into surrounding areas and, on start up and shut down, packages will not receive the normal dose. To obviate these difficulties, the plant can be loaded initially with dummy material having similar absorption characteristics to the process material. This dummy material will then be progressively displaced as process material enters and will follow the process material back into the plant at the end of a processing run.

15.5.3. SAFETY

It is clear from a comparison of the lethal dose for a man and the doses required for various processing operations that operating personnel must be protected from the radiation generated in the plant they tend. To monitor the efficiency of such precautions, operating personnel should wear a personal dose-measuring device, as described in Section 15.4. The chief protective agent is an envelope of radiation-absorbing shielding surrounding the plant. Lead, concrete and purified water are the chief shielding materials in use. A sufficient thickness of material is required to reduce the dose rate outside the plant to an acceptable level (say 0.75 mille-rad/h[9]). This thickness is roughly inversely proportional to the density of the shielding material. Lead shielding is used in the transport of radioactive source rods or in transportable demonstration irradiators because its high density reduces the thickness of shielding required and allows such units to be as compact as possible. High density concrete is used for permanent installations. Figure 15.4 shows a plant constructed in 1973. The concrete shielding can clearly be seen in the diagram and some idea of its thickness can be gained from the fact that the circular turntable in the irradiation chamber is 5 m in radius. Finally, a deep tank of purified water is used, as in the plant illustrated in Fig. 15.4, to provide a safe location into which radioactive sources can be retracted when maintenance must be carried out in the irradiation zone. An alternative to this is 'dry pit' storage, where the source is lowered into a concrete lined pit and covered with a lead or concrete lid to prevent escape of radiation.

Some access points must be provided through the shielding material, but these should not lead to an escape of radiation. Conveyors handling the product pass through maze-like passages in

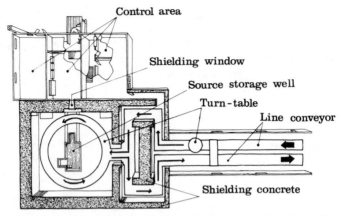

FIG. 15.4. A plan view of the irradiation cell of the potato irradiation plant at Hokkaido, Japan. (From 'Food Irradiation Information', No. 3, June (1974) p. 79.)

the shielding (*see* Fig. 15.4). Access doors are also constructed so that there is no direct path for radiation to escape round their edges. Stringent safety precautions are necessary to ensure that no personnel are present in the irradiation area when processing resumes or can obtain access to the area during operation.[9]

REFERENCES

1. Goldblith, S. R., 'Historical Development of Food Irradiation', *in* 'Food Irradiation'. (International Atomic Energy Agency, Vienna: 1966.)
2. Anon., Food Irradiation Information No. 2, 43 (Sept. 1973).
3. Anon., Food Irradiation Information No. 3, 79 (June 1974).
4. Adamiker, D., Food Irradiation Information No. 5, 19 (Nov. 1975).
5. Anon., Food Irradiation Information No. 1, 73 (Nov. 1972).
6. Anon., 'Report of the Working Party on Irradiation of Food', Ministry of Health, Committee on Medical and Nutritional Aspects of Food Policy. (HMSO: 1964.)
7. Bongirwar, D. R., and Weiss, J., 'Ceric-cupric Sulphate Dosimeter', *in* 'Radiation Preservation of Food'. (International Atomic Energy Agency, Vienna: 1973.)
8. Hannan, R. S., 'Scientific and Technological Problems Involved in Using Ionizing Radiations for the Preservation of Food', DSIR, FIB, Special Report No. 61. (HMSO: 1955.)
9. Anon., 'Factories Ionizing Radiations (Sealed Sources) Regulations, 1961' Statutory Instrument 1961, No. 1470. (HMSO: 1961.)

CHAPTER 16

FOOD STORAGE

16.1. INFLUENCE OF STORAGE CONDITIONS
ON THE PRODUCT

16.1.1. INTRODUCTION

Food being stored may become spoiled by three mechanisms:

(i)   living organisms (*e.g.* vermin, insects, fungi or bacteria) may feed on the food and contaminate it,

(ii) biochemical activity within the food itself (*e.g.* respiration, staling, browning and rancidity development) may in time diminish its quality and usefulness, and

(iii) physical processes (*e.g.* bursting and spillage of the contents of packages or recrystallisation phenomena in sugar confectionery, fats and frozen products) may have the same effect.

The three main factors of the storage environment which influence the storage life of a particular commodity are the temperature, humidity and the composition of the store atmosphere. In addition, rough handling, careless packing or unsuitable packaging can reduce storage life, but these matters are outside the scope of the present chapter.

16.1.2. STORE TEMPERATURE

The rate at which biochemical reactions occur in food increases with increasing temperature.

The relationship frequently observed between reaction rate and temperature is similar to that already noted in connection with the thermal destruction of bacterial spores by moist heat in Chapter 11. That is, the logarithm of the reaction rate is a linear function of temperature. In the present instance, however, the rate of change of the reaction rate is more frequently measured in terms of Q_{10} (the ratio of the rate at one temperature to that at a temperature $10\,^\circ\text{C}$ lower) than by z (the temperature range over which the rate changes 10-fold). The gradient of the plot of the logarithm of the reaction rate against temperature is expressible in terms of both quantities, *i.e.*

$$\text{gradient} = \frac{1}{z} = \frac{\log Q_{10}}{10}$$

whence

$$z = \frac{10}{\log Q_{10}}$$

The concept of Q_{10} values was introduced by vant' Hoff, who found that the Q_{10} for many chemical reactions was about 2, *i.e.* the reaction rate approximately doubled for each $10\,^\circ\text{C}$ temperature rise. The rate of respiration of harvested fruit, however, has a Q_{10} of about 2·5 and that for vegetables is of the same order[1] while the quality deterioration of frozen strawberries has a Q_{10} about ten times greater again than this.[2]

Thus the lower the storage temperature the more slowly do foods suffer degradation by those biochemical spoilage reactions listed in the previous subsection. In addition, the rate of growth of bacteria is reduced as the temperature falls and low temperature storage—particularly frozen storage—has some bactericidal effect. Fungi, like bacteria, have a temperature range over which growth is possible at a given water activity (see Section 16.1.3) and an optimum growth temperature within this range. This optimum is nearer the upper end of the range and at, or above, normal ambient temperatures. Near the limiting temperatures, growth takes place only very slowly, so again it may be said that lowering the temperature of the product will reduce its rate of deterioration. Most insect activity is inhibited below about $4\,^\circ\text{C}$, although some insect species and insect eggs are capable of surviving long exposures to these temperatures. Flour and grain mites are active near $0\,^\circ\text{C}$, breeding at temperatures which render other insects inactive from cold.[3, 4]

From all this it might be inferred that a reduction in storage temperature inevitably results in an extension of storage life. This is, however, by no means the case. Foods containing water will freeze if their temperature is lowered much below $0\,^\circ\text{C}$, the actual freezing temperature depending on the nature of the aqueous solutions in the food. The act of freezing and thawing alters the food, sometimes very extensively, and the properties of 'fresh' produce such as fruits and vegetables are adversely affected should they freeze during storage. For fresh meat stored in the frozen state there is the problem of 'drip'

This is a red fluid which exudes from muscle cells damaged by the freezing and thawing process and which, if extensive, spoils the appearance of the meat and results in loss of weight. If canned foods are allowed to freeze, the cans may burst, and if such goods contain gels or emulsions these may break down.

Even if held above the freezing temperature, deleterious physiological changes can result in the spoilage of fresh fruits and vegetables. Apples stored close to their freezing point can exhibit forms of injury not observed at slightly higher temperatures. Soggy or Low Temperature breakdown (where a clearly defined moist breakdown of the tissues midway between the core and surface develops), Internal Browning (where a browning occurs radiating out from the core area while the tissues remain firm) and Brown Core or Core Flush (where the flesh around the seed cavity browns) result from storage at 0 °C and are not a problem at 3–4 °C.[1]

Apples are not alone in suffering from this sort of injury. Table 16.1 shows the temperatures below which chilling injury can be observed in a variety of tropical fruits and vegetables. There is evidence that ripe tomatoes can be stored at a lower temperature than green tomatoes,

TABLE 16.1
The susceptibility of various tropical fruits and vegetables to chilling injury

Product	Approximate temperature below which chilling injury may be observed (°C)
Avocado (other than West Indian), Cucumber and Lime	5
Papaya and Pineapple	6
Avocado (West Indian)	10
Lemon	11
Banana	13

Based on data from Pantastico.[5]

which can suffer cold injury below 7 °C resulting in abnormal ripening and susceptibility to rots.[5] Storage of potatoes below 3 °C is undesirable as they are susceptible to chilling injury. However, even above this temperature there can be a change in the starch–sugar balance leading to the accumulation of sugar in the tissues making the tubers unsuitable for processing into chips or crisps. Storage at 10–13 °C is recommended to avoid this.

Another factor to be taken into consideration, even when low temperature storage will increase the storage life of a commodity, is the cost of such storage. To the prime cost of foods put into storage must be added the cost of maintaining them under the chosen storage conditions. Thus stored foods appreciate in cost even if they do not in value. Storage at below ambient temperature is more expensive than unrefrigerated storage, and the lower the storage temperature the higher the cost. Clearly storage conditions need be no more elaborate than those required to maintain the stored commodity in good condition up to the time of use. The maintenance of conditions sufficient to provide a shelf life for the material in excess of that required will usually be economically disadvantageous.

This concept has been applied, particularly, to the storage and distribution of frozen food products. Here, provided the products are suitably packaged, the deterioration is almost entirely a function of temperature. By using organoleptic testing procedures, the duration of storage at a given temperature before some specified degree of quality loss is observed can be determined. Such an exercise forms the basis for Fig. 16.1, where the 'high quality life' is plotted for a range of products as a function of temperature. The form of Fig. 16.1 is to be expected, following the discussion at the beginning of this section, since the storage life is in inverse relationship to the rate of deterioration. The Q_{10} values for deterioration may be seen to range from about 3 to 20, that for raspberries (curve 8) being particularly high.

Care must be taken in interpreting charts such as Fig. 16.1, since their meaning will depend on the initial quality of the product tested and the degree of deterioration taken to signal the end of the storage life. The 'high quality life' of Fig. 16.1 is the time a product may be stored at a given temperature before a fall from the initial quality is just detectable by a trained taste panel. Thus the food will still be in sound marketable condition at the expiry of this period.

The analogy between Fig. 16.1 and the relationship of decimal reduction time and temperature (Fig. 11.3) has already been pointed out and, making use of the mathematical approach of Section 11.1, the effect of storage at different temperatures at different periods of the storage can be evaluated in the same way as the effect of an arbitrary temperature history on bacterial destruction was evaluated in equation (11.2). If, during storage, the temperature remained for a differential time, dt, at a value where the 'high quality life' was H, then a fraction dt/H of the high quality life was expended and the total loss of 'high quality life' throughout the process was $\int(dt/H)$, the integration being taken over the entire process. Clearly, values of this integral greater than unity will indicate that a loss of quality *can* be detected, but the extent to which quality loss is acceptable is a matter for commercial judgement.

It may now be seen that three main factors influence the choice of the storage temperature for a particular commodity: the temperature

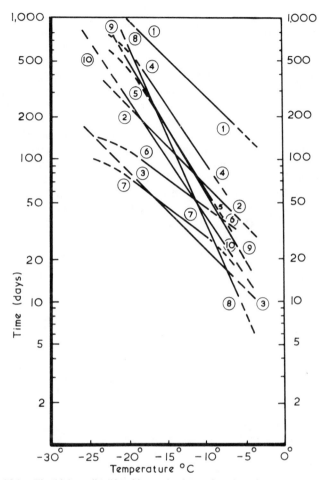

Fig. 16.1. The 'high quality life' of frozen foods as a function of storage temperature. (1) Raw chicken pieces—good packaging. (2) Raw chicken pieces—poor packaging. (3) Fried chicken pieces. (4) Beef. (5) Pork. (6) Lean fish. (7) Fatty fish. (8) Raspberries. (9) Peas and French beans. (10) Spinach. (Courtesy of the Institut International du Froid.)

dependence of the rate at which spoilage processes occur, the risk of cold injury to the commodity, and the economic balance between storage costs and the maintenance of product quality. Recommended conditions for the refrigerated storage of perishable produce have been published.[1, 6] Recommended temperatures for land transport[7] and sea transport[8] of perishable foods are also available. Transport conditions may be less stringent than storage conditions. This is because the provision of refrigeration and the control of product temperature during transport present more problems and are relatively more costly than in stationary storage. Since the duration of land transportation, in particular, is often relatively short, the fraction of the high quality life expended during transportation at temperatures rather above those recommended for storage is comparatively small. It is of greater importance, if a further storage period is to follow transportation, to ensure that, subsequently, the goods are rapidly cooled to the new storage temperature since the persistence of the higher transport temperature during the subsequent storage period may well lead to loss of quality. This problem is intensified since the heat gain will most likely take place when the bulk of the product is broken down into small units for loading and unloading transport vehicles. Heat penetration will then be rapid, due to the extended surfaces and small product depths involved. However, if the product is subsequently returned to bulk storage the re-cooling can be much slower since it must take place from a large body of

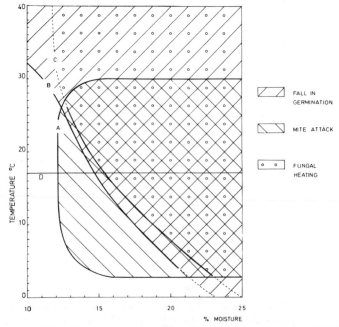

FIG. 16.2.   Effect of grain moisture content and temperature on insect heating (above line D), fall in germination to 95 % in 35 weeks storage (to right of line B), damp grain heating (to right of line C) and mite attack (shaded area within line A).[3] (Originated by the Pest Infestation Control Laboratory. Reproduced by permission of Controller, HM Stationery Office.)

material. Reducing the temperature rises during handling to a minimum is desirable.

The temperature conditions for storage of less perishable items are by implication less rigorous. The keeping qualities of sugar are independent of temperature between 10 and 30 °C.[9] Canned goods must, of course, be protected from frost damage. Figure 16.2 shows that dry grain can be safely stored at temperatures up to 17 °C, while with increasing moisture content storage at reduced temperatures becomes more necessary. In general terms, the cooler and drier seeds can be stored, the longer their storage life. Some nuts will store quite well at 20 °C, though longer storage periods are possible at reduced temperatures. For instance, shelled peanuts will store for 4 months at 20 °C, 2 years at 1 °C and 5 years at −4 °C.[4]

16.1.3. STORE HUMIDITY

If the humidity of a store atmosphere is below the equilibrium relative humidity (or ERH—see Chapter 13) of the food being stored, that food will lose moisture to the atmosphere. Conversely if it is above the ERH of the food, the latter will absorb water. Thus, ideally, the relative humidity of the store atmosphere should be adjusted to the ERH of the stored product. For instance, granulated white sugar has a moisture content of about 0·02 % and an ERH of about 60 %. If the moisture content rises to 0·06 %, the sugar is in danger of caking. Therefore storage relative humidities below 60 % are recommended for this product. Conversely brown sugar has a moisture content of 4 % which must be maintained if the product is to retain a workable texture, so relative humidities of 60–70 % are recommended for long term storage.[10] Again, peanuts become brittle and may split due to dehydration if the storage relative humidity is below 70 % RH and are liable to mould spoilage above this ERH.[4] Thus, as with temperature, there is often an optimum condition for storage.

The ERH of a product has a considerable bearing on its vulnerability to microbial attack. When expressed as a fraction, instead of a percentage, the ERH is known as the water activity (a_w) of the material. Figure 16.3 shows the a_w limits below which various classes of organism are inhibited and also indicates the a_w of various classes of food. As may be seen, bacterial growth may be a major problem in foods with a high a_w—for instance fresh fruits and vegetables, meats and fish—but in materials with a lower a_w it is the fungi that cause the most trouble. Insects can also flourish in foods of comparatively low a_w.

In the case of fresh fruits and vegetables the store humidity cannot

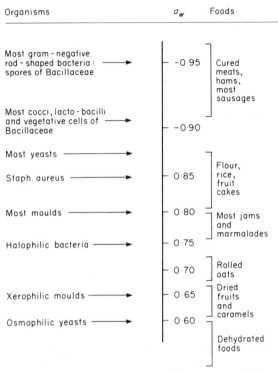

Organisms a_w Foods

Most gram - negative
rod - shaped bacteria : ⟶   - 0·95   Cured
spores of Bacillaceae   meats,
                                                           hams,
                                                           most
                                                           sausages

Most cocci, lacto - bacilli
and vegetative cells of ⟶
Bacillaceae   - 0·90

Most yeasts ⟶
                                                           Flour,
Staph. aureus ⟶   0·85   rice,
                                                           fruit
                                                           cakes

Most moulds ⟶   0·80   Most jams
                                                           and
Halophilic bacteria ⟶   0·75   marmalades

                                     0·70   Rolled
                                                           oats

                                                           Dried
Xerophilic moulds ⟶   0·65   fruits
                                                           and
Osmophilic yeasts ⟶   0·60   caramels

                                                           Dehydrated
                                                           foods

FIG. 16.3. Diagram showing the approximate limiting water activities for various classes of micro-organism and the water activities of various classes of foods. At the a_w indicated, the micro-organisms listed will just be inhibited. Marginally above these a_w values, their growth will be very slow.

be maintained high enough to prevent shrivelling and wilting since mould growth would rapidly develop on the product. A compromise relative humidity must therefore be adopted for storage, in which some wilting is accepted as the price for reducing microbial attack. A certain drying of the surface of meat also slows the development of bacterial slime and is sometimes required in the case of long distance transport. In these cases there is no equilibrium between the store atmosphere and the material in store and the effective a_w at the surface is below that in the bulk of the produce.

Packaging can be used to isolate the environment of the food from the store air and so allow foods to be held at the ERH in storage atmospheres of undetermined relative humidity. Occasionally treatment of the surface of foods achieves the same purpose. Thus shell eggs lose water freely and require high humidity environments if they are not to experience excessive weight loss. This may lead to microbial growth on the egg shell and consequent tainting of the egg. Treating the shell with oil improves its water vapour barrier properties and allows the humidity of the store to be lowered, so avoiding mould growth.

As with storage temperature, recommended levels of store relative humidity have been published for many products.

16.1.4. COMPOSITION OF STORE ATMOSPHERE

A variety of food materials are advantageously stored in atmospheres different from normal air. The most noteworthy example of this occurs in the refrigerated storage of fruit.[8] Fresh fruit respires, taking up oxygen and evolving carbon dioxide. The rate of respiration can be reduced by cooling, so extending storage life, but can be further reduced by storing the fruit in an atmosphere richer in carbon dioxide and poorer in oxygen than normal air. In the case of apples and pears, particularly, worthwhile increases in storage life are possible and this technique, which is known as 'controlled atmosphere' or 'gas' storage, is in extensive commercial use. The oxygen and CO_2 levels used vary markedly between varieties and are controlled to optimum values, since too great a modification of the storage atmosphere can lead to secondary spoilage.[11] This technique is used extensively for the storage of fruits such as apples, pears and oranges and is receiving some attention for improving the quality of vegetables in storage and transportation.

When strawberries and raspberries are cooled and transported in an atmosphere containing about 20 % by volume of carbon dioxide in air, the development of fungal rots and ripening is delayed. Storage in carbon dioxide was at one time also used with meat. Chilled beef was shipped to England from Australia in an atmosphere of 10 % carbon dioxide in air, approximately doubling the storage life obtainable up to that time. However, improvements to meat processing in Australia have now rendered this treatment unnecessary. More recently a similar technique has been tried for the road transportation of beef in Canada.[17]

If grain is stored in an air-tight silo, insects, mites and moulds can be controlled by the atmosphere they generate. These organisms use up the oxygen in the enclosed space and asphyxiate themselves before becoming numerous enough to cause damage. Dry grain can be stored in this manner with little loss of its functional properties. However, wet grain will lose its powers of germination, making it unfit for seed or malting, and develop a taint which is transmitted to baked goods made from it—though it remains suitable for animal feed.[3] Air-tight storage is more satisfactory for non-viable food materials sufficiently dry to be protected against microbial growth, *e.g.* ground, roast coffee. In such cases oxygen may be excluded from the container or package by replacing the air in it by an inert gas (nitrogen or carbon dioxide) or by a vacuum.

16.1.5. ODOURS AND TAINTS

Stored produce may pick up foreign odours and flavours from other foodstuffs stored with it,[12] from inappropriate packaging materials[13] or from the storage chamber and environment. Foods with strong odours—spiced meats, smoked fish, citrus fruit, etc., and spoiled meat and fish are likely to cause tainting. Packaging materials may either themselves contribute odours or be contaminated during production. Adhesives and printing materials may also cause trouble. Finally the constructional materials of the store may become contaminated or taints may be absorbed from vapours entering the store from outside. While such taints do not alter the nutritional status of the food, its commercial value can be seriously affected.

Fatty foods are particularly liable to absorb odours. Butter is very subject to tainting, and meat shipped to England has, on occasions, been found to be tainted by diesel and fuel oil fumes, smoke and fruit (particularly oranges).[14] Eggs will also pick up taints fairly easily. Tables have been prepared indicating commodity combinations which are liable to cause tainting problems in refrigerated shipping space.[15]

The most satisfactory method of avoiding problems of tainting during storage is to avoid storing taint-absorbing foods in the presence of odorous materials. Suitable packaging can help to preserve food untainted, and both activated charcoal and ozone have been used for removing odorous volatiles from food stores. Unfortunately the concentrations of ozone for efficient action are toxic and so require special care, both in their use and in the purification of the air in the chamber afterwards. To be efficient, after these treatments the surfaces of the chamber and refrigerator should be thoroughly cleaned, treating all surfaces with a disinfectant. It is worth remembering that these processes are all more effective the higher the temperature of the chamber when they are carried out.

16.1.6. LIGHT

The ultra-violet light in the sun's rays will quickly impart a taint to butter and milk by oxidising their fats. Potatoes exposed to light will ·

turn green due to the formation of chlorophyll. While this is in itself harmless, a parallel production of the toxic substance, solanine, often takes place. In storage buildings the effect of light on produce is normally unimportant since daylight does not penetrate into them and only a low level (about 12 W/m^2 floor area[16]) of artificial light is provided. Where problems have recently arisen is in supermarkets, where high intensity lighting from fluorescent tubes is used to display foods. The ultra-violet rays from such lights are more intense than those from tungsten filament lighting and have been shown to be sufficient to oxidise fats, bleach colours and to green potatoes. Packaging in coloured plastic film or the use of colour filters on the light fittings will reduce the effects, but are not necessarily satisfactory from a commercial point of view.

16.2. VARIABILITY IN STORAGE CONDITIONS

Both spatial and temporal variations may be found in the conditions in a food store. Temporal variations may either be transient —resulting, say, from recently introduced material coming to an equilibrium state in the store—or they may be periodic in nature and a permanent feature of the storage situation. The main causes of variability in storage conditions are:

(i)   the equilibration of products to storage conditions,
(ii) respiratory activity (either of the food, in the case of fruits and vegetables, or due to insect infestation or spoilage micro-organisms),
(iii) variation of climatic conditions (*e.g.* temperature, pressure, insolation and wind force) external to the store,
(iv) fluctuations in the performance of refrigeration and other equipment designed to maintain the storage conditions at the desired levels, and
(v)   the activities of operating personnel (*e.g.* in loading or unloading the store).

The effects of such variations are often complex, inter-related changes occurring in the temperature, humidity and atmosphere composition throughout the store. As an example of this, consider a bin of wheat, a small volume within which is infested with insects. These insects, in respiring, will absorb oxygen and generate heat and carbon dioxide. The local temperature will therefore rise. The higher temperature at the site of insect activity will result in the grain in that place drying, the moisture being transferred to the surrounding grain, particularly that above the area of infestation. The conditions at the original site of infestation are now less favourable to insect growth; the grain is drier and the oxygen tension low. Thus infestation will spread away from this site, although it will remain warm by being surrounded by a zone of heat generation. The rise of temperature and humidity in the region surrounding the zone of infestation may, if sufficient, cause wheat germination and mould growth (see Fig. 16.2) which in its turn can result in sufficient heat generation to initiate a fire.

The magnitude of spatial variations in storage conditions is considerably influenced by the mode of transfer of heat and gases

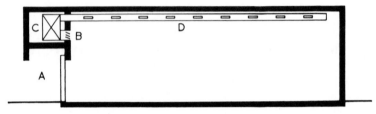

Fig. 16.4.   A forced convection store using a ducted air supply (longitudinal section). A, loading area; B, air inlet to cooler; C, air cooler; D, cool air delivery duct.

within the stack of stored material. If the store air does not move through the stack, diffusional mechanisms and thermal conduction predominate and larger variations will be observable than when the store air moves and promotes additional convective transfer. Thus in order to maintain uniform conditions throughout the store, such air movement is desirable. The produce must therefore be so stacked in the store that air flow through the stack is facilitated, particular care being taken with items such as rectangular cartons, which can be stacked in a solid block. 'Dunnage', say in the form of lengths of timber, may be placed on the floor or at intervals in the stack to create air passages. The pallets in a palletised stack will serve as dunnage and dunnage may be fitted as a permanent feature to the walls and floors of refrigerated containers. It is desirable that floor dunnage should be removable for easy cleaning.

Air circulation through the stack may either be fan assisted (forced convection) or due solely to the thermally generated density gradients in the air (natural convection). The latter system is more frequently used today because the cooling systems are less bulky and cheaper. The most frequently used forced convection systems use a cooling system and fan located in a separate enclosure connected to the store by delivery and return air ducts (Fig. 16.4), located in a floor mounted vertical duct (Figs. 16.5 and 16.7) or built into a compact unit which may be suspended from the ceiling of the store (Fig. 16.6). These last units use finned heat exchangers.

It is sometimes advantageous if the fan and duct systems in forced ventilation stores are so constructed that the direction of air flow can be reversed. Periodic air reversal can reduce the spatial temperature

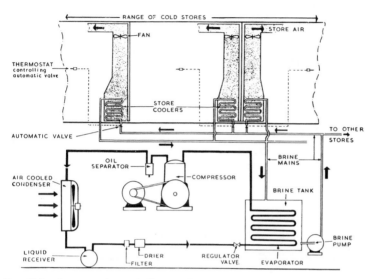

FIG. 16.5. Layout of an indirect refrigeration plant using brine. (From Mechanisation Leaflet for Farmers and Growers 12, by courtesy of the Controller of H.M.S.O.)

variations during the initial cooling of a room full of, say, fruit to storage temperature.

It has already been noted that fluctuating conditions external to the store can affect storage conditions. Annual (summer to winter) and diurnal (day to night) temperature variations may be taken as examples. Consider a large body with an extended plane surface (strictly speaking a 'semi-infinite solid' extending, in a Cartesian co-ordinate system, throughout the region $x \geq 0$ with a plane face defined by $x = 0$). If heat transfer within such a body is by conduction and its surface is subjected to a sinusoidal temperature variation of period T, a temperature wave will be propagated into the body with a velocity

$$\left(\frac{4\pi K}{T}\right)^{1/2}$$

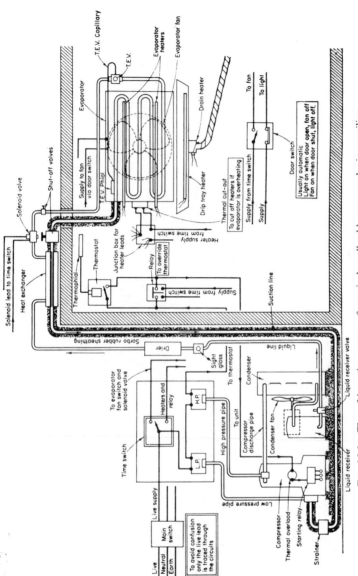

Fig. 16.6.   The refrigeration system of a typical small cold room employing a ceiling-mounted evaporator unit and automatic electric defrosting. The time switch periodically closes the solenoid valve, stopping the flow of refrigerant through the expansion valve (T.E.V.) to the evaporator. The pressure in the evaporator and suction line therefore falls and the low pressure switch (L.P.) stops the compressor. The time switch also operates the heaters which melt the ice on the finned evaporator surface. The high pressure switch (H.P.) is a safety device to protect the refrigerator compressor. (By courtesy of the editor of Modern Refrigeration and Air Conditioning.)

—where K is the thermal diffusivity of the body. The amplitude of the temperature oscillations at depth x within the body is reduced by a factor

$$\exp\left[-x\left(\frac{\pi}{TK}\right)^{1/2}\right]$$

below that at the surface. Now consider a large silo of bulk wheat ($K \simeq 0.30\,\text{m}^2/\text{month}$). From the above expressions it can be seen that 3·4 m from the outer surface the annual thermal oscillations

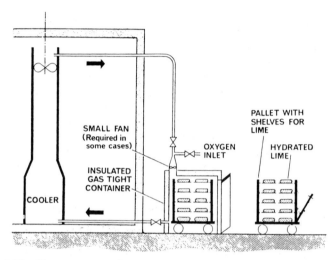

FIG. 16.7. The arrangement of a controlled atmosphere store employing a scrubber using fresh hydrated lime in bags. (From Mechanisation Leaflet for Farmers and Growers 12, by courtesy of the Controller of H.M.S.O.)

would be reduced to 5 % of their initial value, the temperature maxima being propagated into the silo at a velocity of 0·56 m/month. Thus not only will annual temperature fluctuations be measurable well within the stack, they will be appreciably out of phase with the seasons. The diurnal fluctuation will be reduced to 5 % of its initial value only 18 cm below the surface of the silo and so has little effect on storage. Similarly the diurnal temperature variations within the exposed insulated walls of refrigerated stores are rapidly attenuated and the heat leakage into the store remains fairly constant at an average value corresponding to the climatic season. Again, unrefrigerated underground storage locations insulated only by the mass of the subsoil around and over them will maintain a temperature approximately equal to the local year-round average ambient. This form of storage is known as cellar storage. Underground storage chambers of this type have been used traditionally in many parts of the world—particularly for the storage of grain.

16.3. MAINTENANCE AND CONTROL OF STORAGE CONDITIONS

16.3.1. TEMPERATURE

Refrigerated storage rooms are thermally insulated to reduce heat leakage. The insulation, low bulk density porous or fibrous inert material (*e.g.* cork, foamed plastics, glass wool, etc.), is normally fixed to the structural walls, ceiling and floor of the room—though prefabricated unit panels have recently become more common, used in conjunction with a steel or concrete load-bearing framework. Underground chambers and the floors of rooms built directly on the ground are not necessarily insulated, since the thickness of the surrounding earth or rock compensates for the comparatively high thermal conductivity of these materials. Insulation is sometimes desirable in unrefrigerated storage. For instance, root vegetables and potatoes can be stored in clamps or barns using either earth or straw as an insulating material. The purpose of the insulation is to minimise the effects of sudden ambient changes on the produce and so prevent frost damage. Canned goods may be transported in insulated vehicles for the same reason if sufficiently low ambient temperatures might be encountered to give a risk of freezing. While too little insulation will lead to high refrigeration costs, over insulation will be initially more expensive and will reduce the available storage space in a building, cabinet or container. While local costs and special requirements determine the insulation installed, conventional British practice leads to wall leakages of about 7–8 W/m^2. Data and procedures for estimating the heat leakage through different insulated structures are available.[18]

Another important source of heat leakage into a refrigerated store is air exchange at the door. This exchange is reduced by a variety of methods. The time the door is open may be minimised by automatic opening and closing mechanisms. Small hatchways may be used for loading by conveyor. Double doors may be installed, forming an air-lock, or an 'air-curtain' fixed above the outside of the doorway. This latter consists of a fan and duct system that directs a stream of the external ambient air downwards, and slightly outwards, in a sheet across the door opening so preventing the ingress of warm air.

If the refrigeration requirements for a store are to be estimated, heat generation within the store and the cooling of stored produce must be taken into account as well as heat leakage into the store.

Published data[18] suggests that the magnitude of the heat load from all causes, except wall leakage and heat generation by stored produce, during conventional store operation is, very approximately, given by: $0.003V^{0.6}$ kJ/s for every °C difference between the inside and outside of the room. V is here the volume of the room (m³).

Most refrigerated stores are cooled by vapour compression refrigerators using ammonia or halogenated hydrocarbon refrigerants. The cooling effect in such machines is produced by boiling the refrigerant at a low temperature in the pipes of an evaporator. This evaporator may either cool the store air directly (a 'direct expansion' system—see Fig. 16.6) or cool a liquid (say a calcium chloride solution, or 'brine') which is in turn fed to a heat exchanger to cool the air (an 'indirect' system—see Fig. 16.5). The control of refrigeration in indirect systems is particularly simple and the temperature difference across the air cooler can be minimised by keeping the brine velocity sufficiently high. However, such systems are more complex, and therefore more costly, than direct expansion.

Other cooling systems are available and are used, particularly, in food transport. Here there are problems in providing, powering and maintaining vapour compression refrigerators under conditions where reliability is essential while the equipment is unattended. Water ice, aqueous eutectic mixtures, solid carbon dioxide and liquid gases (carbon dioxide, nitrogen and air), all of which refrigerate by absorbing latent heat, have found applications in this field, mainly to supply non-mechanical refrigeration throughout the journey.

In recent years the great advance in this field has been the development of container transportation. Sealed box-like containers of standardised dimensions have been built which can transport foods directly from supplier to consumer, whether by lorry, railway flat-car or in a specially designed ship, without the need for any handling of the goods during the whole transport chain. Containers with built-in refrigeration equipment have found greatest application in road transportation, because there is a driver always in attendance to ensure that the equipment is operating. Solid CO_2 has been widely used to cool rail containers in the UK, though the use of mechanical refrigeration is growing. For transportation between Australia and the UK, containers can be serviced with cold air from a central source on shipboard and equipped with clip-on mechanical refrigeration units for distribution from the port of arrival.[19] Liquid carbon dioxide has also been used to provide an initial boost to the cooling system at the time of loading. Precooling of the transport container and minimisation of heat gain by produce during loading are essential to reduce refrigeration requirements during the journey. The rapid cooling that results from spraying liquid carbon dioxide into the container after loading can be used to effect this.

16.3.2. MOISTURE AND HUMIDITY

Heat passing through the walls of a refrigerated storage chamber must first be supplied to the outer surface of these walls by transfer from the outside air and by solar radiation. When solar radiation does not predominate, the outer wall surface will be below the temperature of the air outside the store wall. If the dew point of this air is higher than the surface temperature of the wall, water will condense on the wall surface, a circumstance which can result in deterioration of the fabric of the wall. Increasing the thermal insulation of the room will reduce the heat leakage and increase the temperature of the outside wall. The avoidance of surface condensation can be a determining factor in wall insulation when the humidities in the air external to the wall are likely to be high. Even under normal conditions, surface condensation can occur at locations where, due to design faults, the thickness of insulation is reduced by structural members, pipes or fixing bolts.

Whether surface condensation occurs or not, there is often a higher partial pressure of water vapour in the air outside the store than in that inside it. Thus there is a water vapour concentration gradient which will tend to cause diffusional flow of water vapour through the wall into the store. If the water vapour pressure at any point within the store wall equals the saturated vapour pressure of water at the local temperature, water will condense from the vapour phase at that place. Since the low thermal conductivity of insulating materials depends on their porous or cellular nature, water logging seriously affects their efficiency. To prevent condensation within the wall, a barrier to water vapour flow must be provided. Some insulating materials are comparatively resistant to vapour flow—notably 'closed cell' foamed plastics, where the plastic membrane is continuous around the air bubbles in the material. Other materials are formed into boards and provided with a prefabricated barrier, say of aluminium foil, on one side. Again, the adhesive fixing the insulation to the structural wall may provide the barrier. It is essential that any barrier should be on the outer face of the insulation to prevent water vapour reaching this vulnerable material.

It has already been noted (Section 16.3.1) that the insulating effect of the subsoil is considerable for stores built directly on the ground. If no precautions are taken and the store is operated below 0 °C, the 0 °C isothermal surface under the store may, particularly during the winter, be in the subsoil below the floor. When this occurs any water in the subsoil will freeze and, owing to the lowered vapour pressure in the region, ice will tend to accumulate due to diffusional water movements. These ice accumulations usually form lens-shaped masses below the store floor and in time damage the structure of the building, giving rise to a condition known as 'frost heave'. Frost heave is a particular danger when the water table in the subsoil is high and when the subsoil contains fine silts and clays. Frost heave of stores built on difficult subsoils can be prevented by installing a heating system—say an electrical heater mat—beneath the floor insulation so that the 0 °C isothermal surface does not pass through the subsoil.

The equilibrium relative humidity of many foods (fruits, vegetables and meat for instance) is greater than the humidity recommended for their storage. There will therefore be some desiccation of the produce by the store air. Moisture will also enter a refrigerated store through air exchange at doors, etc. The relative humidity established in the store air represents a dynamic equilibrium between the take-up of moisture by the air and the dehydrating effect of the air cooler. If the temperature of the cooler surface falls relative to the air temperature, the dehydrating effect of the cooler is increased, and *vice versa*. Thus in stores designed to operate at a high humidity, extended cooling surfaces and small temperature differences are used. Conversely, where a low relative humidity is desired, a restricted cooling surface at a correspondingly lower temperature is employed. A temporary method of lowering the humidity of an existing storage chamber is to introduce heat into the room to enable a lower cooler temperature to be employed without changing the store air temperature. Steam or atomised water from sprays may be used to increase store humidities.

The moisture removed from the store air by the cooling system will either condense as water on the surface of the cooler or form frost upon it. Sometimes coolers are kept wetted by brine solutions or cooling effected by spraying brine through the store air. In such cases the brine will become diluted by the condensing water. Steps must be taken to dispose of this deposited moisture. Frost formation provides the most difficult problem since the ice crystals stay where they form on the cooler surface. Such is the thermal conductivity of the frost layer and the heat transfer coefficient at the frost-air interface that considerable frost formation may occur on an isolated pipe before heat transfer becomes impaired (see Appendix II). More serious is the effect the frost has on air flow through the cooling equipment. Regular defrosting of the coolers is therefore required. This can be effected by circulating hot brine through indirect units, by discharging hot refrigerant gases through direct expansion coolers or by shutting off the refrigeration and melting the frost with electric heaters (see Fig. 16.6).

Frozen foods are best stored at their equilibrium relative humidity to prevent desiccation. If such produce, cooled to the required temperature, is enclosed in a water-vapour impermeable container maintained at the same temperature, the space within the container will rise to the equilibrium relative humidity of the food whereupon desiccation of the produce ceases since, as there is no heat generation in the produce, there are no temperature variations to give rise to the vapour pressure differences required to maintain water vapour diffusion. This conception forms the basis of the 'jacketed' store, which may be used for the long-term storage of frozen produce. The container is made only a little smaller than the insulated room and is supported within the room so as to leave a space all round it. A cooling system maintains this 'jacket' space at the required storage temperature and removes heat leaking through the walls. The air humidity in this jacket is irrelevant since it is external to and separated from the storage space. An auxiliary system is used for cooling the produce within the inner chamber to storage temperature initially. While this technique has been used for the storage of fresh fruit, its advantages here are less obvious since the jacket space and chamber walls must be maintained at a temperature below that desired for storage so as to remove the respiratory heat of the fruit stored inside. Thus condensation will take place on the cabinet wall and some desiccation of the produce will occur.

16.3.3. STORAGE ATMOSPHERE COMPOSITION

The chief concern here, as explained in Section 16.1.4, is the maintenance and control of storage atmospheres containing more carbon dioxide and less oxygen than normal air. The required carbon dioxide can be generated, and the surplus oxygen absorbed, by respiration in the stored produce. This method is employed in the controlled atmosphere storage of apples and pears and the hermetic storage of grain. Alternatively, the carbon dioxide required for the storage atmosphere may be supplied from outside, either from liquid carbon dioxide held in cylinders or, as in the transport of berry fruits, by the evaporation of solid carbon dioxide. In the latter instance the solid carbon dioxide both generates the required gas and provides the refrigerant; the carbon dioxide concentration in the store is therefore determined by the dynamic equilibrium between the rate of sublimation (which is controlled by the refrigeration requirements) and leakage of the gas from the chamber. When the first two methods are employed, however, the storage chamber should be as free of gas leaks as possible, either to minimise the time taken for respiration to supply sufficient carbon dioxide to achieve the required storage conditions, or to minimise the requirements for externally supplied gas. The normal water vapour barrier (Section 16.3.2) is insufficient for this purpose, and the required barrier is often provided by metal sheet or foil cladding on the inside of the store walls, or by multi-layer bituminous preparations. Close attention must be paid to the sealing of doorways. Metal gas-tight covers may be fitted across door openings behind a normal insulated refrigerator door.

If fruit is placed in such a gas-tight storage chamber, the oxygen tension in the store atmosphere will fall as this gas is converted by respiratory activity into carbon dioxide. Since one volume of oxygen will convert to one volume of carbon dioxide, the sum of the percentages by volume of these gases in the store will remain constant at its initial value (*i.e.* the value for normal air—about 21 %). When the carbon dioxide concentration reaches a predetermined value (say x % by volume) a controlled ventilation of the store with air can be used to maintain the atmosphere composition constant throughout subsequent storage. The oxygen concentration will thus be automatically maintained at $(21 - x)$ %. Such conditions have been found satisfactory for some varieties of fruit, but others have been found to require lower oxygen concentrations than are attainable by this method. For such fruit a system such as that shown in Fig. 16.7 is employed. The rate of supply of oxygen by ventilation with fresh air is reduced. The excess carbon dioxide produced by respiration is removed by feeding the storage atmosphere at a controlled rate to a 'scrubber'. This unit may take a variety of forms. The cheapest and most widely used scrubbers are based on passing the store atmosphere over bags of hydrated lime or through sprays of caustic soda solution to absorb the carbon dioxide. These methods have the disadvantage that the absorbent cannot easily be regenerated. Regenerative scrubbers have been constructed using mono- or tri-ethanolamine, potassium carbonate, or water.

Storage chambers for controlled atmosphere storage are not large, since it is desirable to fill the stores and close them within 7 days to get the full benefit of the artificial atmospheres. The maintenance of these chambers in such a degree of leak-tightness that the store atmosphere can be rapidly brought to the required composition is a not negligible charge on the process. One alternative to maintaining a highly sealed store is to accept a certain measure of leakage and inject gases to modify the atmosphere rather than rely solely on the respiratory activity of the fruit. Nitrogen gas, generated from liquid nitrogen holding tanks, or the exhaust gases produced from burning hydrocarbon fuels in air can be used. The expense of these systems, of course, increases the less gas-tight the store, but they do offer a way of building up to the desired atmosphere quicker than can be achieved by relying on the fruit alone.

Fruit packed in perforated or partly closed plastic containers can develop local atmospheres differing from air. Such storage has been called 'Modified Atmosphere' storage, but it suffers from the disadvantage that the atmosphere composition is not susceptible to close control.[20] Another method of modifying the storage atmosphere is to reduce the air pressure around the fruit, say to about 100 torr ($13 \cdot 1 \, kN/m^2$). The effect appears to be largely one of mechanically reducing the oxygen concentration and the method has yet to receive commercial exploitation.[11]

In a store equipped with a scrubber, the oxygen level can be controlled by ventilation with air and the carbon dioxide level by controlling the feed to the scrubber. Such operations are normally carried out manually. Routine measurements of gas concentration are therefore required and, while conventional methods of volumetric gas analysis (using, say, an Orsat apparatus) are available, they are unsuited to routine use by unskilled operators under industrial conditions. Thermal conductivity methods are more generally employed. The major components of the store atmosphere, oxygen, nitrogen and carbon dioxide, have thermal conductivities of $0 \cdot 025$, $0 \cdot 024$ and $0 \cdot 015 \, W/m \, °C$ respectively at $0 \, °C$. Thus, since the values for oxygen and nitrogen are so close, the thermal conductivity of the store atmosphere may be regarded as a function of the carbon dioxide concentration alone. If now a sample of the store atmosphere is passed over heated carbon so that all the oxygen is converted to carbon dioxide, a second determination of the thermal conductivity will give the sum of the oxygen and carbon dioxide concentrations, from which the oxygen can be deduced by subtraction. Instruments to read the oxygen concentration directly have been produced, based on the paramagnetic properties of that gas.

REFERENCES

1. Ryall, A. L., Lipton, W. J. (Vol. I), and Pentzer, W. T. (Vol. II), 'Handling, Transportation and Storage of Fruits and Vegetables' (2 vols.). (AVI: 1974).
2. Van Arsdel, W. B., Copley, M. J., and Olson, R. L. (Eds.) 'Quality and Stability of Frozen Foods'. (Wiley-Interscience: 1967).
3. Sinha, R. N., and Muir, W. E. (Eds.) 'Grain Storage: Part of a System'. (AVI: 1974).
4. Woodroof, J. G., 'Peanuts: Production, Processing, Products', 2nd ed. (AVI: 1973).
5. Pantastico, B. (Ed.) 'Postharvest Physiology, Handling and Utilization of Tropical and Subtropical Fruits and Vegetables'. (AVI: 1975).

6. Anon., 'Recommended Conditions for Cold Storage of Perishable Products'. (I.I.R: 1967).
7. Anon., 'Recommended Conditions for Land Transport of Perishable Foodstuffs. (I.I.R: 1974).
8. Anon., 'The Carriage of Refrigerated Cargoes'. (I.I.R: 1973).
9. Hugot, E., 'Handbook of Cane Sugar Engineering', 2nd ed. (Elsevier: 1972).
10. McGinnis, R. A. (Ed.) 'Beet Sugar Technology'. (Reinhold: 1951).
11. Salunkhe, D. K. (Ed.) 'Storage, Processing and Nutritional Quality of Fruits and Vegetables'. (CRC Press: 1974).
12. Hall, E. G., Food Technol. in Australia, **10**, 537 (1958).
13. Harvey, H. G., 'Survey of Odour in Packaging of Foods'. (Institute of Packaging: 1963).
14. Cromarty, R. W., 'Contamination by Odours from Different Cargoes Carried and Procedures for De-contamination', *in* 'Marine Refrigeration'. Annexe 1965–5 to the Bulletin of the I.I.R.
15. Boyes, W. W., 'Perishable Commodities which may be Stowed in the Same Ship Spaces or Hatches without Danger of Cross-taint', *in* 'Marine Refrigeration'. Annexe 1965–5 to the Bulletin of the I.I.R.
16. Anon., 'Practical Guide to Refrigerated Storage'. (Pergamon Press *for* I.I.R.: 1965).
17. MacNabb, T. C., and Bethune, A. E., *in* Proceedings of the 13th International Congress of Refrigeration, 481. (AVI *for* I.I.R.: 1973).
18. Anon., 'ASHRAE Guide and Data Book—Fundamentals and Equipment'. (American Society of Heating, Refrigerating and Air Conditioning Engineers: 1963).
19. Burton, G. A., *in* Proceedings of the 13th International Congress of Refrigeration, 361. (AVI *for* I.I.R.: 1973).
20. Cowell, N. D., and Scott, K. J., J. Hort. Sci., **37**(2), 87 (1962).

PART IV
ANCILLARY TECHNIQUES

CHAPTER 17

PLANT HYGIENE—HYGIENIC DESIGN, CLEANING AND STERILISING

17.1. INTRODUCTION

In the past, food processing operations were often carried out as small-scale batch operations, numbers of batches of material being processed during a working day. The duration of the working day often depended on raw material availability or on consumer demand, and items of process plant were cleaned by hand after production ceased, using such cleaning agents as were then available, often no more than soap and water. Contamination and spoilage of food materials by microbiological infection and, more seriously, contamination by pathogenic organisms capable of leading to outbreaks of food poisoning could, and did, occur. More recently, the scale of many food processing operations has greatly increased. Larger batch sizes and, in many cases, continuous operation have replaced the more traditional small-scale batch techniques, in the drive for greater productivity. Round the clock operation is becoming common and 'in-place cleaning' is gradually replacing the more traditional methods of cleaning, where applicable.

In the tonnage-capacity production plants of today, the problems of microbiological contamination are exactly those of the small-scale operator, but are much magnified. Adulteration and spoilage of large quantities of product, rather than a few kilograms, can occur, and the much larger consumer markets put at risk—should an outbreak of food poisoning arise—a far greater number of people.

Food processers must continuously guard against contamination of their products and, by correct design, operation and maintenance of their processes and equipment, must reduce to a minimum the risk of costly losses and danger to the health of the consumer.

The area of activity concerned with preventing the contamination of food materials during processing and storage is called 'hygiene', but it must be emphasised that hygiene in the food processing plant is not simply concerned with cleaning.

17.2. HYGIENIC DESIGN

Hygienic requirements should be considered in detail when the factory is being designed. Hygienic design embraces the design of the plant, equipment and building, including both construction and layout, the supply of services, such as bacteriologically acceptable water supplies and waste disposal facilities, as well as the design and installation of facilities for the cleaning and sterilising of raw materials, plant and equipment.

Hygienic design factors must be taken into consideration in all stages of factory development, including:

(i)   Site selection.
(ii) In the design of buildings housing process equipment.
(iii) In the design and lay-out of the processing equipment.

17.2.1. SITE SELECTION

Important hygienic requirements at this stage include:[1, 2]

(i)   the availability of a satisfactory water supply suitable for all likely production requirements and of waste-disposal facilities for both liquid and solid wastes. (These aspects are discussed in Chapter 18).

(ii) the absence of possible centres of pollution from other manufacturers, such as land-fills, streams, etc., used for waste disposal by other producers. These sources of possible contamination are particularly prevalent in industrial areas and can make site selection difficult. Swamp areas and heavily wooded land should be avoided since both harbour rodents and insects and provide breeding grounds for micro-organisms.

17.2.2. DESIGN, CONSTRUCTION AND LAY-OUT OF BUILDINGS

Raw materials commonly arrive at the factory in a contaminated condition, requiring preparation before processing. Vegetables, for example, are contaminated with soil, foreign matter, bacteria, etc. (*see* Chapter 2). Areas where grossly contaminated materials are handled should be recognised and segregated from other processing areas. Careful planning of such areas at this early stage will prevent contamination problems later. Buildings of single-storey construction can be used to advantage where hygienic considerations are important. Large roof spans free from supporting pillars become possible, permitting more efficient utilisation of floor space, easier house-keeping and better lighting. Materials handling is often simpler with this type of construction.

17.2.2.1. Walls and ceilings. Interior wall surfaces of processing rooms should be smooth and easy to clean. They should be free from cracks and crevices which shelter insects and aid microbiological growth. Impervious surfacing materials such as glazed tiles are favoured, and other materials such as brick, cement, wood, etc., should be coated with a material capable of withstanding the action of steam, acids, and alkaline solutions commonly encountered in the food industry. Dust, splashes of food material and other unfavourable deposits collect on exposed ledges, window sills and roof trusses. These surfaces should be curved or sloped to discourage such accumulation and to permit easy cleaning and draining after washing. Corners and crevices must be avoided and unavoidable corners, as, for example, those between floors and walls, should have curved, water-tight joints. False ceilings can harbour dust, rodents and insects besides complicating ventilation and lighting arrangements, and should not be permitted.

17.2.2.2. Floors. Like walls, floors should be constructed of impervious materials which can be easily cleaned. They must be capable of carrying the loads imposed on them and of standing up to the wear encountered under all likely working conditions. They should be chemically resistant to all materials likely to come into contact with them. Floors likely to receive large quantities of water during processing and cleaning should be sloped to permit adequate drainage. Stagnant pools of water must be prevented at all costs since these soon become sources of contamination. Pitches of about one in fifty ($\frac{1}{4}$ in per linear foot) are usually adequate.

Drains should be vented to the outside atmosphere and should carry screens to prevent access of rodents to the plant. Smooth floors, when wet, can become very slippery and present a safety hazard to operating personnel, especially when the latter wear protective rubber footwear. Roughened, slip-resistant flooring materials providing continuous surfaces free from crevices are available. Flooring materials are discussed by Ziemba[3] and others.[4]

17.2.2.3. Ventilation. The provision of adequate ventilation is important.[5,6] Poor ventilation leads to condensation which can support the growth of micro-organisms on walls and ceilings. Ventilation of retorts, cooking and boiling vats, etc., is best carried out by providing hoods over these vessels, trunking carrying vapours away through the roof to the outside atmosphere. The trunking should be designed to avoid dirt collection, a cylindrical cross-section being favoured. Extraction fans can be fitted in the trunking if forced ventilation is considered necessary. Ventilation outlets should be screened to prevent insects and birds entering the system.[7, 8]

Since many food materials readily acquire odours and flavours from the atmosphere in contact with them during processing, areas used for handling a variety of products, including meat and materials containing small quantities of fats—dried milk products, flour and cocoa—are better processed in well-ventilated rooms supplied with clean air under controlled humidity conditions. The whole process area is maintained at a pressure slightly greater than atmospheric. Only treated air enters. The positive pressure ventilation system prevents ingress of insects, dust, etc.

17.2.2.4. Lighting. Adequate lighting of a process area is essential. It affects the health and safety of the operatives as well as the efficiency with which they work. Satisfactory illumination shows up any accumulation of dirt as well as general untidiness and exposes unhygienic working conditions. By encouraging good 'housekeeping', lighting conditions directly influence the overall standard of hygiene within the plant.

17.2.3. EQUIPMENT DESIGN

It is now generally accepted that equipment design and plant lay-out, based on considerations both of utility and of hygienic design, increases the likelihood of success in food processing operations. This conclusion is recognised by food processers, equipment manufacturers and health authorities, all of whom are now collaborating in the production of 'codes of practice' for hygienic or sanitary design. It is intended that these standards[9 – 13] be used as a guide for those engaged in the design, installation, operation and maintenance of food processing plants.

Hygienic design requirements vary to some extent, depending on the nature of the food being processed. However, the underlying principles are common to the design of all food processing equipment. In general, the design, materials of construction and methods of installation of a food-processing plant should be chosen so as to facilitate cleaning and sterilisation of the plant.[14, 15] For this reason the equipment must be easy to dismantle and reassemble quickly, using simple tools. Alternatively, it must be designed for in-place cleaning (Section 17.3.3).

17.2.3.1. Nature and materials of construction of contact surfaces.

All surfaces in contact with food materials must be smooth and free from pits and crevices. They must be non-absorbent and unaffected by either the food material or cleaning agents with which they come into contact.

Toxic substances, likely to endanger health if consumed with the product, must not be used in the construction of food equipment if contact with edible material can occur. Contaminating metals commonly placed in this category include copper, iron, zinc, cadmium, antimony and lead. Some standards allow the inclusion of lead in solder in amounts not exceeding 5%.[15] Dissimilar metals, capable of promoting chemical or electrolytic action if in contact in a liquid environment, must be avoided. Plastic materials,[16] if used, must be abrasion resistant and must be free from constituents which migrate to the foodstuff.

Stainless steel is very widely used in the fabrication of food processing equipment.[17] This material can be polished to a high surface finish giving a smooth, crevice-free surface, ideal for cleaning. Stainless steel offers a high corrosion resistance in a variety of environments but is not recommended for use with salt brine solutions.[18] Aluminium and its alloys are also extensively used in food plant, but since the metal is attacked by both acids and alkalis, care must be exercised in the selection of suitable cleaning agents.

Other materials encountered include Monel metal (a copper–nickel alloy), brass, copper and bronze when suitably tinned and, in more recent years, titanium. In certain applications the advantages offered by this latter material of construction—high corrosion resistance, mechanical strength and cleanability—outweigh its high initial cost.[19] Glass pipelines and vessel linings are also popular in the food industry. Corrosion problems are negligible and inspection to ensure cleanliness of pipe runs becomes possible. With correct installation and handling, breakage, with the attendant risk of glass contaminating the foodstuffs, is minimal. Due to its absorbent properties and the difficulties associated with its cleaning, wood is not recommended as a material of construction for food contact surfaces. Nevertheless, wood is still widely used for cutting surfaces in the preparation of meat and in the hand slicing and dicing of speciality vegetables and fruits. More recently, several toughened rubbers have been developed for these applications. These have more favourable surface characteristics and are finding increasing use.

17.2.3.2. Plant construction.

In the construction of food plant items much can be done to streamline the flow of materials over internal contact surfaces, thus avoiding those undesirable accumulations of food soils which are a potential source of contamination when trapped in less accessible areas of the equipment. Recesses, seams, ledges, inside threads, rivets, bolts and screws should be avoided as these promote stagnant regions which assist deposition and soiling. Permanent joints in metal parts should preferably be butt-welded, and the weld should be ground flush with adjacent surfaces, taking care to avoid pits and crevices (Fig. 17.1a). Lap welds (Fig. 17.1b) should be contoured to promote drainage.

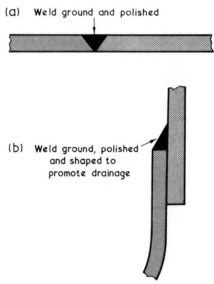

(a) Weld ground and polished

(b) Weld ground, polished and shaped to promote drainage

FIG. 17.1. (a) Butt weld. (b) Lap weld.

All surfaces in contact with food materials must be constructed and installed so as to be self-draining to reduce undesirable build-up of food material. To assist complete emptying, bottoms of vessels can be dished or, if flat-bottomed, pitched (Fig. 17.2). A minimum bottom slope of about one in a hundred ($\frac{1}{8}$ in/ft) is recommended. When dished bottoms are fitted, drain lines from vessels should be flush fitting and sited at the lowest point to avoid stagnant pools of liquid. Sharp interior corners should be avoided, minimum radii of about 7 mm ($\frac{1}{4}$ in) being preferred.

Shaft seal assemblies and bearings for pumps and agitators used with liquid or semi-liquid products should be located outside the product contact zone. The shaft seals must be readily removable to facilitate cleaning and inspection of both seals and sealing materials.

All packing materials must be non-toxic, non-porous and non-absorbent, and must be inert to food materials and cleaning compounds.

Equipment should be designed to prevent contamination of the contents from external sources. Readily removable covers must be provided for vessels, and all access points must be covered when not in use. These covers should be designed to permit free drainage of any liquid inadvertently coming into contact with them, the pitch of the

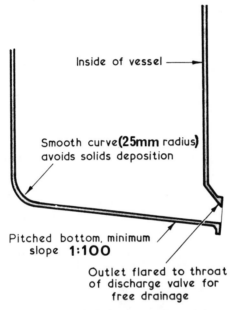

Fig. 17.2.   Hygienic design features for tank bottom.[15]

surface carrying the liquid away from the access point. Lid hinges should also be of a simple take-apart type, permitting easy cleaning. Adequate ventilation and correct design of hoods and trunking will, of course, overcome the nuisance and constant contamination risk caused in so many plants by condensation drips from steam-heated blanchers, retorts, evaporators and boiling pans.

The importance of good house-keeping in maintaining satisfactory hygienic standards cannot be overstressed, and any design leading to a higher standard of cleanliness is highly desirable. For this reason even exterior non-product contact surfaces should be easily cleanable. They should be contoured so as to prevent build-up of soils and other deposits which encourage the growth of micro-organisms and insect pests in and around the equipment. This means that external surfaces should be free from open seams, crevices and other inaccessible recesses. Lagging around heat transfer equipment should be sealed to prevent ingress of insects.

17.2.3.3. Installation of equipment. The design of supporting steelwork and masonry shows a lack of appreciation of hygienic design principles in some plants. Bed-plates and support foundations for food equipment often serve as breeding grounds for insects and bacteria. Food material can become trapped in inaccessible gaps where satisfactory cleaning is not possible. Equipment should be installed on a floor or foundation of non-absorbent, easily cleanable material. Narrow gaps between the undersides of equipment and the floor must be avoided. The clearance must be sufficiently high to permit access for inspection and cleaning. Alternatively, the equipment or supports can be completely sealed into the floor. Joints must, however, be water-tight and flush-fitting or contoured to permit free drainage.

17.2.3.4. Installation of pipework. All pipes and pipe fittings used with food materials should be capable of easy dismantling for inspection and cleaning. Pipe connections and valve entry and exit ports should be provided with hygienic-type fittings having easily cleanable external threads (Fig. 17.3) or gasketed joints with snap-on

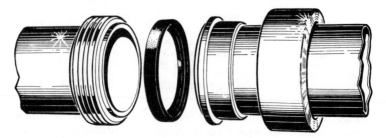

FIG. 17.3.   APV type stainless steel sanitary pipe fittings. (By courtesy of The APV Co. Ltd, Crawley.)

couplings. Both pipes and fittings must be completely self-draining, and adequate pipe supports are necessary to prevent sagging of pipe runs since this could lead to the retention of pockets of food material. 'Dead ends' must also be avoided. To minimise the risk of scale, paint or condensate getting into the food, overhead pipes should not pass directly over vessels or process lines carrying food exposed to the atmosphere. Pipes carrying services such as steam, water or air to process vessels should pass behind the vessels rather than over them. To assist in house-keeping, pipes, vessels, instrument-consoles, in-place cleaning panels, etc., should not be fitted too close to walls or floors. Adequate space to permit cleaning of both the equipment and the floor area must always be allowed.

With the plant and equipment designed to take advantage of modern hygienic principles, an essential step towards hygienic operating conditions in the factory will have been taken. However, acceptable standards of hygiene will only be achieved if correct cleaning and sterilising procedures are followed.

17.3. PLANT CLEANING AND STERILISATION

17.3.1. INTRODUCTION

Cleaning and sterilisation operations are essential in a food processing plant if edible food materials are to be produced under safe, hygienic conditions. These operations may be carried out on the raw material and product streams in certain processes—as in the preparation of fruits and vegetables—but must be performed on the plant and equipment in every food factory. Cleaning and sterilisation of plant and equipment is considered here. Raw material cleaning is discussed in Chapter 2 and sterilisation of foodstuffs by heat and ionisation in Chapters 11 and 15. Cleaning and sterilisation operations must not be considered as optional extras by plant operatives. They are an integral part of plant operation requiring a certain technology of their own. The performance of these cleansing operations must be co-ordinated with those involving the actual processing of food material. For efficient performance the development of a satisfactory programme of operations will necessitate detailed study using techniques such as network analysis. Such a study will show up both bottle-necks and areas where savings in time can be realised.[20, 21]

Food equipment must be cleaned immediately after use and requires sterilising before re-use. These two operations are quite distinct, although satisfactory sterilisation is much easier to achieve on a clean surface.

In cleaning, residual food materials in the plant and soils deposited during processing are physically removed by brushing, by the action of highly turbulent fluids, or by a combination of both these agencies. This removal is usually aided by the addition of detergents and conditioners which assist the wetting of the surface of the soil and its subsequent removal from equipment surfaces. This detergent cleaning should be followed by a clean water rinse. Care must be taken to ensure that dislodged soil is not deposited in other parts of the plant. Detergent cleaning is best preceded by a clean water rinse which often removes much of the soil.

In removing soils, large numbers of contaminating micro-organisms will have been removed. Nevertheless, micro-organisms will remain on the equipment surfaces after cleaning and these must be destroyed if the risk of contamination is to be avoided. The contact surfaces will require sterilising, using either steam, hot water, or a chemical sterilant.

The development of combined detergent-sterilants in recent years has, in certain cases, made possible the combining of cleaning and sterilising into a single operation. This has the advantage of reducing process downtime. However, many chemical sterilants (Section 17.3.4.2) are less effective when combined with detergents and, although this can be overcome by increasing the concentration of sterilant, cleaning costs will rise.

17.3.2. 'CLEANSING'—TERMINOLOGY AND METHODS FOR 'CLEANSING'

There is an element of ambiguity in the nomenclature associated with food plant sterilisation. The term sterilisation refers to a process which will destroy all living organisms, and a sterile surface is one free of all micro-organisms. This condition is approached in 'aseptic filling' but not in general plant cleansing.[22, 23] The terms commercial sterility and near sterility are both used to describe those conditions where acceptably few micro-organisms have survived the sterilisation treatment.[24] 'Sanitiser' is a term preferred in North America to 'sterilant' for a chemical agent that reduces the number of microbial contaminants on food contact surfaces to safe levels as regards public health,[22] and sanitising or sanitisation are often used to denote an operation leading to physical as well as microbiological cleanliness. A disinfectant destroys disease organisms. In Britain, disinfection is often preferred to the term 'commercial sterilisation' while cleansing is preferred to sanitising when both physical and microbiological cleanliness is required.

The standard method for cleansing food plant and equipment involves:

(i)   Cleaning, using water and a detergent suited to the soil, the hardness of the water, the material of construction of the equipment and the cleaning technique used.

(ii)   Sterilisation (disinfection, sanitisation), using the heat in steam or hot water as a sterilising medium, or a chemical sterilant (bactericide, disinfectant, sanitiser).

These two aspects of cleansing will now be discussed in more detail.

17.3.3. CLEANING

The cleaning operation can be performed in one of two different ways, modern food processing plants being designed to permit cleaning by either:

(i)   Dismantling and cleaning, or
(ii)   In-place cleaning or cleaning-in-place (CIP).

17.3.3.1. Dismantling and cleaning. This older method of cleaning, still widely practised and very efficient when carried out correctly, requires the plant to be constructed so as to permit rapid dismantling. After dismantling, the plant surfaces are cleaned by brushing and flushing with detergent solution. Residual detergent is rinsed away with clean water, the detergent being selected to ensure that food material and released soil film is carried away in solution or suspension. This method of cleaning allows visual inspection of plant contact surfaces to ascertain that cleaning is complete.

A wide variety of cleaning equipment is available. Brooms, mops, buckets, scrapers and 'squeegees' are standard requirements. Manual and mechanical brushes are also useful. Compressed air jets are invaluable for removing powdered soils from machinery surfaces. Vacuum cleaners also find extensive application in solids cleaning. Water jets operating at both low and high pressures are useful, when used with discretion—they can, however, disperse dirt over very wide areas. Two-phase cleaning guns have very wide application in food plant cleaning. These include steam-water jets and steam-detergent jets. Steam guns are also used for cleansing plant surfaces. They should not be used in the vicinity of plant moving parts—gear trains, pulleys, etc.—since they rapidly strip lubricant off bearing surfaces. For small items of equipment, soak-tanks containing detergent solution are convenient. After pre-rinsing in a water stream, items can be left to soak before brushing *in-situ*. A final rinse with hot water at about 82 °C (180 °F) will ensure natural drying.[25]

For larger items of equipment, such as storage vessels, spraying is preferred to manual cleaning. Manual internal cleaning can be difficult, whereas the use of correctly designed spraying heads can thoroughly clean relatively inaccessible surfaces. A variety of types of head are available (Fig. 17.4). Head and fittings can be temporary or permanent fixtures, but permanent installation is preferred. The head should be designed to hygienic standards, being self-cleaning and self-draining. Leakage of cleaner to the food product during processing operations should not be possible. The incorporation of permanent cleaning facilities into major items of process plant is a big step towards in-place cleaning.

Foam cleaning and gel-cleaning[26] are finding increasing use where larger areas—walls, working surfaces, etc.—need to be cleaned.

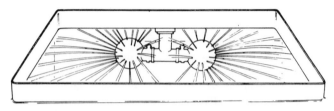

FIG. 17.4.   In-place cleaning sprays operating inside a stainless steel tank. (By courtesy of The APV Co. Ltd, Crawley.)

With foam cleaning a foaming agent is added to the detergent solution. This produces a longer-life, thick foam, which clings to the surface being cleaned thus increasing contact time between dirt and detergent. Pressure activated foaming equipment is now available. The use of foam cleaning gives visual evidence of the area actually contacted by the cleaner.

In gel-cleaning a gelling agent added to the detergent produces a mixture which sticks to inclined and to vertical surfaces thus giving long contact times for efficient softening of the soil.

With both foam cleaning and gel-cleaning the need for mechanical flushing remains and the cleaning agent used must be capable of easy removal with a water rinse.

17.3.3.2. In-place cleaning. Food processing plants require frequent cleaning. Dismantling plant for cleaning leads to long periods of downtime and high labour usage. Continual dismantling and reassembly can also result in mechanical damage and increased maintenance charges. Manual cleaning of the inside surfaces of larger capacity vessels—storage tanks, spray drier chambers, calandria evaporators, etc.—is arduous, and even a conscientious operator can overlook the small pocket of dirt that could lead to the spoilage of product.

To obviate the disadvantages inherent in dismantling and cleaning, in-place cleaning has been developed for use in plants handling liquid foodstuffs.[27]

In principle, the method used is the same as that for dismantling and cleaning, As before, detergent solutions are used to strip food residues and soiling films from the internal surfaces of the system, following an initial, wash water rinse. Sterilisation of the cleaned surfaces, using a chemical sterilant, follows the rinse. However, no time-consuming dismantling or reassembly is required. The exact arrangement of the cleaning system depends on the complexity of the plant layout. Basically, a make-up or storage tank containing the cleansing solution is piped into the system. Under normal operating conditions this tank is suitably isolated to avoid leakage of chemical solutions into the process stream. With the system empty and ready for cleaning after a production run ceases, raw material storage tanks and product receivers are isolated and the cleansing solution storage tank opened to the system. The desired solutions are circulated through the equipment and back to the storage tank on a sequential basis, using a circulation pump. Water rinses can be passed through the system to a drain. The detergent and sterilant solutions can be made up to the desired concentration in the make-up tank, prior to cleaning. Alternatively the calculated quantity of concentrated chemical can be metered into a circulating water stream, using a dosing pump.

By incorporating automatic valves and a sequential timing system the cleaning process can be made almost fully automatic and independent of human operators, thus affording considerable labour savings.

17.3.3.3. Factors influencing the degree of cleaning achieved. Factors influencing the degree of cleaning, whether by dismantling or CIP, include:

(i)   temperature, composition and concentration of detergent solutions,
(ii) contact time between detergent solutions and the soil deposit,
(iii) degree of turbulence promoted, and
(iv) the nature and thickness of the soil film.

Detergent composition governs the ability of the process to remove soil deposits in a given system. The detergent will be selected following laboratory trials with the particular type of solid and expected degree of deposition. Solution concentration and temperature affects the rate of reaction between soil and detergent. Solution temperature can be adjusted by steam injection. With CIP the degree of turbulence promoted and the circulation time will influence the scouring effect produced by the flowing liquid stream. It is this scouring effect which replaces the brushing in manual cleaning, so the piping system should be designed to produce high Reynolds numbers (Appendix I) in the circuit. Flow velocities for pipeline sizes commonly encountered should not be less than 1·5 m/s (5 ft/s).[28]

The quality of the water supplied to the plant is also important. If the water is bacteriologically acceptable and has been softened (Chapter 18) only detergent need be added, but if the mineral content of the water is high, water conditioners (sequestering agents such as sodium polyphosphates) must be added to prevent precipitation on pipeline and equipment surfaces (Section 17.3.3.5).

If the soil deposits are not great, the cleaning and sterilising solutions can be mixed and circulated together.

17.3.3.4. Detergents. Detergents are almost invariably used in the wet cleaning of food contact surfaces. The nature of the soil to be removed and the material of construction of the plant surfaces will dictate the type of detergent required. They should be readily soluble in water so as to avoid the possibility of deposition of unwanted solids. The resulting solution must not attack the contact surfaces, corrosion being avoided by correct selection of detergent for the particular material of construction. With stainless steels, the almost automatic first choice for food plant fabrication, risk of corrosion is slight. It must be remembered, however, that stainless steel is not universally inert to chemical corrosion and, in any case, alternative, cheaper materials of construction might well be used (Section 17.2.3). The detergent solution must be able to emulsify or disperse fats and oils, adequately wet the surface of the soil, and penetrate to the soil-contact surface interface thus dislodging the soil. It should also be able to dissolve or disperse the food materials released and have good rinsing properties. A wide variety of detergents are available.[22] They may be classified as:

(i)   Detergents composed principally of inorganic alkalis.
(ii)   Inorganic and organic acid detergents.
(iii)   Detergents composed principally of surface active agents.
(iv)   Alkaline polyphosphates, used for their water conditioning capabilities rather than their alkalinity.

Inorganic alkaline detergents. Alkaline detergents have good emulsifying properties and can dissolve food solids such as protein. They include:

(*a*) *Sodium hydroxide.* Caustic soda solution is a powerful detergent with excellent emulsifying and dispersing properties. It is an effective bactericide and is widely used in mechanical bottle washing. Solutions of caustic soda are strongly corrosive to certain metals, aluminium and zinc being rapidly attacked. Use of the solution involves a safety hazard, and protection of personnel must be considered.

(*b*) *Sodium metasilicate.* Another useful detergent having good wetting, emulsifying and deflocculating properties, sodium metasilicate, is much less corrosive than caustic soda and actually inhibits corrosion of aluminium and tin. It is often used with a sodium polyphosphate, the mixture being recommended for use where water hardness exceeds 100 mg/litre $CaCO_3$.

(*c*) *Sodium orthosilicate and sodium sesquisilicate.* Both are compounds giving highly alkaline solutions which are powerful saponifiers. They attack greases and protein readily. The sesquisilicate is not as corrosive as the orthosilicate but care is necessary when using either of these solutions.

(*d*) *Trisodium phosphate.* A solution of trisodium phosphate has excellent emulsifying and dispersing properties. It is a water softening agent and, as such, is used in conjunction with other detergents as a water conditioner in general cleaning compounds.

(*e*) *Sodium carbonate—soda ash.* Soda ash as well as the bicarbonate and sesquicarbonate of sodium have been used both as water softeners and as cleaners but their main use is as buffering agents in a number of cleaning compounds.

Acid detergents. The employment of acid detergents in food plant cleaning has increased in recent years, although they are by no means as commonly used as alkalis. Inhibited inorganic acids such as hydrochloric, nitric and phosphoric acids have been used in the past to remove hardness scale (Chapter 18) and, in dairies, to remove 'milkstone' (inorganic deposits, consisting mainly of calcium phosphate, which build up on hot surfaces during milk processing). Both deposits are relatively insoluble in alkaline solution but are successfully removed by acids. Plant corrosion and operator safety are major considerations when using these inorganic acids. Such acids are now being replaced in these applications by relatively non-corrosive organic acids such as sulphamic, citric, tartaric and gluconic acids.[22] Gluconic and sulphamic acids are widely used in the descaling of heat transfer equipment such as evaporators and pasteurisers. Acid detergents can be safely used in conjunction with iodophors in formulations for detergent-sterilants (Section 17.3.4.2).

Detergents composed of surface active agents. A variety of surface active agents are available and they are often added to detergent formulations to enhance wetting and penetrating properties. Many are excellent emulsifying agents and can disperse oils, fats, greases, etc. Surfactants stable under both acid and alkaline conditions are available. They are compounds containing both water soluble (hydrophilic) groups and oil-soluble (lipophilic groups) (Chapter 5). In the presence of water–oil systems the hydrophilic part dissolves in the water phase and the lipophilic part in the oil. A firm bond is established between water and oil. In a turbulent water stream the emulsion is carried away from an oil or grease contaminated surface and cleaning achieved.

Surface active agents can be classified as either: (a) Anionic, (b) cationic, or (c) non-ionic.

(*a*) *Anionic surfactants.* With *anionic surfactants*, the active ion in solution is negatively charged. Many synthetic varieties are on the market. They have excellent dispersing and wetting powers and are especially useful in the removal of fatty acids or inorganic (polar-type) soils. They are poor bactericides and are used solely for their detergent properties.

(*b*) *Cationic surfactants.* These surfactants give positively charged active ions in aqueous solution. They are poor detergents but excellent bactericides and are used for their sterilising properties (Section 17.3.4.2).

(*c*) *Non-ionic surfactants.* Non-ionic surface active agents are not dissociated in solution. Consequently they are virtually unaffected by water hardness. They are powerful emulsifiers and are used to emulsify colloidal soils, being inert to the electric charge present on colloids. Non-ionic surfactants have a pronounced foaming action which can lead to difficulties, especially in the disposal of detergent contaminated wastes.

Some anionic surfactants exhibit synergistic effects with other compounds, the detergent capability of the mixture being better than that of individual components. However, it must be realised that mixing of anionic and cationic detergents should be undertaken with caution since such mixing can reduce the efficiency of both, with a consequent deterioration in cleaning performance. Non-ionic forms can safely be combined with anionic or cationic varieties.

17.3.3.5. Water conditioners. (a) *Sequestering agents.* If hard water is used for cleaning purposes the efficiency of cleaning is likely to be reduced and hardness scale will develop on pipeline and equipment surfaces. Since hardness is due to the presence of salts of calcium and magnesium (Chapter 18), additives capable of preventing the precipitation of these ions from solution will prevent scale formation. Such additives are known as 'water conditioners' and the restraining action as sequestering. Sodium polyphosphates are widely used sequestering agents. Tetrasodium pyrophosphate is the cheapest of these. It is reasonably stable in hot, highly alkaline solutions, and is often used in mechanical bottle washers and soak-tanks. It is not very soluble and is a poor sequestering agent for calcium. Two other polyphosphates, the tri- and tetra-polyphosphates of sodium, are effective sequestering agents for both calcium and magnesium. They are readily soluble in warm water but lose their efficiencies at higher temperatures. Sodium hexametaphosphate is widely used with waters high in calcium but it is less effective with 'magnesium hardness'. Like the tri- and tetra-polyphosphates it decomposes to the less effective pyro- and ortho-phosphates at higher temperatures.

(*b*) *Chelating agents.* Like the polyphosphates, chelating agents can prevent hardness constituents depositing on plant surfaces. The hardness constituents and other metal ions are bound in a chelate ring structure and are not precipitated. The most important chelating agents are ethylene-diamine-tetra-acetic acid (EDTA) and its sodium or potassium salts. Besides their capacity for preventing the deposition of scale on plant surfaces, both EDTA and sodium hexametaphosphate solutions are used to soften existing scale when detergent cleaning. The use of these agents in hard surface cleaning is discussed by Jennings.[29]

17.3.4. STERILISATION

The methods selected for plant sterilising operations must be kept under rigid bacteriological control.[30] Either heat or chemical sterilants are used.

17.3.4.1. Heat sterilisation. For heat sterilisation, either steam or hot water is used. The use of saturated steam under pressure is a most effective means of controlling micro-organisms, being excellent for the sterilisation of storage tanks, process vessels, pipelines, etc. Thorough cleaning before sterilisation is essential, otherwise food soils on heavily contaminated surfaces can become baked on to the plant surfaces. These soils can provide excellent nutrients for the subsequent growth of micro-organisms which may have survived the heat treatment, owing to the heat insulating properties of the baked surface formed.

Moisture plays a part in the destruction of micro-organisms by thermal treatment, dry heat being less effective than the heat in steam or hot water.[31] Steam jets are widely used for sterilising both interior and exterior surfaces of plant and equipment (Section 17.3.3.1), but steam should be used with care on plastics. Hot water is also useful for sterilising food plant. In this case appreciable quantities of bacteria are also removed by the scouring action. Time and temperature conditions for both steam and hot water sterilisation must be determined. An extended discussion of steam sterilisation is given by Chalmers.[32]

17.3.4.2. Chemical sterilisation. The two most popular groups of chemical sterilants used in the food industry are: (1) chlorine compounds, and (2) quaternary ammonium compounds.

These sterilants are very convenient for use with in-place cleaning systems and, provided the plant contact surfaces are clean, their lethality to micro-organisms is no less than that of heat treatment. They can be used in cold dilute solution thus reducing the possibility of corrosion. Newer sterilants include 'iodophors' and amphoteric 'bactericides'.

Chlorine compounds. An aqueous solution of sodium hypochlorite is the most commonly used chlorine containing compound, a fresh commercial solution containing 9–12% of available chlorine. The recommended concentration for use in stainless steel plant is 150–250 mg/litre of available chlorine with a contact time of 15 min. A method more suitable for larger vessels, storage tanks, etc., involves spraying contact surfaces with a solution containing 250 mg/litre available chlorine for 5 min. For maximum wetting, spraying should start at the lowest point and rise up the surfaces. A concentration of 200 mg/litre available chlorine should not be exceeded in aluminium plant. At these recommended concentrations chlorine exerts a rapid bactericidal action against both Gram-positive and Gram-negative bacteria[33] leaving non-toxic residues (sodium chloride). A disadvantage of hypochlorite solution is its decrease in bactericidal efficiency in the presence of organic matter. For this reason, contact surfaces should be thoroughly cleaned and rinsed free of organic detergent compounds before sterilisation.

Quaternary ammonium compounds. The use of these cationic detergent compounds—quats—has grown in recent years. They are ammonium salts having some or all of the hydrogen atoms in the $[NH_4]^+$ radical replaced by alkyl or aryl groups, one of these being a long chain (C_8—C_{18}) group. The inorganic anion is usually chloride or bromide, as, for example, in 'alkyl trimethyl ammonium bromide' and 'lauryl dimethyl benzyl ammonium chloride'. Their mode of action against micro-organisms is not certain, but they are very effective against Gram-positive and, to a lesser extent, Gram-negative bacteria. The bactericidal efficiency of some quats is reduced in the presence of organic matter, but others retain their lethality to micro-organisms under these conditions. Since they are cationic, quats should not be mixed with anionic detergents and contact surfaces should be free of anionic surfactant before disinfecting with a quat. These compounds are available as powders and pastes but their use in aqueous solution is preferred. They are stable to heat, colourless, odourless and, at solution concentrations suitable for use, are non-toxic. Quats have a pronounced foaming tendency which can be troublesome. Non-foaming cationic bactericides based on guanidine (and said to be particularly effective against Gram-negative bacteria such as *Salmonella*) have been developed.[23]

For a fuller discussion of 'quats' and their use in the food industry *see* Lawrence.[34]

Iodophors. Iodophors are soluble complexes of non-ionic surface active agents and iodine. They can be formulated so as to possess detergent as well as bactericidal properties and are finding use as detergent-sterilants. They have rapid bactericidal action in cold, acid solution and are unaffected by water hardness. They are stable, non-toxic and do not impart stains, objectionable odours or tastes.[35]

Amphoteric–ampholytic bactericides. This group of bactericides are organic materials—usually substituted amino-acids or betaines—containing both acidic and basic groups. They exhibit anionic or cationic properties depending on pH. They are surface active, some having excellent wetting and penetrating powers, others being better bactericides.[36]

17.3.5. BACTERIOLOGICAL CONTROL

Cleaning and sterilising methods selected for plant cleansing operations must be kept under rigid bacteriological control. The modes of action, methods for testing the efficiency of sterilants, and contact surface tests for disinfection are discussed by Sykes.[30]

REFERENCES

1. Brown, C. B., and Derwas, J. L., *in* Cremer, H. W., and Watkins, S. B. (Eds) 'Chemical Engineering Practice', Vol. II. (Butterworths: 1959.)
2. Joslyn, M. A., and Heid, J. L., 'Food Processing Operations', Vol. III. (AVI: 1964.)
3. Ziemba, J. W., 'Know Your Floors'. Fd Engng, **36**(10), 74 (1964).
4. Anon., 'Surface for Finishing Floors'. Fd Process Ind., **42**(506), 35 (1973).
5. Kell, J. R., *in* Cremer, H. W., and Watkins, S. B. (Eds) 'Chemical Engineering Practice', Vol. V. (Butterworths: 1963.)
6. Slade, F. H., 'Food Processing Plant', Vol. 2. (Leonard Hill: 1971.)
7. Evans, M., 'Planned Insect Control'. Fd Mf., **48**(9), 29–37 (1973).
8. Anon., 'Insect Infestation—The Problem and the Plant and Services to Cope With It'. Fd Process Ind., **44**(519), 36–40 (1975).
9. '3A Sanitary Standards'. Formulated by International Association of Milk, Food and Environmental Sanitarians, United States Public Health Service and The Dairy Industry Committee.
10. 'Recommendations for Sanitary Design'. National Canners Association, Washington, D.C.
11. 'Sanitation Standards'. Baking Industry Sanitation Standards Committee, New York.
12. 'Guide for the Sanitary Design and Construction of Food Equipment'. Bureau of Food and Drugs of the New York City Health Department, New York City, USA.
13. Joint Technical Committee, FMF/FMA, 'Hygienic Design of Food Plant'. Food Manufacturers' Federation and Food Machinery Association (undated).
14. Wilson, C. K., 'Sanitation in Machinery Design and Use', *in* Proceedings Third International Congress On Canned Foods'. (Rome: 1956.)
15. Milleville, H. P., and Gelber, P., 'Sanitary Design of Food Processing Equipment'. Food Processing, **25**(10), 93–114 (1964); also, **26**(4), 170–177 (1965).
16. Briston, J. H., and Katan, L. L., 'Plastics in Contact With Food'. (Anchor Press Ltd: 1974.)
17. Connolly, B. J., 'Stainless Steels in Food and Drink Processing'. Process Engng, December (1969).
18. Wilson, C. K., 'Your Sanitary Food Equipment'. Food Engineering, **29**(3), 72–76 (1957).
19. Bamberger, H. B., Bedford, G. T., and Lorz, R. M., 'Why Not Try Titanium?', Food Engineering, **29**(8), 97–100 (1957).
20. Lockyer, K. G., 'An Introduction to Critical Path Analysis'. (Pitman: 1964.)
21. Bluesnel, E. L., 'A New Look at Network Analysis for the Smaller Companies'. Chemistry and Industry, 916 (1966).
22. Parker, M. E., and Litchfield, J. H., 'Food Plant Sanitation'. (Reinhold: 1962.)
23. Thomas, G. A., 'Chemical Sterilants in the Food Industry'. Chemistry and Industry, 1198–1202 (1960).
24. 'In-Place Cleaning of Dairy Equipment'. Society of Dairy Technology (1959).
25. Graham-Rack, B., and Binstead, R., 'Hygiene in Food Manufacturing and Handling', 2nd ed. (Food Trade Press: 1973).
26. Bensink, J. C., 'Cleaning in the Food Industry'. CSIRO, Fd Res. Q., **34**, 49–61 (1974).
27. Seiberling, D. A., 'Equipment and Process Design as Related to Mechanical/Chemical Cleaning Procedures', *in* Opila, R. L., and Schultz, J. S. (Eds) 'Bioengineering-Food'. Chemical Engineering Progress Symposium Series No. 86, Vol. 64, 94–104 (American Institute of Chemical Engineers: 1968).
28. Blois Johnson, W., 'Hygienic Considerations in Food Plant Design'. Chemistry and Industry, 1203–1205 (1960).

29. Jennings, W. G., *in* Chichester, C. O., and Mrak, E. M. (Eds) 'Advances in Food Research', Vol. 14. (Academic Press: 1965.)
30. Sykes, G., 'Disinfection and Sterilization'. (Spon: 1965.)
31. Ball, C. O., and Olson, F. C. W., 'Sterilization in Food Technology'. (McGraw-Hill: 1957.)
32. Chalmers, C. H., 'The Value of Steam as a Sterilizing Agent'. Journal of the Society of Dairy Technology, **14**(2), 72–75 (1961).
33. Frazier, W. C., 'Food Microbiology', 2nd ed. (McGraw-Hill: 1967.)
34. Lawrence, C. A., 'Quaternary Ammonium Surface-Active Disinfectants', *in* Lawrence, C. A., and Block, S. S. (Eds) 'Disinfection, Sterilisation and Preservation', CL 26, 430–52 (Lea and Febiger: 1968).
35. Davis, J. G., 'Iodophors as Detergent-Sterilizers'. Journal of Applied Bacteriology, **25**(2), 195–201 (1962).
36. Kornfeld, F., 'Ampholytic Surfactants'. Food Manufacture, **41**(8), 39–46 (1966).

CHAPTER 18

WATER SUPPLIES AND WASTE DISPOSAL

18.1. INTRODUCTION

Two requirements often vital to the successful operation of a modern food processing plant are (a) an adequate supply of water of various qualities, and (b) satisfactory facilities for the disposal of waste materials.

Such is the importance of these two facilities, that failure of the water supply, either in quantity or quality, or an inability to discharge waste materials safely and cheaply, can quickly bring the most efficient process line to a standstill. Their availability influences the choice of a factory site and they are factors which must be fully examined during an initial 'site survey'.

18.2. WATER SUPPLIES

18.2.1. WATER QUALITY REQUIREMENTS

The multiplicity of uses for water in the food industry (cleaning, blanching, sterilisation, cooling and steam generation for power, process heating and direct 'in-process' use) calls for enormous quantities of this commodity.

Water used in the food and beverage industries can be classified as:

(i)   General purpose water.
(ii) Process water.
(iii) Cooling water.
(iv) Boiler feed water.

(i) General purpose water for cleaning and preparation of food materials, for the washing of plant and ancillary equipment, etc., is used in the greatest quantities. These waters should be clean and wholesome, that is, potable and clear, colourless, free from tastes, odours and toxic ions and bacteriologically acceptable.[1,2]

(ii) The requirement for a process water depends on the process. In addition to being potable, these waters may require softening to remove soluble salts which can influence the texture of certain vegetables, cause unsightly deposits on equipment surfaces, on bottles during washing, etc., and can lead to scale formation in heat exchange equipment.

(iii) The water quality requirement for a cooling water is less stringent. The water may be non-potable if contamination of food materials can be eliminated. Removal of colours, tastes and odours is not so important. A hard cooling water should be softened to prevent scale formation. Since large quantities of cooling water are required, re-use of this water is recommended whenever possible.[3, 4]

(iv) With boiler feed water the removal of 'hardness' to avoid scale formation may be sufficient treatment. With water for higher pressure boilers a reduction in total solids content is advisable if priming (*i.e.* the carry-over of large quantities of water with steam) is to be avoided.[5, 6]

18.2.2. NATURAL WATERS—SOURCES AND QUALITY

The source of all water for factory use, excluding those plants using sea water for such specialised applications as cooling and fish freezing, is meteoric water—water precipitated as rain, snow or hail over the land masses of the earth.

The nature of the water collected depends on the atmosphere through which it descends and on the terrain on which it falls. Falling rain water is relatively pure. It contains little dissolved and suspended solids and very little bacterial flora. However the quality of the water reaching the factory 'intake' or the municipal water plant is very variable. Chemical substances which the water contacts are both dissolved and retained in suspension, organic matter is leached from decaying vegetation and a variety of micro-organisms find such an environment congenial for growth. Whatever the source, natural waters will contain impurities. These impurities will vary in different supplies.

Natural water supplies may be classified as either (a) surface or (b) ground waters.

(*a*) *Surface waters.* These come from rain falling on open uplands and moorlands. The rain subsequently drains into lakes and man-made reservoirs.

(*b*) *Ground waters.* These originate from wells or springs and consist of rain water which has percolated into the ground to become trapped in underground pockets.

Surface waters are open to direct contamination with human and animal refuse and industrial wastes. They may contain mineral matter, organic matter and micro-organisms, be turbid, highly coloured and possess unpleasant odours and tastes. These waters require treatment before use. Ground waters possess lower turbidities and bacterial contents but may have high soluble solids contents. With surface waters the composition may vary frequently, changing, for example, after sudden rainfall. With deep wells and large lakes the composition may remain relatively constant over many years. Any likely variation in composition must be considered when drawing up a water treatment flowsheet for a particular process.

18.2.3. CHOICE OF SUPPLY: MUNICIPAL SUPPLY OR FACTORY TREATMENT?

Many factories purchase their water supplies direct from the municipal authorities, the price per unit of volume usually falling with increasing requirement.[7] In general, these municipal supplies will have been clarified, filtered and sterilised, to produce a potable water.

For use in the food industry further treatment may be necessary. The treatment necessary for the production of a water of satisfactory quality for a particular consumer depends on the use for which the water is required. Where large quantities are needed, it is often advantageous for the user to purchase raw, untreated water and purify it to his own specific requirements.

18.3. WATER PURIFICATION: TYPES OF IMPURITIES AND METHODS FOR REMOVAL

The major impurities requiring removal are:

(1) Suspended matter, (2) micro-organisms, (3) organic matter—colours, tastes and odours, (4) dissolved mineral matter, (5) iron and manganese, (6) dissolved gases.

18.3.1. REMOVAL OF SUSPENDED MATTER

Water containing suspended matter is undesirable for most uses. Suspended impurities are of variable character, silt, clay, silica, finely divided vegetable and animal matter all being common.

The size range of the solids may be wide. Coarse solids (sediment) settle out rapidly on standing. Fine particles may remain in suspension imparting turbidity to the waters. Underground water supplies are likely to be free of turbidity excepting after periods of heavy rain, owing to the filtration undergone as water percolates through permeable strata.

The method selected for removing suspended matter depends on the volume of water to be treated and on the size range and nature of the suspension. Settling, coagulation and filtration are used.

18.3.1.1. Settling. With large volumes, storage in reservoirs and ponds will often allow sufficient residence time for the removal of much suspended matter by gravity sedimentation. With smaller volumes of water, settling tanks are sometimes used.

Fine particles can be agglomerated by coagulation.

18.3.1.2. Coagulation. The addition of a flocculating agent causes agglomeration of fine particles.[5, 8] The clumps of particles so formed behave as single particles of larger diameter and settle out more quickly. Thus a combination of coagulation and settling permits the separation of smaller particles in a relatively short time. The water produced is clear enough for many industrial uses.

The coagulants used in water treatment are generally salts of aluminium or iron. Aluminium sulphate, sodium aluminate and ferrous sulphate are often used.[7]

A solution of coagulant is metered into the mixing zone of a flocculating tank (Fig. 18.1). Here it meets raw water. The 'floc' of

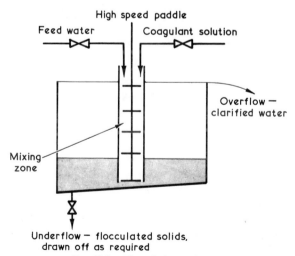

Fig. 18.1. Flocculating tank.

aluminium or iron hydroxide formed, settles to the bottom of the vessel, carrying with it suspended matter, micro-organisms, etc. The water then rises through a sludge of previously deposited floc. The upward velocity of the water is too low to permit carry over and a reasonably clear water is produced. Using a coagulant with a suitable coagulant aid such as activated silica, colour, turbidity, suspended matter and appreciable quantities of micro-organisms are removed.

For complete removal of very fine particles or for reduction in the time required for gravity separation, the coagulation and settling stage is often followed by filtration of the partially clarified waters.

18.3.1.3. Filtration. The filters used for water treatment in food plants are often pressure type sand filters (Fig. 18.2). Water is passed

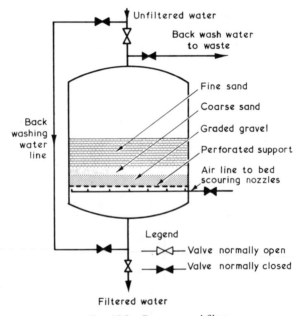

FIG. 18.2.   Pressure sand filter.

downwards through a filter bed consisting of fine sand supported on a layer of graded gravel. Suspended matter is removed. Filtration is continued until the pressure drop across the bed indicates that the filter is becoming choked. The bed can be cleaned by backwashing with an upwards stream of clean water. The capacity of these rapid sand filters is often taken as $2.5 \times 10^{-3} \, \text{m}^3/\text{s}$ per m^2 ($0.5 \, \text{ft}^3/\text{min}$ per ft^2) of filter bed area, and backwash flow rates for efficient washing should not be less than $1 \cdot 0 \times 10^{-2} \, \text{m}^3/\text{s}$ per m^2 ($2 \, \text{ft}^3/\text{min}$ per ft^2) of bed area.[9]

In general, factory water treatment for removal of suspended solids involves a combination of coagulation, settling and filtration.

18.3.2. REMOVAL OF MICRO-ORGANISMS

Micro-organisms are commonly encountered in surface waters. Their content in waters from deep wells is usually low. Commonly occurring micro-organisms in surface waters[10] include diatoms, fungi, algae, protozoa, rotifera and nematodes together with a variety of non-pathogenic bacteria. Should the supply be contaminated by sewage, pathogenic bacteria may also be present.

If introduced into food processing plant, living micro-organisms and their decomposition products may give rise to off-colours, tastes and odours in food equipment and foodstuffs, while pathogenic bacteria not only cause spoilage of the product but also food poisoning.[11] To minimise such introduction, process waters must be free from micro-organisms.

On a large scale (treatment of lakes, etc.) algae and similar flora are controlled by dosing with copper sulphate, bacteria and other micro-organisms being subsequently removed by a combination of chlorination, coagulation, settling and filtration.

For 'on-site' water treatment, coagulation, settling and filtration, followed by sterilisation, usually produces water of acceptable bacteriological quality.

The usual method of sterilising water supplies is by treatment with chlorine or chlorine derivatives.[13, 14] Liquid chlorine is employed for large-scale treatment: for smaller capacities, chlorine dioxide and hypochlorites are used. Since suspended matter absorbs chlorine, turbid waters should be filtered before chlorination.

The effectiveness of disinfection depends on chlorine concentration, contact time, temperature, pH, and on the amount of organic matter present.

Chlorine reacts with organic nitrogenous matter in the water. The amount of chlorine required for complete reaction is called the 'chlorine demand'. To ensure complete destruction of all bacteria, 'residual chlorine' must remain in the water after a specified contact time. This contact time increases with water pH and decreases with temperature.

The reaction between chlorine and water is reversible:

$$Cl_2 + H_2O \rightleftharpoons HOCl + HCl$$

The hypochlorous acid reacts with nitrogenous matter to give chloramines

$$HOCl + NH_3 \rightarrow NH_2Cl + H_2O$$

$$2HOCl + NH_3 \rightarrow NHCl_2 + 2H_2O$$

Although less powerful bactericides than chlorine, chloramines are more stable and give a degree of protection after treatment, not afforded by chlorine alone. Holden[15] discusses an ammonia-chlorine treatment which takes advantage of this extra protection.

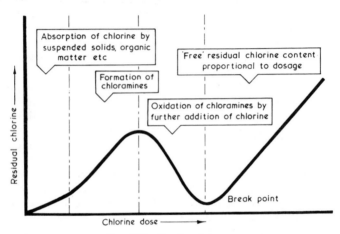

FIG. 18.3.   Break point curve.

When dosing with chlorine, the 'residual chlorine' initially rises with chlorine dose. This occurs while chlorine is absorbed by organic matter and chloramines are formed. Further addition of chlorine causes oxidation of the chloramines and the residual chlorine content again starts to increase when oxidation of chloramines is complete. The position of minimum residual chlorine is known as the 'break point' (Fig. 18.3). After the break point the free residual chlorine content becomes proportional to dosage. In the 'break point' method of chlorination the aim is to achieve a small residual of free chlorine sufficient to destroy micro-organisms present in the water without imparting a chlorine taste or odour. Chlorine dosage and contact time must be adequate to ensure sterilisation and must be confirmed by bacteriological examination of the treated waters. In another chlorination method, particularly suited to 'on-site' treatment, a much greater dose of chlorine is added to the water. At these higher concentrations bacteria are rapidly destroyed and contact times are short. Since the residual chlorine content is considerably higher than that desired, this technique is called 'superchlorination'. Knowing the final chlorine content acceptable for the particular application, the excess is removed by dechlorination. This is brought about by contact with suitable chemical agents. Sulphur dioxide is commonly used: alternatively the water can be passed through a bed of activated carbon which absorbs excess chlorine.[15] With improvements in equipment for the production of ozone, interest in the use of this material for the sterilisation of potable water has been growing in recent years. In France, over 500 installations are employing ozone and its use is spreading to other countries. The advantages claimed for ozone include: superior bactericidal action; elimination of tastes, especially those from phenolic wastes and from algal contamination; and avoidance of residuals other than a high dissolved oxygen content.[14, 16]

18.3.3. REMOVAL OF ORGANIC MATTER, COLOUR, TASTES AND ODOURS

Surface waters usually contain organic material leached from decaying vegetable matter with which it has been in contact. These waters can be both turbid and highly coloured, especially in swampy areas. Peat bogs often give rise to colour in ground waters.

Evidence suggests that a large part of the colouring in water is due to the presence of a colloidal suspension of ultramicroscopic particles, as well as to dissolved impurities in 'true' solution. Colour of natural waters can also be influenced by the presence of iron and manganese (Section 18.3.4).

Tastes and odours are normally confined to surface waters, although some deep well waters contain hydrogen sulphide and may carry a 'metallic' taste due to the presence of iron.

Practically all odours in natural water supplies are associated with the organic matter present. Death and decay of algal growths and other micro-organisms can give rise to undesirable odours and unsightly appearance. Chlorophenols, produced when water contaminated with traces of tar, phenols, etc., is chlorinated, can impart disagreeable tastes to water.

The use of ozone avoids these taste problems[16] but the removal of organic compounds, often only present in trace amounts, *e.g.*, organic pesticides, is an important step in the production of a potable water.[17]

In general, organic matter, colours, tastes and odours are unacceptable in a water to be used for food and beverage products. Several methods are available for their removal from water supplies. A combination of coagulation, settling and filtration is generally employed. With highly coloured waters the use of coagulant aids such as activated silica is recommended. Break-point chlorination has been used with success in the removal of certain colours but only experiment will determine its utility in any particular case. Aeration and super-chlorination are also employed.

The removal of colour, taste and odour producing substances from water by adsorption with activated carbon is, in general, the most efficient method available. Normally a slurry of powdered activated carbon is added to the water in a mixing vessel, the contaminated carbon then being removed by sand filtration. Alternatively filtration through granular beds of activated carbon is used.[15]

18.3.4. REMOVAL OF DISSOLVED MINERAL MATTER

All natural waters contain dissolved mineral matter, sulphates, chlorides and bicarbonates of sodium, magnesium and calcium being common. Other constituents include iron, manganese, silica and nitrates. For water treatment purposes it is convenient to examine the effects of these soluble impurities under three separate headings:

(i)   Alkalinity.
(ii) Hardness.
(iii) Iron and manganese.

18.3.4.1. Alkalinity. Almost all waters contain alkalinity due to the presence of the soluble bicarbonates of calcium, magnesium, sodium and potassium. In some waters soluble carbonates and hydroxides also give rise to 'alkalinity' which can be regarded as the capacity of a water to receive acid without substantially lowering the pH. Alkalinity is determined by titration with a standard acid solution using phenolphthalein and methyl orange as indicators. The titration enables 'bicarbonate alkalinity', 'carbonate alkalinity' and 'caustic alkalinity' to be determined.[9] Low alkalinity waters are required for certain mineral waters and beers. Boiler feed water should also have a low alkalinity if 'caustic embrittlement' (a form of 'crack corrosion') caused by caustic soda is to be avoided. Caustic soda is formed by the decomposition of sodium bicarbonate deposited in steam boilers using high alkalinity feed waters. Hydrogen zeolite treatment will remove 'alkalinity' when necessary (*see* below).

18.3.4.2. Hardness. *Effects of hard water.* Soluble calcium and magnesium salts dissolved in water give rise to 'hardness'. A water may contain 'temporary hardness' (carbonate hardness) due to the presence of calcium and magnesium bicarbonates, or 'permanent hardness' (non-carbonate hardness), due to sulphates, chlorides and nitrates of these elements.

The use of a hard water can lead to difficulties in food processing. Calcium and magnesium salts in process water produce a marked toughening of the skin of certain vegetables during blanching and canning.[18, 19] Washing operations using soap or other alkaline detergents are more difficult with hard water and softening leads to appreciable savings in detergent. A tough scale of calcium carbonate and sulphate is deposited on the walls of heat exchange equipment—pasteurisers, water heaters, steam boilers, etc.—when the water supply is hard. Besides reducing the flow capacity of equipment, these deposits inhibit heat transfer and, in boilers, can result in the failure of boiler tubes through overheating.[5, 19, 20]

Water softening. Of water softening processes commonly encountered, viz. (a) precipitation, (b) base exchange, and (c) demineralisation, the first two, either in combination or individually, provide the soft water requirements for most of the food industry.

(a) *Precipitation process.* Hydrated lime $Ca(OH)_2$ and sodium carbonate (Na_2CO_3) are added in metered quantities to the hard water. The lime removes temporary hardness precipitating the hardness salts as their insoluble carbonates.:

e.g.

$$Ca(HCO_3)_2 + Ca(OH)_2 = 2CaCO_3 + 2H_2O$$

$$Mg(HCO_3)_2 + Ca(OH)_2 = MgCO_3 + CaCO_3 + 2H_2O$$

Similarly soda ash removes permanent hardness:

e.g.

$$CaSO_4 + Na_2CO_3 = CaCO_3 + Na_2SO_4$$

So bicarbonates, chlorides, sulphates and nitrates of calcium and magnesium are removed.

A coagulant is usually added to flocculate the finely divided precipitate which is then separated by filtration if completely clear water is required. The cold lime-soda process reduces hardness of a water to about 70 mg/litre ($1\cdot0$ mg/litre as $CaCO_3 \equiv 0\cdot07$ grains/Imp. gallon).

For complete removal of hardness, the precipitation can be followed by a 'base exchange' or 'zeolite' process.

(b) *Zeolite process* (*base exchange*). Zeolites are complex silicates.

Natural zeolites can exchange sodium ions for ions of calcium, magnesium, iron and manganese in solution

e.g.

$$Ca(HCO_3)_2 + Na_2Z = 2NaHCO_3 + CaZ$$

Water to be softened is passed downwards, under gravity or pressure, through a bed of granulated zeolite. The cation exchanging properties of the zeolite remove the hardness. Exhausted zeolite is regenerated by backwashing with clean water followed by sodium chloride solution (salting). This removes the Ca and Mg as soluble chlorides leaving the bed in its original condition:

e.g.

$$CaZ + 2NaCl = Na_2Z + CaCl_2$$
$$\text{or} \qquad\qquad\qquad \text{or}$$
$$MgZ \qquad\qquad\qquad MgCl_2$$

Zeolite softeners produce water of zero hardness. Hydrogen cation exchanging, synthetic zeolites have been developed. Ca, Mg and Na ions in water are removed, an equivalent amount of hydrogen being given up as carbonic acid, sulphuric acid or hydrochloric acid

e.g.

$$CaSO_4 + H_2Z = CaZ + H_2SO_4$$
$$\text{or} \qquad\qquad\qquad \text{or}$$
$$MgSO_4 \qquad\qquad\qquad MgZ$$

Hydrogen zeolites are regenerated by treatment with mineral acid, so acid resistant materials of construction are required.

Zeolite exchangers are best operated as 'duplex' units, one section being 'on-stream' while the 'off-stream' section is undergoing regeneration.

(*c*) *Demineralisation.* For extremely pure, special-purpose, waters, demineralisation, using mixed beds of synthetic anion and cation exchange resins, is used.[7, 9]

18.3.4.3. Iron and manganese. Iron and manganese are found in many water supplies, commonly as bicarbonates. Iron may also be present as a consequence of dissolved oxygen corrosion.

Waters containing organic matter in addition to these metals can give rise to 'iron-bacteria' or 'manganese-bacteria'.[15] The development of iron-bacteria can lead to the deposition of slimes and hard scales on the insides of pipes and vessels. These bacterial growths can rapidly clog pipe lines and fittings, besides producing unpleasant odours.

Staining and discoloration of equipment is also encountered with waters containing these metals.

Aeration, followed by settling and filtration, is a common treatment when iron is present as soluble bicarbonate. The bicarbonate is oxidised to insoluble, higher oxides. Sodium hexametaphosphate may be added as a sequestering agent. Manganese is not oxidised by aeration but insoluble oxides are produced by treatment with chlorine, the insoluble solids being removed by filtration. If the water is to be softened, a zeolite water softener will remove ions of both metals. Salting will remove the iron and manganese as soluble chlorides during regeneration of the zeolite. This process gives a soft, iron and manganese free water, satisfactory for many food processing operations.

18.3.5. REMOVAL OF DISSOLVED GASES

Natural water supplies may contain carbon dioxide, oxygen, nitrogen and hydrogen sulphide, in solution. Most of the carbon dioxide arises from the decay of organic matter. Oxygen and nitrogen come from aeration of the water, although oxygen may also be produced by photosynthesis. The proportion of carbon dioxide and oxygen present depends on algae content, sunlight, water depth, etc., during storage.

The presence of dissolved gases in process water can lead to a variety of difficulties. Incondensable gases, introduced into steam-raising plant and process-heating equipment using steam *via* boiler feed water, form troublesome films which act as resistances to heat transfer during the condensation of vapours.[20, 21] Free carbon dioxide dissolved in water reacts with iron, a common material of construction, leading to corrosion and iron pick-up. Oxygen, dissolved in water, vigorously attacks iron, galvanised iron, steel and brass, all commonly used in water systems. Oxygen attack is accelerated by increase in temperature and also by the presence of carbon dioxide. Hydrogen sulphide, found in sulphur waters, gives a corrosive solution which rapidly attacks iron pipes. The ferrous sulphide formed is either deposited on the pipe walls, or is carried away in the water stream as a fine, black suspension. Sulphur bacteria may develop in waters containing hydrogen sulphide. *Beggiatoa*, for example, produces thread-like, clogging growths on surfaces in contact with these waters.[15]

Carbon dioxide and dissolved air can be removed by boiling the water and venting off these non-condensable gases. Boiler feed-water is often deaerated in this way.[9] Chemical dosing for removal of oxygen and prevention of dissolved oxygen corrosion is also used, both sodium sulphite and hydrazine solutions being employed as oxygen scavengers. A mixture of sodium silicate and caustic soda solutions is also used to inhibit oxygen corrosion in water systems. For treatment of waters containing small quantities of hydrogen sulphide, chlorination is of value. With higher proportions of the gas, forced draught aeration followed by chlorination is used. With high concentrations, degassing, using carbon dioxide stripping, has been successfully applied.[9]

The method selected for the on-site treatment of waters for use in food processing depends on the quality of the raw water supply and on the quality of the water required. This latter requirement varies with the process. In general, a combination of coagulation, settling, filtration, softening, chlorination and degassing will be required.

In both the selection and maintenance of satisfactory water supplies and waste-water disposal facilities in the food factory, a knowledge of certain important chemical and physical properties of the water is required. Commonly required are: alkalinity; hardness; nitrogen content in various forms; dissolved oxygen; biochemical oxygen demand (BOD); chemical oxygen demand (COD); total solids; suspended solids; and settleable solids. Another frequent requirement is the concentrations of a number of metallic and other ions. Details of laboratory procedures for the analysis of water and waste samples are given in Standard Methods for the Examination of Water and Wastewater.[22]

18.4. WASTE DISPOSAL

18.4.1. INTRODUCTION

Every food processing plant takes in raw materials which are converted to finished products. Besides finished products, waste materials are produced. Typical wastes, indicating the variety encountered, include: foreign matter, peelings and contaminated water from fruit and vegetable preparation plants; blood, fats and greases from meat and poultry processing; waters contaminated with milk products from the dairy industry; detergent solutions from plant sanitary operations and waste wash water and human sewage from facilities used by plant operatives.

In earlier times many food processors used to lose their wastes down some convenient hole in the ground or in some near-by stream. This cheap but short-sighted solution is no longer possible. With the increasing pollution problems created by our expanding technological society, the disposal of industrial wastes (effluents) becomes a vital economic factor in the efficient operation of any plant.

With liquid wastes, the disposal of untreated effluent to a municipal sewage plant may be possible in urban areas. Much depends on the nature, strength and volume flow rate of the effluent. For municipal disposal a relatively constant strength effluent at a steady flow rate is preferred and the installation of storage balance tanks at the factory site may be all that is necessary.

In country areas municipal disposal facilities may not be available, and in towns the nature of the effluent may be such that the local authority insists on some form of pretreatment before discharge to their sewers. In these circumstances on-site treatment facilities must be provided. In general, municipal sewage treatment is cheaper than factory treatment and is the method recommended whenever possible.

18.4.2. FACTORY TREATMENT

A complete survey of factory operations, including the determination of material balances over individual plants within the site, is an essential pre-requisite to the installation of a waste treatment plant. A full knowledge of the various material streams in each part of the factory may show up unexpected losses of finished product, excessive usages of water and contamination of other wastes capable of re-use within the factory. The survey may indicate a need for better control of water in the plants, for the recirculation of 'once-through' water, the re-use of non-potable water streams as cooling media, or the desirability of separating heavily contaminated waters from those capable of re-use. The separation of concentrated and dilute effluent streams is particularly important if the wastes contain materials capable of being profitably recovered. In this case it is important to prevent over-dilution of the effluent since the profitability of a recovery process decreases with increasing initial dilution. An overall survey of factory material flow streams may lead to substantial savings on plant operating costs, as well as to a much reduced effluent load and consequent cheaper waste treatment facilities.[24]

Some processors give little consideration to their effluent until faced with a pollution problem demanding action. Under these circumstances the first requirement is to stop the offending pollution.

Ideally, the requirements for waste treatment should be fully considered while the factory is at the design stage. The treatment plant then becomes an integral part of the overall factory design embracing:

(i) Avoidance of waste as far as possible.
(ii) Maximum utilisation of waste products.
(iii) Prevention of pollution at the effluent loading expected under maximum production conditions.

Food processing wastes are generally stronger than domestic sewage. They contain a large proportion of organic matter and have high 'biochemical oxygen demand'. The 'biochemical oxygen demand' (BOD) is a measure of the quantity of oxygen required for the oxidation of organic matter in water by micro-organisms present, in a given time interval at a specified temperature. The time is usually 5 days, the temperature $18 \cdot 3\,°C\,(65\,°F)$ in Britain and $20\,°C\,(68\,°F)$ in the US.

Food wastes having high BOD values, when discharged to rivers and streams, give rise to pollution. The high organic content can lead to rapid putrefaction and odour problems, the growth of pathogenic organisms and a diminution in the oxygen content in the water, resulting in damage to aquatic flora and fauna. Pollution can render water unfit for human, animal or industrial use.[25] Waste materials must be pretreated before discharge so that organic material undergoes decomposition to a more stable form harmless to subsequent users of the water. The important quantities determining the strength of a food waste are the BOD and the suspended solids content. These values are normally quoted in parts per 100 000, or in milligrams per litre (parts per million) of the sample. Since the BOD test is time-consuming, another commonly used test for the polluting nature of specific contaminants is the Chemical Oxygen Demand or COD test. Details of the various tests used in waste treatment and pollution control may be found in Standard Methods for the Examination of Water and Wastewater.[22]

18.4.3. WASTE TREATMENT PROCESSES

Food wastes may be subjected to:

(i) Physical treatment.
(ii) Chemical treatment.
(iii) Biological treatment.

Examination of a few typical values for the polluting strengths of some food wastes:

Waste	BOD_5 (mg/litre)
Fruit and vegetable preparation	500–2 500[26, 27]
Cannery—baked beans	2 000
peas	4 000
Milk washings	75–1 500[28]
Meat processing	200–3 000[29]

shows them to be considerably stronger than domestic sewage (BOD_5 = 200–400 mg/litre), with which they are often compared. So food waste liquors are likely to require all three treatment stages. Physical and chemical treatments, whether singly or in some combination of the two, are often called 'primary treatments'. Biological treatment is then known as 'secondary treatment'. The BOD of a typical food waste stream is a consequence of (a) suspended solids, and (b) dissolved solids. The removal of suspended solids by physical and/or chemical means considerably reduces the BOD before the biological treatment stage. Material separated by primary treatment may be a possible source of valuable recovery products.[30]

18.4.3.1. Physical treatment. This preliminary treatment affords a separation of suspended solids and other high BOD materials (fats, greases, oils, etc.) from the bulk of the aqueous effluent. The size range of solids is wide and several separation methods are used. A common method involves the separation of coarse material, using screens. Stationary bar screens, vibrating screens and rotary drum screens are all used. Screen apertures range from 25 mm down to micrometre sizes, depending on the application. Since these screens are prone to 'blinding', facilities for 'in-place cleaning', such as mechanical rakes or wash water jets, should be incorporated. Preliminary screening can be followed by passage through a gravity sedimentation tank (Fig. 18.4). Entering the cylindrical vessel, the liquid stream slowly rises to the top of the tank to be removed *via* an overflow launder as a clarified liquid stream. Denser solids settle to the bottom as a thick sludge underflow. Slow speed scraper blades help compact the sludge and drive it to the centre off-take pipe for continuous removal. Residence times in these units are insufficient for anaerobic decomposition to occur, being of the order of 1–3 h.[31, 32]

If the effluent contains large quantities of inorganic matter, as in the

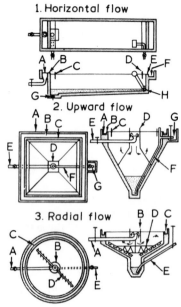

FIG. 18.4.   Gravity sedimentation tanks. (1) Horizontal-flow tank. A, inlet channel; B, inlet weir; C, baffle; D, scum-board; E, outlet weir; F, outlet channel; G, sludge draw-off; H, floating arm (or other device) for removing supernatant liquid before de-sludging. (2) Upward-flow tank. A, effluent channel; B, effluent weir; C, scum-board; D, baffle box; E, inlet pipe; F, sludge pipe; G, sludge well. (3) Radial-flow tank. A, inlet pipe; B, baffle box; C, effluent channel; D, power-driven scraper; E, sludge pipe. (From Southgate, B. A., 'Treatment and Disposal of Industrial Waste Waters', by permission of the Controller of HMSO.)

preparation of fruit, vegetables, etc., then a simple gravity settler or grit tank should be installed. Grit tanks consist of long, narrow channels designed to produce a low liquid flow velocity (about 0·3 m/s). At this order of velocity the more dense inorganic matter settles out. Since some organic material also settles, the resulting sludge should be removed continuously to avoid decomposition.

Certain food wastes (*e.g.* from meat processing) contain oils and fats in large quantities. Besides giving rise to high BOD values and consequent pollution if discharged untreated, these materials also represent valuable by-products and should be recovered.

These organic materials are immiscible with the aqueous effluent stream and float to the surface after passage through suitably designed residence tanks. Residence times of about an hour are required with flow velocities of about 0·3–0·6 m/s. The layer of fat can then be mechanically skimmed from the surface of the bulk liquid.

An alternative method of oil and fat removal is by aeration–flotation.[32, 33] Controlled aeration of the effluent stream by injection of air under pressure to the bottom of a flotation tank gives a mass of small bubbles which rise through the liquid, carrying grease and fine solids to the surface. The addition of certain surface active agents can assist this process. The separated surface layer is then removed. Lash and Kominek give a concise account of available physical treatment methods for waste treatment.[34]

18.4.3.2. Chemical treatment. In principle, chemical treatment for removal of solid matter in food wastes is identical to that used for the removal of suspended solids in natural waters (Section 18.3.1). A coagulant solution (often lime and ferrous sulphate) is added to the effluent. The floc formed carries down suspended solids. The coagulant dose depends on effluent pH, alkalinity and solids content. In batch operation the coagulant solution is added to the effluent in a mixing tank. The floc formed is allowed to settle. Underflow and overflow can then be separated. The process can also be carried out continuously.

With both physical and chemical methods for separating solid materials, large volumes of wet sludge and clarified liquors are produced. The sludge passes to sludge drying beds which can occupy large areas. If space is not available, dewatering centrifuges (Chapter 7) may be required to reduce the volume of sludge handled. The disposal of sludge from both primary and secondary treatment plants poses a major problem to food processors and is currently the subject of much investigation (Section 18.4.4).

In some applications a combination of physical and chemical treatments is sufficient to lower the solids content and BOD to acceptable values for discharge to rivers and lakes. With very many food wastes the BOD of the clarified liquors would still be unacceptably high. Biological treatment then becomes necessary.

18.4.3.3. Biological treatment (secondary treatment). This treatment involves the conversion of unstable organic materials to more stable forms by the action of micro-organisms. The microbial action can be:

(i)   Aerobic.
(ii) Anaerobic.

Aerobic biological treatment. Several biological treatment processes are used including: (a) Trickling or percolating filters, (b) activated sludge systems, (c) lagoons, and (d) spray irrigation.

(*a*) *Trickling filters* (Fig. 18.5). A trickling filter for on-site food waste treatment normally consists of a cylindrical concrete tank 2–3 m (6–10 ft) in depth and 7·5–15 m (25–50 ft) in diameter. The tank is packed with crushed stone or other porous media, the bed being underlaid with drains. Clarified effluent liquor is fed on to the upper surface of the bed by spray nozzles or rotating distributor arms. The liquid trickles through the bed and a slime of biologically active material forms on the surface of the stones. The large surface area of the bed permits intimate contact between air, effluent liquor and the

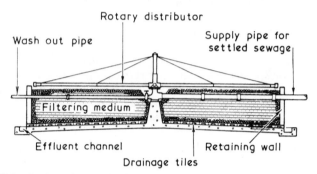

FIG. 18.5.   Section of a trickling filter. (From Southgate, B. A., 'Treatment and Disposal of Industrial Waste Waters', by permission of the Controller of HMSO.)

active growth, facilitating biological attack on organic matter contained in the effluent. Organic matter is removed, nitrifying bacteria oxidise ammonia to nitrates and a relatively clear effluent suitable for discharging to a river can be produced. A suspension of solids (humus) is usually found in the treated liquors. These are removed by passage through a settling tank.

Low-rate percolating filters have a randomly packed medium about 40–50 mm (1·5–2 in) in size. This gives a voidage of some 45–55 %. The conventional form of percolating filter is also employed for the partial purification of waste liquor before discharge to a sewer for municipal treatment. In this case a somewhat coarser packing medium is used.[35]

The active slime on the medium takes time to develop and it can be poisoned by the addition of toxic chemical substances. The efficiency of a trickling filter is also affected by over-loading. Over-loading leads to clogging of the bed and the development of a pool of water on the upper surface of the filter, a symptom of mal-operation known as 'ponding'. Alternating double filtration is often used in the treatment of food wastes, particularly dairy wastes.[25, 28] During biological oxidation in conventional trickling filters the biomass produced tends to block the filters. The nature of the growth ranges from tenuous bacterial slimes (with aqueous wastes low in organic content) to thick masses of fungal mycelium (from some strong wastes). Passage of treated effluent breaks down the growth. With two filters in series, one performs the actual filtration while the second is 're-generated'. Periodically the sequence of filtration is reversed. Up to 95 % removal of BOD is reported with trickling filters working on food wastes.[36]

Macro-invertebrate organisms such as fly larvae and worms play an important part in preventing blockage of low-rate trickling filters and there is evidence to suggest that they improve the settling characteristics of suspended solids in the treated liquid.[35]

In recent years there has been growing interest in the use of plastic media in so-called 'high-rate' trickling filters. Plastic media possess low bulk densities, high voidages (90 %) and can be fabricated with a wide range of specific surfaces. Because of their low bulk densities, plastic packings are normally used in packed towers. The consequent reduction in ground-area required is one of the advantages claimed for high-rate tower filters. They are finding extensive use as 'roughing filters' for the partial treatment of liquors before passage to a municipal sewer or to a conventional trickling filter for further reduction in BOD.[37]

(*b*) *Activated sludge systems.* These are alternative aerobic oxidation systems, used instead of (or sometimes in conjunction with) trickling filtration for the treatment of a variety of food wastes.

In these processes a high concentration of micro-organisms, in the form of a floc, is maintained in suspension in the partially treated waste-liquor resulting from primary treatment. Suspension is normally brought about by a combination of aeration and agitation. The synthesis of microbial cells utilises organic matter in the aerated waste with a consequent reduction in BOD. The liquid suspension is referred to as 'mixed liquor suspended solids' (MLSS). After a period of aeration the mixed liquor flows to a settling tank. Clarified liquor 'overflows' with BOD values of 20 mg/litre and less can be obtained. Part of the sludge 'underflow' from the settling tank is recycled to the aerator to maintain the biological activity. The disposal of the excess sludge can present problems (Section 18.4.4). It is necessary to achieve rapid adsorption and oxidation of organic material while producing a rapidly settling sludge possessing good handling characteristics and the ability to dewater, hence dispose of easily. To realise these objectives mixed liquors of suitable concentrations and activity are required. This makes the activated sludge process somewhat sensitive to changes in waste-liquor composition, concentration, etc. For this reason activated sludge processes are regarded as less reliable than trickling filters by some operators.[23, 25] Several variations of the 'conventional' activated sludge process are in use. These involve different arrangements for introducing the waste-liquor and air, and in variations in the rate of dissolved oxygen uptake. These latter variations give rise to 'high-rate', 'conventional' and 'extended aeration' activated sludge systems.[23]

(c) *Lagoons (stabilisation ponds or oxidation ponds)*. If a sufficient area of land is available lagooning becomes a simple and convenient method for the treatment of some food wastes. This is particularly the case where operations are seasonal and capital expenditure on expensive equipment is difficult to justify. Lagooning is extensively used for the treatment of cannery wastes. Lagoons normally consist of water-tight embankments enclosing a lake of waste liquor. The simplest lagoons involve both aerobic and anaerobic decomposition in the break-down of organic matter in the waste. For efficient operation they depend on surface aeration. Algal growth also plays a part in making oxygen available. For optimum aeration, depths of 0·9–1·5 m (3–5 ft) are recommended. Bacterial decomposition and algal growth are both affected by low temperatures and under these conditions anaerobic decomposition can predominate, giving rise to odour problems. Sodium nitrate is sometimes added to produce additional oxygen to encourage aerobic oxidation. With some food wastes having high organic contents—fats, proteins, etc.—anaerobic decomposition is encouraged. In anaerobic decomposition, sludge production is low and high BOD removal rates are possible. Anaerobic lagoons are deeper than those for aerobic treatment, the layer of active anaerobic sludge being at the bottom of the lagoon. The method is frequently encountered in meat-processing waste treatment and in this application a layer of grease, several centimetres thick, is allowed to accumulate to form a cover for suppressing odours, retaining heat and maintaining anaerobic conditions.[38]

Aerobic ponds are increasingly being used in conjunction with mechanical aeration. Forced aeration permits the size of the lagoon to be significantly reduced. Lagoons often act as sedimentation tanks and flow equalisation tanks, and as such are useful adjuncts to a waste treatment plant. Waste stabilisation pond use and design are discussed by Gloyna.[39]

(d) *Spray irrigation*. This method is popular where land with a suitable (reasonably porous) soil is available within economic pumping distance of the source of the waste-liquors. Screened liquor is pumped to the irrigation site (fields carrying a variety of grass crops are commonly used) and distributed over the area by sprinklers. The method is cheap, avoids pollution of water-courses, if carried out under controlled conditions, and can be used to irrigate edible crops. Spray irrigation is used satisfactorily on milk and cannery wastes.[40]

Anaerobic biological treatment. As discussed above, anaerobic biological treatment is used in some special applications of waste stabilisation ponds, *e.g.* meat-processing wastes. One of the major areas using this type of bacterial process, however, is in the treatment of wet sludges which arise in almost all waste treatment processes. The large volumes of wet sludge produced in both primary and secondary stages of waste treatment have to be dewatered before disposal. Sometimes these sludges can yield a useful recovery product (Section 18.4.4) but more frequently they are discarded. Anaerobic sludge digestion produces a reduced volume of relatively inert material having little unpleasant odour and which can be easily dewatered. The overall process results in the destruction of organic matter and the formation of carbon dioxide and methane.

Sludge digesters. These are tanks equipped with heating coils for accurate temperature control. They are often agitated to aid the digestion. Residence time may be several days and up to 95 % BOD removal can be achieved.

After settling, the reduced volume of digested sludge passes to drying beds. The liquid, after aerobic treatment, is sometimes chlorinated before discharge to a river. Since anaerobic fermentation is accompanied by the formation of hydrogen sulphide and ammonia, unpleasant odours can arise. The digesters are usually covered, to reduce the likelihood of odour nuisance and to permit gas collection. In large treatment plants the combustible gas collected can be used as a source of energy.

18.4.4. DISPOSAL OF WASTE SLUDGE AND SOLIDS

The disposal of solid wastes and sludge solids from food industry waste-treatment plants poses special problems. The possibility of profitable recovery of material from the waste stream must always be considered.[30] If the residues are valueless then it is necessary to arrange for their 'ultimate disposal' in a manner which cannot cause offence due to contamination or pollution of the environment.

Sludges arise from primary separations using screens, settling tanks, filters, etc., and from secondary treatment as humus (from trickling filters) and excess activated sludge. Primary sludges are likely to be mixtures of fats, carbohydrates, proteins, siliceous matter and anything else introduced into the factory drainage system, and it is these that offer the best 'recovery' prospects. Though seemingly quite dense a typical sludge is likely to consist mainly of water so a major factor in sludge disposal is dewatering. As a first step, before attempting costly mechanical separations, 'sludge-conditioning' using chemical or thermal methods should be considered.[41] Synthetic organic polyelectrolytes, for example, are finding increasing use in improving the filtering of sludges by addition to the sludge in controlled amounts. It has long been known that heat-treatment can also be of assistance in the dewatering of biological sludges. Heating is particularly useful in breaking down gel-structures which are a characteristic of many food structures. By subjecting the sludge to high temperatures, thermal effects bring about rupture of the cellular structure, so releasing trapped liquid.

Methods for the ultimate disposal of solid food wastes include:

(*a*) *Dumping.* The waste material is transported to a suitable dump and disposed of by 'land-filling' under hygienic conditions. The nuisance caused by odour, rodents, insects, etc., can be a major problem. This method of disposal is coming under increasing suspicion in these pollution-conscious times.

(*b*) *Incineration.* Incineration of solid wastes at temperatures as high as 650 °C results in complete destruction of all organic matter liable to cause pollution.[42] In such a system the generation of smoke and odours must be carefully controlled. Incinerators capable of handling low calorific-value organic materials having very high water contents are now available. This type of unit is likely to find increasing use for the disposal of valueless food waste sludge.

(*c*) *Composting.* Composting[43] of waste materials under controlled conditions can produce a humus suitable for agricultural purposes.

REFERENCES

1. O'Keefe, J. A. (Ed.) 'Sale of Food and Drugs (Bell)', 14th ed. (Butterworths: 1968).
2. Public Health Service, US Department of Health, Education and Welfare, 'Public Health Reports', 61, 378–384 (1946).
3. International Union of Pure and Applied Chemistry, 'Re-use of Water in Industry'. (Butterworths: 1963.)
4. Anderson, D., 'Developments in Effluent Treatment in the Food Industry'. BFMIRA Golden Jubilee Conference, No. 9. (BFMIRA: 1969.)
5. Hamer, P., Jackson, J., and Thurston, E. F., 'Industrial Water Treatment Practice'. (Butterworths: 1961.)

6. James, G. V., 'Water Treatment'. (The Technical Press: 1949.)
7. Cremer, H. W., and Watkins, S. B., 'Chemical Engineering Practice', Vol. 10. (Butterworths: 1960.)
8. Purchas, D. B., 'Flocculation and Coagulation'. Process Biochem., **3**(10), 17 (1968).
9. Nordell, E., 'Water Treatment For Industrial and Other Uses', 2nd ed. (Reinhold: 1961).
10. Curds, C. R., and Hawkes, H. A., 'Ecological Aspects of Used-Water Treatment, Vol. 1, The Organisms and their Ecology'. (Academic Press: 1975.)
11. Frazier, W. C., 'Food Microbiology', 2nd ed. (McGraw-Hill: 1967.)
12. Mercer, W. A., and Somers, I. I., 'Chlorine in Food Plant Sanitation', *in* Mrak, E. M., and Stewart, G. F. (Eds), 'Advances in Food Research', Vol. VII. (Academic Press: 1957.)
13. Mrak, E. M., and Stewart, G. F. (Eds), 'Advances in Food Research', Vol. VII. (Academic Press: 1957.)
14. Johnson, J. D., 'Disinfection—Water and Wastewater'. (Ann Arbor Science: 1975.)
15. Holden, W. S. (Ed.), 'Water Treatment and Examination. A Successor to "The Examination of Waters and Water Supplies", by Thresh, Beale and Suckling'. (Churchill: 1970.)
16. Lowndes, M. R., 'Ozone for Water and Effluent Treatment'. Chemy Ind., 951–956 (1971).
17. Gauntlett, R. B., and Packham, R. F., 'The Removal of Organic Compounds in the Production of Potable Water'. Chemy Ind., 812–817 (1973).
18. Murray, R. V., and Peterson, G. T., 'Water for Canning'. Research Bull. No. 22. Continental Can Company, Inc., Chicago, Ill. (1951).
19. Joslyn, M. A., and Heid, J. L., 'Food Processing Operations', Vol. 1 (AVI: 1963).
20. Lyle, O., 'The Efficient Use of Steam' (HM Stationery Office: 1947.)
21. 'The Efficient Use of Fuel'. (HM Stationery Office: 1958.)
22. Standard Methods for the Examination of Water and Wastewater. 13th ed. (American Public Health Association, American Water Works Association and the Water Pollution Control Federation: 1971).
23. Furness, C. D., 'Biological Treatment of Effluents', The Chemical Engineer, **282**(2), 102–107 (1974).
24. Anon., 'A Guide for Waste Management in the Food Processing Industries'. (National Canners Association: 1969.)
25. Southgate, B. A., 'Treatment and Disposal of Industrial Waste Waters'. (HM Stationery Office: 1948.)
26. Holdsworth, S. D., 'Effluents from Fruit and Vegetable Processing'. Process Biochem., **3**(6), 27–31 (1968).
27. Jones, H. R., 'Waste Disposal Control in the Fruit and Vegetable Industry'. (Noyes Data Corporation: 1973.)
28. Wheatland, A. B., 'Treatment of Waste Waters from Dairies and Dairy Product Factories—Methods and Systems'. J. Soc. Dairy Technol., **27**(2), 71–79 (1974).
29. Jones, H. R., 'Pollution Control in Meat, Poultry and Seafood Processing'. Pollution Technology Review No. 4. (Noyes Data Corporation: 1974.)
30. Birch, G. G., Parker, K. J., and Worgan, J. T. (Eds) 'Food From Waste'. (Applied Science Publishers: 1976.)
31. Foust, A. S., Wenzel, L. A., Clump, C. W., Maus, L., and Andersen, L. B., 'Principles of Unit Operations'. (John Wiley: 1960.)
32. Gurnham, C. F., 'Principles of Industrial Waste Treatment'. (John Wiley: 1955.)
33. Anon., 'Air-Flotation Can Economize Your Waste-Water Treatment'. Food Engineering, **27**(9), 107 (1955).

34. Lash, L. D., and Kominek, E. C., 'Primary Waste Treatment Methods'. Chemical Engineering, Desk Book Issue, **82**(21) (1975).
35. Bruce, A. M., 'Percolating Filters'. Process Biochem., **4**(4), (1969).
36. Parker, M. E., and Litchfield, J. H., 'Food Plant Sanitation'. (Reinhold: 1962.)
37. Askew, M. W., 'Plastics in Waste Treatment', Part 1. Process Biochem., December 1966. Part 2, January 1967.
38. Hammer, M. J., 'Water and Waste Water Technology'. (John Wiley: 1975.)
39. Gloyna, M. J., 'Water Stabilization Ponds'. Monograph Series No. 60. (World Health Organization, Geneva: 1971.)
40. Butters, J. R., 'Spray Disposal of Food Waste'. Fd Mf., **47**(5), 29–32 (1972).
41. Anderson, D., 'Disposal of Sludge Solids from Food Industry Waste Treatment', *in* Thomas E. Furia (Ed.) 'Critical Reviews in Food Technology', Vol. 3, Issue 1 (Chemical Rubber Company: 1972).
42. Burgess, J. V., 'Developments in Sludge and Waste Incineration'. Process Biochem., **8**(1), 27–28 (1973).
43. Gray, K. R., Sherman, K., and Biddlestone, A. J., 'A Review of Composting'. Part 1, Process Biochem., **6**(6), 32–36 (1971). Part 2, **6**(10), 22–28 (1971).

CHAPTER 19

MATERIALS HANDLING

19.1. GENERAL CONSIDERATIONS

19.1.1. SCOPE AND IMPORTANCE OF MATERIALS HANDLING

Materials handling is concerned with the five elements:
Movement — Time — Place — Quantity — Space.[1] Efficient
materials handling is Movement in the most efficient manner at the
right Time, to and from the correct Place, in the required Quantity
with the maximum economy of Space. Handling adds nothing to the
value of the product. It is vital, therefore, to ensure maximum
handling efficiency during all the following movements of the
material:

(i)   *As a raw material* from supply point to store or process.
(ii) *As a material in process* between stages during processing.
(iii) *As a finished product* to packing, storage and despatch.

Any reduction in this defined scope will result in a restricted
outlook with corresponding loss of effectiveness.

Case studies indicate that substantial savings can be effected by
changing from manual to mechanised handling. Savings of the order
of 50 % of the labour bill are not uncommon. An example of this is
given in Fig. 19.1 which shows reductions in labour charges of
40–90 %. These savings are partially offset by increased capital
charges but the overall effect is a large reduction in operating costs.

In addition to direct savings, good handling techniques confer other
advantages, such as:

(i)   Improved utilisation of men, machines and storage space.
(ii) Reduced material wastage.
(iii) Improved control and rotation of stock.
(iv) Improved working conditions and reduced operator fatigue.

These result in increased productivity, improved product quality
and reduced absenteeism.

19.1.2. THE RULES OF EFFICIENT MATERIALS HANDLING

Materials handling technique has improved rapidly over the last few decades, and during this time practitioners have accumulated a set of generally applicable rules which provide valuable guides to action. These rules are not fundamental in any scientific sense. They have been changed and will continue to be changed, from time to time, as new techniques develop. Good handling practice is exemplified by the list of rules reproduced in Table 19.1 which should be studied in conjunction with the text from which they have been abstracted.[2] Applied to materials handling which is not yet, and may never be, a science, the word 'principle' in its strictest sense is inappropriate. For this reason the word 'rule' is preferred here.

19.1.3. PLANNING AN IMPROVED SYSTEM

In order to design an improved handling system, answers to the following questions are required:

(i)   What is the present system of handling?
(ii)   What is the present handling cost per unit of production?
(iii) How can the present system be improved?
(iv) What will the new system cost?
(v)   What savings can be expected from the new system?

Answers to questions (i) and (iii) can be obtained using established planning techniques[1] in conjunction with the rules discussed in Section 19.1.2. Questions (ii) and (v) are, generally, much more difficult to answer accurately. Some cost systems, because of the widespread nature of the handling activity, are unable to provide the required data. In such circumstances a special cost study has to be made.

19.1.4. THE NEED FOR HANDLING KNOWLEDGE

Responsibility for materials handling is, properly, vested in specialist handling engineers, and many food manufacturers adopt this procedure. Almost invariably these specialists take decisions in conference with production executives. Where a specialist handling department is not provided, the responsibility for efficient movement of materials falls on the production manager and his staff. Therefore, in either of these situations, it is important for production executives

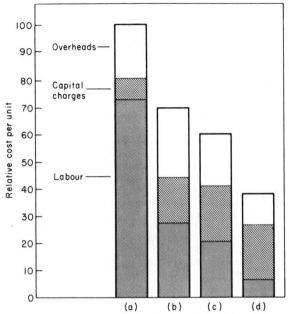

FIG. 19.1.   Comparison of costs of handling flour in a mill producing at a rate of 75 t/24 h. (a) Flour bagged from mill and handled manually in bags. (b) Flour bagged from mill and handled mechanically in bags. (c) 50 % as for (b) and 50 % bulk handled pneumatically. (d) 100 % bulk handled pneumatically.

to have a sound knowledge of the fundamentals of good handling practice.

19.1.5. SAFETY CONSIDERATIONS

There were 24 992 accidents in the food and allied industries in the UK during 1973. Of these, handling accidents, totalling 6613 were the single biggest group.[3] A similar situation exists in the USA where handling accounts for 27 % of all plant accidents. The mechanisation of handling has not reduced the accident rate; it has merely altered the types of handling hazards. The safety provisions embodied in the Factories Act 1961 have been reinforced by the Health and Safety at Work Act 1974[4] which applies severe penalties to both employers and employees who permit or engage in practices which endanger health or safety. The safety aspects of materials handling and movement, therefore, warrant the most careful attention. Hazards in the food industry are discussed by Creber.[5]

TABLE 19.1
The 20 principles of materials handling

In June, 1966, The College-Industry Committee on Material Handling Education, sponsored by The Material Handling Institute, Inc. and the International Material Management Society, adopted the following 20 Principles of Materials Handling:

1. *Planning Principle.* Plan all materials handling and storage activities to obtain maximum overall operating efficiency.
2. *Systems Principle.* Integrate as many handling activities as is practical into a coordinated system of operations, covering vendor, receiving, storage, production, inspection, packaging, warehousing, shipping, transportation, and customer.
3. *Material Flow Principle.* Provide an operation sequence and equipment layout optimising material flow.
4. *Simplification Principle.* Simplify handling by reducing, eliminating, or combining unnecessary movements and/or equipment.
5. *Gravity Principle.* Utilise gravity to move material wherever practical.
6. *Space Utilisation Principle.* Make optimum utilisation of building cube.
7. *Unit Size Principle.* Increase the quantity, size, or weight of unit loads or flow rate.
8. *Mechanisation Principle.* Mechanise handling operations.
9. *Automation Principle.* Provide automation to include production, handling, and storage functions.
10. *Equipment Selection Principle.* In selecting handling equipment consider all aspects of the material handled—the movement and the method to be used.
11. *Standardisation Principle.* Standardise handling methods as well as types and sizes of handling equipment.
12. *Adaptability Principle.* Use methods and equipment that can best perform a variety of tasks and applications where special purpose equipment is not justified.
13. *Dead Weight Principle.* Reduce ratio of dead weight of mobile handling equipment to load carried.
14. *Utilisation Principle.* Plan for optimum utilisation of handling equipment and manpower.
15. *Maintenance Principle.* Plan for preventive maintenance and scheduled repairs of all handling equipment.
16. *Obsolescence Principle.* Replace obsolete handling methods and equipment when more efficient methods or equipment will improve operations.
17. *Control Principle.* Use material handling activities to improve control of production, inventory, and order handling.
18. *Capacity Principle.* Use handling equipment to help achieve desired production capacity.
19. *Performance Principle.* Determine effectiveness of handling performance in terms of expense per unit handled.
20. *Safety Principle.* Provide suitable methods and equipment for safe handling.

Reproduced by courtesy of The Material Handling Institute Inc., Gateway Center, Pittsburgh, Pa., USA.

Handling accidents fall into two groups:

(i)   Unsafe conditions including:

Insufficient working space.
Inadequate aisle space.
Inadequate guarding of running machinery.
Defective equipment.
Inadequate lighting and ventilation.
Unsafe design or construction of equipment.
Bad floor surfaces.

(ii) Unsafe acts such as:

Unsafe loading and stacking.
Disregard of traffic signals.
Carrying out repairs and adjustments on the run.
Operating without authority.
Working at unsafe speeds.
Using incorrect equipment.
Exceeding the capacity of equipment.
Failing to use protective clothing.
Practical joking.

19.1.6. CATEGORISATION OF MATERIALS HANDLING EQUIPMENT

The many types of handling equipment may be classified conveniently into five main groups as set out in Table 19.2. This grouping is used in this chapter as a basis for considering the application of handling equipment in the food industry.

19.2.   CONVEYORS

Conveyors may be described as equipment for inclined or horizontal continuous movement serving a point or path. The service is generally fixed, and conveying takes place at working height, floor level or underfloor. Packaged or bulk solid materials may be transported.

Motion of the material may be imparted either (a) by gravity or manually, or (b) by power. The method of motivation provides a convenient basis for subdividing the many types of conveyor into two main groups as follows:

(i)   Gravity or manually powered: chute, roller, or skate-wheel conveyors.

(ii) Powered: roller, belt, slat, chain, vibratory, magnetic, screw, flight and pneumatic conveyors.

TABLE 19.2
Categorisation of materials handling equipment

Classification	Direction Vert. up	Vert. down	Incline up	Incline down	Horizontal	Frequency Continuous	Intermittent	Occasional	Location served Point	Limited area	Unlimited area	Service nature Permanent	Temporary	Non-fixed	Movement height Overhead	Working height	Floor level	Underfloor	Material state Packaged	Bulk	Solid	Liquid
(1) Conveyors			×	×	×	×			×	×		×			×	×	×		×	×	×	
(2) Elevators	×	×				×			×			×			×				×	×	×	
(3) Cranes and hoists	×	×					×		×	×		×	×			×	×		×	×	×	
(4) Trucks					×		×				×			×			×		×	×	×	
(5) Pneumatic equipment	×	×	×	×	×	×			×			×			×	×				×	×	×

× = applicable.

19.2.1. GRAVITY CONVEYORS

19.2.1.1. Chutes. Chutes are smooth-surfaced inclined troughs used to convey from high to low levels under the force of gravity. The factors to be considered in their design and use are as follows:

(a) *Friction.* An average value for the coefficient of friction of wooden cases on a wood surfaced chute is about 0·5 and for wooden cases on a metal surface is about 0·3. Coulomb's classical laws of friction, although useful, do not explain many observed events and it has become necessary to modify these laws.[6] Thus friction force is now considered to be dependent on the sliding velocity since this affects the temperatures and hence the natures of the sliding surfaces. Again, the friction force is regarded as supplying energy to overcome adhesion between the surfaces and to deform or shear asperities, *i.e.* irregularities, of these surfaces. Sliding surfaces are supported on peaks of the highest of these asperities and the friction force is therefore dependent on this, very small, contact area which will vary with the applied load. With bulk materials, it is necessary to consider both the friction between the material and the chute and the interparticulate friction within the material. The latter determines whether the material slides down the chute or whether it pours down.

(b) *Moisture.* Atmospheric humidity and the moisture content of the conveyed material affect both sliding and interparticulate friction, and this variable must be allowed for in designing chutes.

(c) *Chute inclination.* Steep chutes give high acceleration rates, consequently the risk of product damage is increased.

(d) *Chute length.* The longer the chute the greater the package terminal velocity. Since the kinetic energy of the conveyed unit is proportional to the square of its velocity, conveying on long or steep chutes can result in considerable damage to packages.

(e) *Uniformity of package weight.* Chute conveying of units of mixed weights may lead to excessive damaging of the lighter packages by bumping. Light and heavy units should, therefore, be conveyed separately.

(f) *Position of centre of gravity of package.* A vertical line through the centre of gravity of the package must pass through the surface of the package in contact with the conveyor, otherwise tumbling will result. Similarly, unevenly balanced packages must be conveyed heavy-end down.

These remarks are applicable to conveyance on many other types of inclined conveyors and must be borne in mind if product damage and accident rates are to be minimised.

Chutes may be of wood or metal; they may be straight; they may be curved to effect change of direction or they may be spiralled to effect space economy. Bulk food materials are best conveyed on metal chutes enclosed to restrict product contamination.

19.2.1.2. Gravity and manpowered roller or skate-wheel conveyors. A roller conveyor comprises free running rollers mounted horizontally in a frame so as to form a table on which the packages or containers may be conveyed either at an inclination (by gravity) or horizontally (by manual effort). Skate-wheel conveyors function similarly but consist of sets of wheels mounted in groups of three or more on axles (Fig. 19.2).

These conveyors are used for the handling of: cases, cartons, drums, barrels, trays, and similar units having firm, flat bases. Sacks and similar loose packages can be conveyed only if they are supported on boards or trays. With roller conveyors at least three rollers and with skate-wheel conveyors at least six wheels (two across and three along the conveyor) must be in contact with the package base at all times.

Although these two types are similar in application, the following differences are noteworthy:

(i)   Wheels are better than rollers on curved conveyors since there is less friction between package and conveyor when wheels are used.
(ii) Rollers are better load bearers than wheels.
(iii) Rollers weigh about three times as much as an equivalent skate-wheel assembly. Hence rollers have higher inertia and are more difficult to start and to stop compared with skate-wheels.
(iv) Rollers are more robust than skate-wheels.

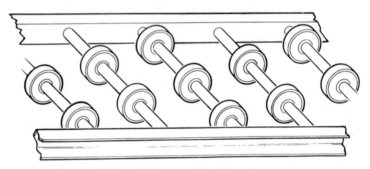

FIG. 19.2.   A skate-wheel conveyor.

Both types are free-running, so they may be used for horizontal or near-horizontal movement; a down-grade of 3 % (2 °) is adequate for gravity transportation of most packages. Gravity, assisted by air (Section 19.6) may also be used for package handling. Special care must be exercised to minimise bumping damage when using these conveyors.

19.2.2. POWERED CONVEYORS

19.2.2.1. Roller conveyors. These may be belt driven (the rollers being mounted above and in friction contact with driven belts) or chain driven (the rollers being fitted with end sprockets which engage with driven endless chains).[1, 7]

Powered rollers are used for packages similar to those carried by gravity rollers (Section 19.2.1.2). They may be used for movement both upwards and downwards at shallow angles (10–12 °). Belt-driven rollers are used for low-speed conveying (0·2–0·3 m/s). Chain-driven rollers are used for heavy duty, high-speed conveying (up to 2·5 m/s). Both types are reversible and may be fitted with switch points and intermediate discharging devices, thus serving a limited path.

19.2.2.2. Belt conveyor. This comprises an endless belt, friction driven at one end and carried on an idling drum at the other end. Belts may be of a wide variety of materials such as: plain or coated canvas, woven wire or stainless steel ribbon. They may be flat (for package conveying) or troughed, using idling rollers or slides (for bulk transfer). Hence they are suitable for moving almost any type of material—wet, dry or packaged. Correct tensioning and tracking of the belt must be ensured at all times. This may be effected by automatic spring-tensioners or by manual adjusters. Plain belts may be used on inclines up to 22° while belts fitted with non-slip devices such as cleats or cross-bars may be used up to 45° of inclination. Information is available for calculating power requirements, maximum belt speeds and capacities of belt conveyors.[7]

Discharge arrangements warrant careful consideration. Belts are costly items and are easily damaged at both loading and discharge points. Again, carry-over of food products, causing fouling of the area beneath the conveyor, can be a problem. Simple arrangements, like belt brushes, are frequently satisfactory with bulk dry materials. Sticky materials can be removed by spring-loaded scraper blades but these often cause excessive belt wear if improperly adjusted.

Apart from their wide applications in transfer operations, belt conveyors find extensive use as in-process conveyors during sorting, cleaning and heat-processing. They may be fitted with load cells or lever systems which measure the deflection of a unit length of belt, thus providing a continuous weighing system which can be used for monitoring, proportioning, feeding and other process operations.[8]

19.2.2.3. Slat conveyors. These comprise wooden or metal slats carried on endless driven chains. This provides a rigid flat surface with excellent load-bearing characteristics which is much less susceptible to damage and more easily repaired than is a belt. They are used for transporting packaged goods and small bulky items like fish and large fruits. In these latter cases careful attention to cleaning is obligatory.

19.2.2.4. Chain conveyors. Milk churns, barrels, crates and trays are conveniently handled by loading directly on to driven chains. Floor level or overhead chains may also be used to transport wheeled trolleys along a fixed, programmed path using hook couplings. Overhead or monorail conveyors using trays or hooks slung from a driven chain find applications in the poultry and meat industry. Bulk conveying by chains is dealt with in Section 19.2.2.8.

19.2.2.5. Vibratory conveyors. These use the inertia of material, conveyed by a relatively slow forward movement of the conveyor surface, to maintain product flow during a rapid backward movement of the conveyor surface. This motion (called 'throws and catches') is repeated at high frequency and may be produced electromagnetically or mechanically.[9] Vibratory conveyors commonly take the form of a trough or vertical spiral. By suitable control of the vibration, the material may be caused to flow forward at a variable rate, to remain stationary or to flow backwards. Thus a spiral unit will convey either upwards or downwards. The accuracy with which the flow of material can be controlled enables these conveyors to be used as feeders for equipment like mills and mixers. Their gentle handling makes them suitable for friable foods (*e.g.* potato crisps) whilst wet, stringy, hot, or abrasive materials are conveyed without difficulty. Vibratory conveying is substantially dustless and is becoming increasingly popular in the food industry.

19.2.2.6. Magnetic conveyors. Electromagnetic and permanent-magnetic belts and rollers are used to convey, hold and orientate ferromagnetic materials.[10] In the food industry, they are used to convey food cans and to hold them inverted for rinsing and drying. Magnetic rollers may be used to discriminate between the open and closed ends of cans. Such conveyors are positive in action and are silent, in distinct contrast with the usual railed conveyors used for can handling.

19.2.2.7. Screw conveyors. These operate on the principle of a rotating helical screw advancing material in a trough or casing. Bulk dry materials (*e.g.* sugar, flour and grain) and semi-liquid non-abrasive materials (*e.g.* sugar-beet pulp and comminuted meat) may be conveyed horizontally, at an inclination, or vertically.

The discharge rate and power consumption are considerably affected by the inclination and conveying distance and for these reasons screw conveyors are best used at or near the horizontal. Screw conveyors are characterised by their uniform discharge rate and, hence, find applications as feeders for mills and other process equipment. Many patterns of screw conveyor are available.[7]

19.2.2.8. Flight conveyors. These conveyors function on the basis of the material being dragged along an enclosed channel by an endless chain.[12] The chain may be a simple link chain (drag-link conveyor) or the links may have ears or flights attached to them (flight conveyors) (Fig. 19.4). The duct is kept filled with material which is conveyed because the interparticulate friction is greater than the wall friction. Flour, grain and similar materials are effectively conveyed at high capacity. Ring systems with intermediate charge and discharge points are common. Alternatively, the return leg may run in the same casing. Chain speeds are relatively low, 0·1–0·15 m/s being typical. Inclination is limited by the tendency of the material to slip back, and with most types a maximum angle of 30° is permissible.

19.3. ELEVATORS

Elevators are conveniently considered as equipment for continuous movement of materials in a vertical path (see Table 19.2).

19.3.1. PACKAGE ELEVATORS

Packages are carried vertically on free-swinging trays suspended between a pair of endless chains. Loads are charged on the upgoing side, pass around the top of the conveyor and are discharged on the downgoing side. Travel speeds of 0·1–0·2 m/s are common (Fig. 19.3). These elevators are useful in multi-storey buildings where access is restricted.[11] Strict safety precautions are necessary with open conveyors of this type.

19.3.2. BULK ELEVATORS

The four types of bulk elevator most commonly encountered are: screw, pneumatic, flight and bucket. Screw conveying (Section 19.2.2.7) is used for elevation but owing to the friction involved, power consumption becomes unduly high at lifts above about 5 m. Pneumatic elevation is discussed in Section 19.6.

19.3.2.1. Flight elevators. Vertical elevation using flight conveyors (Section 19.2.2.8) requires the use of specially designed flights and casings such as those used in the 'en masse'* system.[12] The flight elevator combined with the flight conveyor in a ring circuit provides a

* Redler Conveyors Ltd., Stroud, Glos., England.

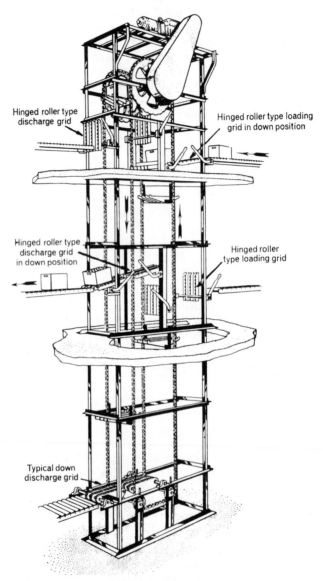

Hinged roller type discharge grid

Hinged roller type loading grid in down position

Hinged roller type discharge grid in down position

Hinged roller type loading grid

Typical down discharge grid

FIG. 19.3.   A vertical swinging tray elevator. (By courtesy of W. & C. Pantin Ltd., Epping, Essex, England.)

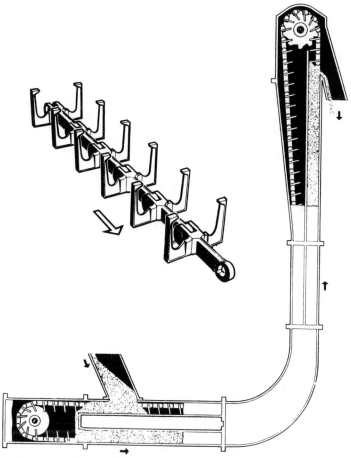

Fig. 19.4.   The Redler 'En Masse' conveyor used as a flight elevator. The inset shows
the elevator chain in more detail. (By courtesy of Redler Conveyors Ltd, Stroud, Glos.,
England.)

flexible, totally enclosed system (Fig. 19.4) suitable for high-capacity
multilevel movement of a wide range of particulate foods.

19.3.2.2. Bucket elevators. These are high-capacity units primarily
for bulk elevation of relatively free-flowing materials such as sugar,
beans, salt and cereals. Light, fluffy, sticky or wet materials can be
dealt with but require special equipment.

The bucket elevator consists of steel or malleable iron buckets
carried on an endless belt or on single or double endless chains. The

more important considerations affecting the design and operation of these elevators are:

(i)   The physical properties of the conveyed material (its moisture content, angle of repose, flow properties and crystal form).
(ii)   The shape and pitch (*i.e.* spacing) of the buckets.
(iii)   The speed at which the elevator is driven.
(iv)   The method of feeding the elevator.
(v)   The method of discharging the elevator.

Drive speed, although dependent on the type of material, is controlled mainly by the method of discharge. There are four main types of discharge—gravity, centrifugal, positive and continuous (Fig. 19.5).

(i)   (ii)   (iii)

FIG. 19.5.   Bucket elevator discharge systems. (i) Centrifugal discharge—the solid is thrown from the bucket to the discharge chute; (ii) positive discharge—the carrying chains are snubbed back to discharge wet or sticky material; (iii) continuous discharge —closely spaced buckets discharge onto the backs of the preceding buckets.

Gravity discharge buckets are carried pivoted on two chains and are tipped mechanically. Large capacity buckets are carried at about 0·25 m/s, usually at an inclination, providing a slow-speed high-capacity elevation system.

Centrifugal discharge types dredge up the material at the feed point (elevator 'boot') and discharge centrifugally into a chute. Commonly, discharge is arranged to take place when the line produced from the bucket centre to the sprocket centre makes an angle of approximately 45° to the vertical. With this method of discharge the linear speed of the drive chains is critical if the product is to be thrown cleanly into the outlet chute with minimal fall into the down-leg. In general it is found that linear velocities of around 1·5 m/s are necessary. At these high speeds, belt carriers are used and considerable wear and tear of the running equipment is encountered. Additionally, stringent anti-explosion precautions are necessary. Centrifugal discharge systems are characterised by high capacity.

Positive discharge may be produced by tipping the buckets by means of a change-of-direction sprocket located on the down-side of the conveyor. This facilitates the discharge of sticky and lumpy materials. This is a slower type, running at about 0·25 m/s, with corresponding reduction in wear and tear and spark risk compared with centrifugal discharge systems.

Continuous discharge is a slow-speed system (0·5 m/s approx.) which overcomes the disadvantage of spillage into the down-leg by discharging into the outlet using the backs of preceding buckets as chutes. The spacing between the buckets is small so that discharge is virtually continuous.

The feeding of bucket elevators must be carefully controlled (*e.g.* by using a screw feeder—Section 19.2.2.7), since the accumulation of material in the elevator boot places considerable strain on the belt or chains carrying the buckets.

Improved feeding is effected in the Econ-O-Lift* bucket conveyor/elevator by the use of interlocking buckets which are carried pivoted on a pair of driven chains. The conveyor stops automatically at the feeding points, the chains are telescoped, and the buckets interlock to permit non-spill feeding. The conveyor re-starts automatically at the end of feeding and the chains resume a linear form, the buckets being tipped mechanically at the discharge points.[12]

19.4. CRANES AND HOISTS

These are used for intermittent movement of materials in a vertical direction with associated horizontal movement, a path or limited area being served (Table 19.2).

19.4.1. CRANES

The main constructional features of a typical crane are shown in Fig. 19.6. The boom pivots on the mast which may be supported by fixed legs or guyed by ropes or cables. 'Derricking' is the act of winching the boom (or jib) up or down so as to alter the elevation of the boom and, hence, the area served by it. The lifting capacity and stability of cranes are considerably affected by the boom inclination. Failure to appreciate this causes many accidents.

Derrick cranes find wide application in handling from holds of barges or ships, from railway trucks and in similar situations where their unique lift and swing motion can be used to maximum advantage. Fixed-elevation jib cranes find many applications in the

---

* Gough Econ Mechanisation. Stoke-on-Trent, Staffs., England.

food industry (*e.g.* the charging of large vertical canning retorts and the handling of heavy packages). Jib-crane attachments are obtainable for fork-lift trucks, providing a mobile unit of wide flexibility.

The overhead travelling crane (Fig. 19.7) is capable of vertical movement serving a large area and finds application in warehousing operations. Cranes of this type give excellent building cube utilisation since aisle requirements are minimal and stacking to within a foot or so of the crane beams is practicable.

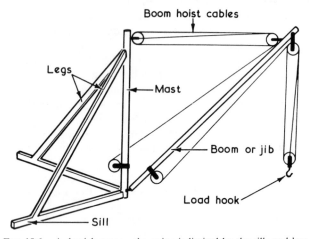

FIG. 19.6.   A derrick crane—the swing is limited by the sills and legs.

19.4.2. HOISTS

The act of hoisting is, primarily, a vertical lifting or lowering movement, so that a crane is a hoisting mechanism motivated by a source of power remote from the load carrier. Hoists referred to in this section are lifting and lowering mechanisms in which the load is carried suspended from the motivator.

Hoists generally employ some type of gear arrangement in order to increase the mechanical advantage of the system (*i.e.* the ratio: weight lifted/effort applied). The types of gearing most frequently encountered in the food industry are:

(i)   Lever hoists which work on the principle of the wheel and axle. The effort is applied by a ratchet lever, and lever hoists handling $\frac{1}{2}$–5 tonnes are common. They have low mechanical efficiency (35 %) and are self-braking.

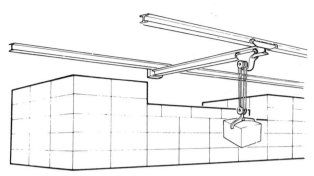

FIG. 19.7.   An overhead crane system.

(ii) Differential hoists which employ a fixed double sheave in conjunction with a movable sheave block and fall system. They are operated by pulling on an endless chain which runs round the pulley wheels. They have low efficiencies (30–40 %), are self-braking and may be used in intermittent, slow movements where accurate positioning is necessary (*e.g.* machinery installation and truck battery handling).

(iii) Worm geared hoists in which a driven worm turns a spur gear which lifts the load. They are capable of producing high mechanical advantage and have corresponding high capacity (up to 20 tonnes).

(iv) Spur geared hoists which use either compound gear trains or epicyclic (*i.e.* planetary) gears. These hoists have high efficiency (up to 85 %).

Types (iii) and (iv) are compact and powerful and are well suited to high-speed electrically powered hoisting. When attached to an overhead runway they provide an inexpensive and flexible system for handling packaged materials. Large hoists of this type are used in port-handling of containerised loads up to 70 tonnes in weight. In one application, self-propelled cars, each with its own operator, winch and lifting beam, run on an overhead track circuit supported by masts travelling on railed tracks.[13]

Air operated hoists have certain advantages over electric hoists: they are spark proof and therefore safe in dusty conditions; they are smooth in operation; they permit accurate positioning of the load and they cannot be overloaded. With a minimum of moving parts, air hoists are cheap to maintain and are resistant to corrosive, hot or wet conditions. Disadvantageously, air hoists require a supply of compressed air at about $800 \, kN/m^2$ and lifts are restricted to the stroke of the piston unless some sort of multiplier is used.

19.5. TRUCKS

19.5.1. GENERAL CONSIDERATIONS

This group includes all handling equipment which is capable of movement in a horizontal non-fixed path. It is convenient to categorise trucks on the basis of their vertical lifting characteristics giving three main groups as follows:

(i)   Trucks with no vertical lift (hand trucks, platform trucks and tractors).
(ii) Trucks with low vertical lift (pallet and stillage trucks).
(iii) Trucks with high vertical lift (fork-lift trucks and stackers).

19.5.1.1. Loads for trucks. Although trucks can handle any load which can be accommodated on the carriers, proper observation of the rules of material handling (Section 19.1.2) requires materials to be handled as *unit loads*.[14] A unit load is a group of items or a mass of bulk material which is handled as a single entity. It is standardised on the basis of weight, number or size. The movement of unit loads instead of single items results in: faster and cheaper handling and stocktaking, reduced product damage, improved stock rotation and better building-cube utilisation. Common forms of unit loads are:

(i)   Assemblies of items on platforms, skids, pallets and flat sheets.
(ii)   Groups of small items or masses of bulk material in containers such as bins, crates, trays or tanks.
(iii) Strapped, taped, baled or bundled assemblies.
(iv)   Loose loads which are handled as assemblies by baling clamps, shovels, etc.

19.5.1.2. Drive systems for trucks. *Drive resistance* considerations affect the size and type of motivator selected. This is an important matter: a drive unit which is too small causes delay and disorganisation; one which is too large contravenes the dead-weight rule (Section 19.1.2). When selecting a drive system, three types of resistance must be considered. These are:

(i)   *Tractive Resistance* (TR) which is the force required to overcome rolling friction when a specified gross weight (truck and load) moves over a given surface. The magnitude of TR is dependent on the nature of the surface, varying from 150 N/tonne (~ 35 lbf/ton) for a smooth concrete surface, to

1500 N/tonne (~ 350 lbf/ton) for clay. For design purposes a value of 200 N/tonne (45 lbf/ton) is assumed for well maintained floors.

(ii) *Acceleration Resistance* (AR) which is the force required to overcome inertia to acceleration. Trucks usually accelerate at around $0.2 \, m/s^2$ (~ $0.6 \, ft/s^2$) and at this rate, AR has a value of 200 N/tonne (~ 45 lbf/ton).

(iii) *Grade Resistance* (GR) which is the force additional to TR required to surmount a specified incline. Inclination is conveniently referred to as 'percentage grade' which is:

$$\frac{\text{vertical travel}}{\text{horizontal travel along the plane}} \times 100$$

Using this concept, for a gross weight of 1 tonne, GR has a value of 98 N per 1 % grade (22.4 lbf per ton per 1 % of grade).

Total Tractive Effort (TE) is calculated by summing these three resistances, hence:

$$TE = TR + AR + GR$$

Thus a man can conveniently move a load of 1 tonne on a hard, smooth, horizontal surface (TE = 200 + 200 + 0 = 400 N or 90 lbf) but if a shallow incline (say 2 % grade) intervenes then TE increases to 400 + 2 × 98 = 596 N or 134 lbf and fatigue rapidly sets in. The considerable effect of ascending gradients on the magnitude of TE and, hence, on the size of drive-system is noteworthy.

In addition to TE, allowance must be made for other energy consuming activities such as: loss of efficiency between motor and drive wheels; energy consumed in load lifting and lowering; and power used for steering and manoeuvring.

Manpowered drives despite their obvious limitations find use in confined areas and when intermittent working at low speed is acceptable. Power-assisted manpower is also of value, high and low lift facilities being added to the manoeuvrability and low capital costs of manpowered equipment.

Battery powered drives have the general characteristics shown in Table 19.3. Trucks driven by this method have a high dead-weight to capacity ratio and are limited by the storage capacity of their batteries. They are best suited to movement over short distance (100 m continuously) and on smooth level surfaces (maximum 10 % grade).

Internal combustion (*IC*) *drives*, using petrol or diesel fuel or liquefied petroleum gas (LPG), find application where long travel distances and steep gradients are involved (Table 19.3).

TABLE 19.3
Characteristics of truck engines

Drive System Characteristic	Electric	Petrol	LPG	Diesel
Risk of product contamination by fuel and exhaust	none	high	moderate	v. high
Type of haul (continuous)	short	long	long	long
Gradient surmountability	poor ($<10\%$)	good	good	good
Noise level	very low	high	high	high
Starting (cold)	easy	mod. difficult	mod. difficult	mod. difficult
Fire and explosion risk in dusty conditions	very low or none[a]	high	moderate	low
Engine wear	low	high	moderate	high

[a] When flashproofed.

IC engines should not be used in conditions where fire risk, product contamination risk or poor ventilation exist. LPG engines are similar in design to petrol engines, differing only in using a gaseous fuel which is said to cause less engine wear than occurs with liquid fuels. The exhaust is cleaner and the fuel less odorous than in petrol and diesel systems. LPG engines are sometimes used inside well-ventilated warehouses.

19.5.1.3. Wheels for trucks. The type of wheel selected should: handle the food gently, not cause floor damage, be easy to start and keep rolling (*i.e.* low AR and TR), and result in the lowest operating cost. The more important characteristics of truck wheels are indicated in Table 19.4 and are discussed, in detail, elsewhere.[15]

TABLE 19.4
Wheels for trucks

Wheel type Characteristic	Iron and steel	Aluminium	Polyurethane and phenolic	Rubber cushion	Rubber pneumatic
Load bearing	*****	**	***	****	***
Floor protection	*	**	***	****	*****
Impact resistance	*****	*	**	***	****
Wear resistance	*****	**	**	***	**
Non-spark properties	*	*****	*****	*****	*****
Oil resistance	*****	*****	****	*	*
Type of ride	*	**	**	***	*****
Noise rating	*	**	****	****	*****
Manoeuvrability	*****	*****	****	***	*

*****—very good;   *—very poor.

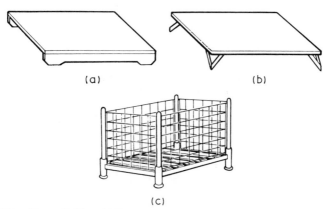

(a)   (b)

(c)

Fig. 19.8.   Types of stillage. (a) Two-way entry. (b) Four-way entry. (c) Collapsible box
stillage.

19.5.1.4. Stillages and pallets. These are the subject of various
standard specifications.[16, 17] Pallets and stillages (or skids) must be
loaded in patterns which ensure stability during transit and storage.
Loading patterns are discussed in detail in the specialist literature.[1]

Stillages (or skids) are platforms mounted on pairs of parallel
runners at each side or on legs at each corner (Fig. 19.8). Stillages may
be 'live' (*i.e.* with four wheeled legs), 'semi-live' (with two wheeled and
two fixed legs), or 'dead' (with fixed runners or legs). They may be
made of wood or metal and are primarily intended for in-use
movement or single-layer storage. Stillages should not be used for
stacking unless load boards are interposed between layers, otherwise
the heavy loading at the runners causes damage to underlying layers.

Pallets are load boards with two decks supported by bearers or,
alternatively, with a single deck supported by at least three bearers.
Pallets may be two-way or four-way entry. In the former type the
decks are separated by solid stringers and in the latter by stringers and
block bearers (Fig. 19.9).

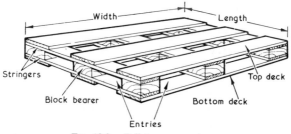

Fig. 19.9.   Pallet components.

19.5.2. TRUCKS WITH NO VERTICAL LIFT

19.5.2.1. Hand trucks. Despite the emphasis on mechanisation, these are available in wide variety. Truck manufacturers are able to offer trucks designed for specialised handling applications at low prices. In special circumstances (*e.g.* in confined areas) hand trucks are valuable handling adjuncts. Their main disadvantage is the tendency to use them in disregard of the performance rule (Section 19.1.2) and in this circumstance inefficiency results.

19.5.2.2. Platform trucks. Manpowered platform trucks, although still used, are being rapidly replaced by powered burden-carriers. Powered trucks with capacities ranging from 1 to 3 tonnes are common. They are used as fork-lift truck economisers, where their lightness, manoeuvrability and relative cheapness may be fully exploited. Both operator-led and operator-carrying types are available. Unpowered platform trucks are used in 'tractor trains' (Section 19.5.2.3).

19.5.2.3. Tractors. A powered tractor towing a train of platform trucks (*i.e.* a 'tractor train') provides an inexpensive high-capacity handling system for unit loads. The trucks are loaded by hoist, crane or by a stacker (Section 19.5.4) and function as an efficient transportation system for serving distant points. In some instances this enables a fork-lift truck to be replaced by a cheaper stacking truck.

The capacities of tractors are indicated in terms of drawbar pull. Tractors capable of moving loads of up to 40 tonnes are common. The capacity is substantially reduced on inclines where grade resistance (GR) must be allowed for. The stated maximum drawbar pull should be scrupulously observed since some types of tractor, if overloaded, are likely to rear up on the back wheels and cause accidents by toppling.

Driverless tractor trains, electronically controlled and running on programmed paths, are becoming increasingly popular.

19.5.3. TRUCKS WITH LOW VERTICAL LIFT

A low-lift truck is a self-loading machine which carries its load on a skid or pallet. The forks or platform are engaged with the load which is lifted sufficiently to allow free movement, the procedure being reversed at the discharge point. These trucks may be manpowered, power assisted, or fully powered and lifts varying from 5 to 10 cm may be produced mechanically or hydraulically. Unit loads up to 1 tonne may be handled conveniently, rapidly and cheaply. Low-lift trucks are very manoeuvrable, requiring only half the aisle space of a fork-lift truck, and they may be moved from floor to floor by elevator since they are relatively light in weight. However, these trucks generally have small-diameter wheels giving high floor loading. Particular care must be exercised in the choice of wheels in this case (Section 19.5.1.3).

Pallet trucks are equipped with forks which are fed, with the help of the booster wheels (Fig. 19.10), into the pallet entry. On actuating the

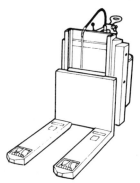

FIG. 19.10. A twin-fork low-lift pallet truck. (By courtesy of Matling Engineering (1962) Ltd, Wednesbury, Staffs.)

lift mechanism, the load wheels (which are normally carried housed in the forks) swivel down and lift the load clear of the ground for transit.

Stillage (or skid) trucks carry their loads on stillages. The lowered platform of the truck is slid beneath the stillage, the platform is then raised and held locked for transit.

19.5.4. TRUCKS WITH HIGH VERTICAL LIFT

Trucks with high vertical lift are primarily intended for stacking activities. Their use for movement over long distances is inefficient and expensive. High-lift trucks range from manpowered stackers to powered lift-trucks handling 10 tonnes and equipped with a large array of ancillaries. Typical examples are shown in Fig 19.11, the stacking truck being specifically for working in narrow aisles, and for relieving or replacing the more expensive and more space-consuming fork-lift truck. The use of this type of equipment is well known and calls for no description. The general characteristics which are operative in selecting and operating high-lift equipment are discussed below.

Load distribution methods may be of different types as follows:

(i)   Counterbalanced trucks which use the rear mounted battery or motor to balance the load, the front wheels acting as a fulcrum.

(ii) Outrigger trucks which carry their loads within the wheelbase, the front wheels being carried on extended legs. Non-straddle trucks have the legs inside the forks whilst straddle trucks have the legs outside the forks so as to clear the base of the load.

(iii) Reach trucks which are characterised by the ability of the forks, the fork carriage, or the whole mast, to move forward horizontally to facilitate manoeuvring of the load.

(iv) Sideloading trucks which carry their loads at right angles to the direction of travel and are used for handling lengthy loads, such as timber and girders.

Masts are usually telescopic and lifts of 3 m are general. The 'free lift' is the maximum lift attainable before the mast starts to telescope out. Lift speeds of 0·2 m/s and lowering speeds of around 0·25 m/s are common. Masts may be fixed, or forward moving as in reach trucks, or swivelling so as to turn the forks at an angle to the direction of movement. It is usual to provide a backward tilt of 10–12° for safe carriage and a forward tilt of 2–3° to permit easy positioning and pick-up of loads.

Load capacity is generally rated as '*W* kg at *X* cm load centres'. This means that the truck is rated to carry a load of *W* kg with its centre of gravity at a horizontal distance of *X* cm from the heels of the forks when these are in the lowered position. Other rating systems are described by Apple.[1] Mast tilt, and lifting or tilting the load, considerably affect load capacity and stability.

Gradient surmountability and underclearance are specified by manufacturers. The presence of ramps and other floor-level projections must be considered when selecting equipment.

Manoeuvrability specifications indicate the minimum aisle widths required for travelling, turning and stacking. Unfortunately, fork-lift trucks, in particular, require wide aisles which reduce maximum utilisation of floor area.

Speeds for battery driven trucks are 8–10 km/h whilst internal combustion types run at 15–20 km/h. In the interests of safety, speed limits must be rigidly enforced.

Ancillaries for trucks include: extension forks, drum and bale clamps, squeeze clamps and crane attachments. The use of these devices should be carefully considered having regard to the rules given in Section 19.1.2.

Automatic pallet loaders are widely used for forming patterned unit loads from regular shaped sub-units such as cartons, boxes and

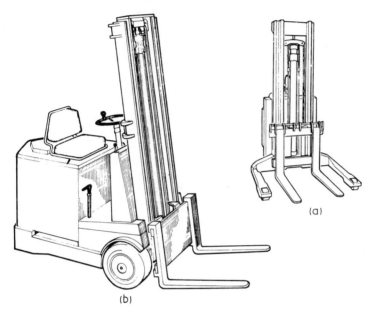

FIG. 19.11.   High-lift free moving equipment. (a) Straddle type pallet truck. (b) Driver controlled counterbalanced type fork lift truck. (By courtesy of Matling Engineering (1962) Ltd, Wednesbury, Staffs.)

sacks. These are conveyed into the palletiser and are formed into tiered layers by means of powered rams controlled by a programming device. Loaders handling 5–15 sub-units/min are common and high-speed units are capable of dealing with 35 sub-units/min.[18] Automatic de-palletisers are also available.[19]

Hiring or leasing of handling equipment of all types is growing, and many organisations find that the nature of their work (*e.g.* seasonal processing of vegetables) makes hiring cheaper than buying. This is particularly appropriate for the more expensive mobile equipment such as fork-lift trucks and cranes.[20] However, one should not be tempted into the use of unsuitable equipment even on a temporary basis.

19.6. PNEUMATIC EQUIPMENT

Pneumatic handling utilises a flow of air to reduce or eliminate solid–solid friction in a system. Three classes of handling may be distinguished:

(i)   Package conveying using the 'air-cushion' principle.
(ii) Conveying of particulate solids fluidised by air (see Appendix I).
(iii) Conveying of particulate solids suspended in air.

19.6.1. 'AIR CUSHION' CONVEYING OF PACKAGED MATERIALS

In one example of this method of handling, packages are conveyed by gravity on an inclined chute. A package placed on the chute depresses patented valves set in the chute surface. These admit air beneath the package to form an 'air cushion'. Another type of air-cushion conveyor which is suitable for conveying both packages and bulk food materials uses a flow of low-pressure air, issuing from louvres punched in the conveying surface, to lift and propel the load.[21] Air-floated pallets using the Hovercraft principle may be used to handle heavy loads (~ 7 tonnes) over uneven surfaces in confined conditions.[22]

19.6.2. FLUIDISED CONVEYING

Particulate solids, contained in silos or bulk transportation vehicles, may be fluidised to assist discharge (Fig. 19.12). Air is introduced in sufficient quantity and at sufficient pressure to produce gravity flow of the material. This is sometimes called 'dense phase' conveying[23] and is characterised by a high solids to air ratio. The beds used in fluidised handling consist of porous ceramic tiles, sintered metal or plastic, fine wire-mesh and similar materials.[24]

Fluidised solids may be forced through pipe-lines by air under pressure as in the 'powder pump' shown diagrammatically in Fig. 19.13. Specially designed road and rail vehicles which discharge bulk loads of flour, salt, sugar, etc., using this principle are commonly encountered.

Solids contained in a pipe-line may be fluidised by passing air through a perforated flexible inner-tube running the length of the pipe-line. The fluidised material is then conveyed by establishing a pressure drop along the pipe-line (Fig. 19.13).

19.6.3. CONVEYING OF SOLIDS SUSPENDED IN AIR

In this widely used method, air flowing axially along a pipe-line is used in sufficient quantity and at sufficient pressure to suspend particulate materials and to convey them through the pipe-line. This method of handling, characterised by a low solids to air ratio, is called 'dilute phase' or 'dispersed phase' conveying.

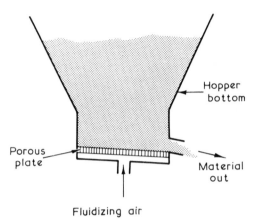

FIG. 19.12.   Fluidised bed discharge.

19.6.3.1. Types of dilute phase conveyor. Figure 19.14 shows the three main types of dilute phase conveyor. The 'positive pressure' or 'push' system operates at super-atmospheric pressure and is used for delivery to several outlets from one inlet. The 'negative pressure' or 'pull' system works at sub-atmospheric pressure and is used for delivery to one outlet from several inlets. The combination or 'push-pull' system is used for delivery to several outlets from multiple inlets.

Recirculation of the conveying air, as in the 'closed' system, reduces contamination of the product by the air and limits product dehydration. However, such systems are often difficult to control and an intercooler may be required to prevent the pump overheating the recirculated air.

19.6.3.2. Factors affecting dilute phase conveying. *Air velocity.* Most food materials may be conveyed satisfactorily at air speeds within the range of 15–25 m/s. Above this, abrasion of tube bends and product damage may become troublesome. At speeds which are too low, solids tend to settle out (saltate) and block horizontal pipe runs.

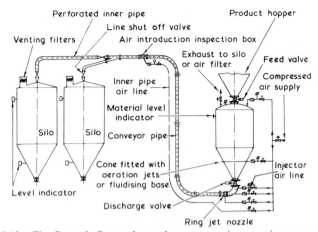

FIG. 19.13. The Pennsalt-Gattys dense phase pneumatic conveying system. (By courtesy of Pennsalt Ltd, Camberley, Surrey, England.)

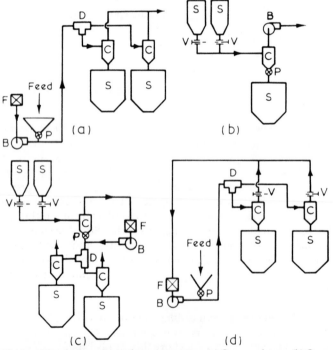

FIG. 19.14. Dilute phase pneumatic conveyor types. (a) Open push type. (b) Open pull type. (c) Open push–pull type. (d) Closed push type. B, blower; C, disengager; D, diverter; F, air filter; P, feeder; S, silo; V, slide valve.

Air pressure. This is required to provide energy to:

(i)   Accelerate the conveying air.
(ii)   Lift the particles.
(iii) Overcome resistances due to interparticulate and particle-wall collisions.
(iv)   Overcome fluid friction in ducting and beds.
(v)   Overcome resistance due to disengagement of the solid at the discharge point.

Thus there will be a pressure drop along the conveyor as the energy in the air is expended. If air at high pressure is used, its correspondingly high initial energy will enable more conveying to be accomplished, per kilogram of air, than if low-pressure air is used. However, high-pressure systems are proportionately more expensive and the maximum pressure used for general purpose dilute phase conveying is about $170 \, kN/m^2$.

Solid-air ratio. Obviously, for maximum efficiency this ratio should be as high as possible. For flour and salt this ratio may be up to $80 \, kg \, solid/m^3$ air while wheat is limited to $30 \, kg \, solid/m^3$. There is an upper limit for this ratio for each material, which if exceeded will cause blockage of the system as a result of saltation.

Material properties. The size, shape, density and surface properties of the particles comprising a material control its behaviour during pneumatic transfer (Appendix I). Other properties such as friability, hygroscopicity and susceptibility to impact and abrasion damage or oxidation must be considered.

19.6.3.3. Components of dilute phase conveyors. *Air movers.* High-speed, single-stage, centrifugal fans deliver air at about $120 \, kN/m^2$ and must be supplied with cleaned air if excessive abrasion of the light impellers is to be avoided. The slower-running, multi-stage, heavy-duty centrifugal fan can deliver up to $140 \, kN/m^2$ and, being slower running, is relatively resistant to particle abrasion. The discharge from centrifugal fans falls markedly as the discharge pressure rises, so solids blockage may occur. Centrifugal fans are used in low-pressure conveyors ($105–125 \, kN/m^2$).

Positive displacement blowers, of the Root's type, pump through driven, intermeshing lobes. The clearance between the lobes is small so that an inlet air cleaner is required to reduce wear. Blowers of this type are less affected by downstream pressure than fans, and produce lubricant-free air. Single-stage blowers generate up to $200 \, kN/m^2$ and double-stage blowers generate up to about $270 \, kN/m^2$. Blowers are, therefore, used extensively in medium pressure systems ($120–200 \, kN/m^2$).

Compressors deliver air at high pressures but require lubrication. This contaminates the air with oil vapour which is difficult to remove. Nevertheless, compressors find applications in high-pressure systems (200–$800\,kN/m^2$) and in dense phase conveying.

Stabilisers. If one air mover supplies several conveyor pipes, each must be unaffected by changes in the others. Figure 19.15 shows an air

air inlet

FIG. 19.15. The sonic valve. (By courtesy of the patentees—Henry Simon Ltd, Stockport, England.)

stabilising valve designed to satisfy this requirement. The valve works on the principle that once the pressure drop across an air nozzle exceeds a certain minimum value, the velocity at the throat equals that of sound and no further reduction in the downstream pressure affects the mass-flow rate through the nozzle. Thus, a constant rate of supply may be maintained against a fluctuating pressure in the conveyor.

Feeders. Figure 19.16 shows two types of feeder. The venturi feeder is only suitable for low-pressure systems. The rotary valve is widely used for feeding medium-pressure conveyors and, although simple in principle, calls for careful design in order to minimise air leakage. Excessive air loss from feeders wastes power, causes dust and leads to

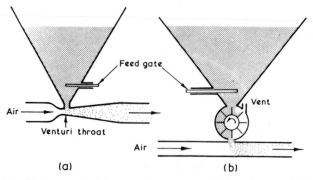

Feed gate

Air

Venturi throat

Vent

Air

(a)   (b)

FIG. 19.16. Feeding devices for pneumatic conveyors. (a) Venturi feeder. (b) Rotary feeder.

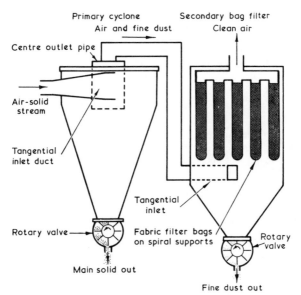

FIG. 19.17.   Separation system for a pneumatic conveyor.

system instability. Rotary valves work well on free-flowing non-abrasive powders and special types are available for more difficult materials.

Separators. Preliminary disengagement of the conveyed material from the conveying air at the discharge point may be affected by discharging into a receiver of sufficient size. The efficiency of this method is improved by fitting an impingement plate in the air path. It is more general, however, to bring about separation by means of a cyclone followed by a bag filter (Fig. 19.17).

19.6.3.4. Safety precautions. Static charges of considerable potential can be developed during the pneumatic conveying of many food materials (*e.g.* sugar, flour and grain). Both product-wall and product-product charges can be produced. These may initiate dust explosions or cause shocks to operators. Charging of the product can also cause wall adhesion, agglomeration and blocking. Ducting should be effectively earthed taking particular care to install bridging plates on ducting joints. Product charging can be reduced by:

(i)   Controlling the product moisture content.
(ii) Inserting charged probes into the product-air stream.
(iii) Ionising the air by radio-active materials.

19.6.3.5. Advantages of the method. A well designed system is self-cleaning, dustless and sanitary. It has high capacity for installation and running costs which compare favourably with other conveying systems and makes good use of the building cube.

REFERENCES

1. Apple, J. M., 'Plant Layout and Materials Handling', 2nd ed. (Ronald Press, N.Y.: 1963).
2. Anon., 'An Introduction to Material Handling'. (The Material Handling Institute Inc., USA: 1966.)
3. Harvey, B., 'Annual Report of HM Inspector of Factories 1973': Cmnd. 5708. (HMSO: London.)
4. Anon., 'Health and Safety at Work Act, 1974'. Chap. 37. (HMSO: London.)
5. Creber, F. L., 'Safety for Industry'. (The Royal Society for Prevention of Accidents, London: 1967.)
6. Bowden, E. P., and Tabor, D., 'Friction and Lubrication of Solids'. (Oxford University Press: 1964.)
7. Anon., 'Cereal Millers' Handbook', Vol. 1. (Burgess Publishing, USA: 1963.)
8. Robinson, R., 'Weighing against the Clock'. Mech. Handl., **62**(3), 42–5 (1975).
9. Coyne, P., 'Hopalong Capacity'. Mech. Handl., **62**(4), 37–9 (1975).
10. Anon., 'Conveyors That Cling On'. Mech. Handl., **61**(11), 45–6 (1974).
11. Anon., 'Interfloor Movement of Goods and Materials'. Mech. Handl., **54**(3), 111–8 (1967).
12. Anon., 'Systems for Conveying'. Fd. Proc. Ind., **42**(5), 62–7 (1973).
13. Anon., 'Continuous Ship–Shore Container Handling'. Mech. Handl., **55**(1), 93 (1968).
14. Hulett, M., 'Unit Load Handling'. (Gower Press: 1970.)
15. Anon., 'Choosing the Right Castor for the Job'. Storage Handling and Distribution, **10**(12), 38 and 45 (1967).
16. Anon., 'Specifications for Pallets for Materials Handling'. British Standard 2629: 1967. (British Standards Institution, London: 1967).
17. Anon., 'American Standard Pallet Sizes'. American Society of Mechanical Engineers, ASA MH 1.1 (undated).
18. Nugarus, A. R., 'Automatic Palletization'. Fd Engng, **37**(4), 89–91 (1965).
19. Anon., 'Fully Automatic Depalletizer'. Mech. Handl., **54**(11), 509 (1967).
20. Anon., 'Lift Truck Rental'. Storage Handling and Distribution, **17**(10), 40–43 (1974).
21. Anon., 'Air Cushion Conveyor'. Fd Mf., **41**(6), 65–6 (1966).
22. Anon., 'Hoverpallets Aboard Ship'. Mech. Handl., **55**(2), 227 (1968).
23. Mumby, K., 'Crossroads for Fluidized Conveying'. Mech. Handl., **52**(11), 513–21 (1965).
24. Kraus, M. N., 'Pneumatic Conveying of Bulk Materials'. (Ronald Press, N.Y.: 1968.)

APPENDICES

FLUID FLOW FORMULAE

I.1. FLOW THROUGH EQUIPMENT

For fluids flowing in pipes and ducts or past solid bodies the 'Reynolds Number' is defined by:

$$Re = \frac{Dv\rho}{\eta} \tag{I.1}$$

where D = a characteristic dimension of the system; v = the mean linear velocity of the fluid; ρ = the density of the fluid; η = the viscosity of the fluid, and the 'Friction Factor' is defined by:

$$f = \frac{D}{2v^2} \frac{dF}{dx} \tag{I.2}$$

where dF is the energy used in overcoming friction when unit mass of the fluid flows from a surface at x to $x + dx$.

For incompressible fluids (*i.e.* liquids) flowing in ducts or channels of uniform cross-section:

$$f = \frac{D(-\Delta p)}{2L\rho v^2}$$

where $(-\Delta p)$ = pressure drop due to frictional losses (in, say, Newtons/(metre)^2); L = length of duct or channel (in, say, metres); and the other quantities are as defined in equations (I.1) and (I.2) and are measured in units consistent with those above.

For flow of incompressible fluids in circular ducts at Reynolds Numbers below 2000 (streamline flow):

$$Re.f = 16 \tag{I.3}$$

At higher Reynolds Numbers, where the flow is turbulent, a number of correlations between Reynolds Number, friction factor and the roughness of the pipe wall have been proposed. For smooth pipes an equation of the form:

$$\frac{1}{(f)^{1/2}} = k_1 \log [Re. (f)^{1/2}] - k_2 \tag{I.4}$$

501

is often used. A number of different values have been proposed for k_1 and k_2, but Nikuradse's proposals ($k_1 = 4{\cdot}0$, $k_2 = 0{\cdot}40$) are commonly employed.[1]

For turbulent flow in ducts and channels of non-circular section it is usually assumed that the above formula may be used, provided the characteristic dimension, D, is taken to be $4R$, where R is the 'hydraulic radius' defined by:

$$\frac{\text{cross-sectional area of duct}}{\text{length of the wetted perimeter}} \qquad (\text{I.5})$$

For flow through a bed of granular material the following equation has been proposed:[3]

$$\frac{(-\Delta p)x^3}{LS_0 u(1-x)} = k_1 S_0 (1-x)\eta + k_2 \rho u \qquad (\text{I.6})$$

where x = the porosity of the bed (*i.e.* the fraction filled with fluid); L = the length of the bed; S_0 = the specific surface of the granules (surface area of unit volume of the *granules*); and u = the superficial velocity, given by:

$$u = \frac{V}{A}$$

where V = rate of volume flow through the bed; A = cross-sectional area of the *bed*.

The constant k_1 in equation (I.6) takes values between about 4 and 5, depending on the geometry of the granule bed[2] and k_2 has a value of about $0{\cdot}3$.[3] For streamline flow (*i.e.* at comparatively low flow rates) the second term on the right-hand side of equation (I.6) can be neglected.

I.2. FLUIDISATION

If flow takes place vertically upwards through a granular bed, equation (I.6) will apply until the pressure drop across the bed balances the weight of the bed. If the flow is increased above this level, the bed expands and the granules forming it are no longer all in static contact; the bed is then said to be fluidised and the pressure drop across it is given by:

$$-\Delta p = g(1-x)(\rho_s - \rho)L \qquad (\text{I.7})$$

where ρ_s = the density of the granules; g = the acceleration due to gravity.

If the flow is further increased so that the viscous drag on the granules exceeds their weight, the granules will be carried along in the fluid stream (fluid-solid conveying). This case is discussed by Foust *et al.*[3]

An important parameter of a fluidised bed is the Froude Number (*Fr*), given by:

$$Fr = \frac{u^2}{gD}$$

where D = the average diameter of the granule.

At Froude numbers below unity 'particulate' fluidisation occurs, the bed being essentially uniform in nature. At Froude numbers above unity the bed takes on a 'boiling' appearance with 'bubbles' of a dilute suspension rising through the bed ('aggregative' fluidisation).

REFERENCES

1. McCabe, W. L., and Smith, J. C., 'Unit Operations of Chemical Engineering'. 2nd ed. (McGraw-Hill: 1967).
2. Coulson, J. M., and Richardson, J. F., 'Chemical Engineering'. Vol. II, 2nd ed. (Pergamon Press: 1964).
3. Foust, A. S., Wenzel, L. A., Clump, C. W., Maus, L., and Andersen, L. B., 'Principles of Unit Operations'. (John Wiley: 1960.)

HEAT TRANSFER FORMULAE

II.1. THERMAL CONVECTION

This occurs in fluids when heat is transferred by the motion of the fluid. Two types of convection are distinguished: 'forced' convection, in which the motion of the fluid is caused by external agencies and there is a net fluid velocity in the system, and 'natural' convection, in which movement occurs by virtue of density gradients generated by differential thermal expansion of the fluid.

II.1.1. HEAT TRANSFER COEFFICIENTS

The rate of heat transfer by convection from an area dA of a solid surface (temperature θ_1) to a fluid (temperature θ_2) under steady conditions

$$= h\,dA(\theta_1 - \theta_2) \tag{II.1}$$

where h is the local heat transfer coefficient at the fluid–solid interface.

This heat transfer coefficient is expressed in dimensionless form in the Nusselt Number (Nu):

$$Nu = \frac{hD}{k} \tag{II.2}$$

where D is a characteristic dimension of the system and k is the thermal conductivity of the fluid.

In a heat exchanger where two fluids (a and b) flow on opposite sides of a barrier, the overall heat transfer coefficient between them (U—Section II.2.1) being constant over the heat exchange surface (area A), the rate of heat exchange between them

$$= UA\,\Delta\theta_m \tag{II.3}$$

where

$$\Delta\theta_m = \frac{(\theta_a - \theta_b) - (\theta_a' - \theta_b')}{\ln(\theta_a - \theta_b) - \ln(\theta_a' - \theta_b')} \tag{II.4}$$

and θ_a, θ_b, θ'_a, θ'_b are the temperatures of the fluids a and b at one end and the other end of the heat exchanger respectively.

II.1.2. FORCED CONVECTION

For fluid flowing turbulently, the Nusselt number may be expressed approximately as a function of the Reynolds and Prandtl Numbers by:

$$Nu = a(Re)^b (Pr)^c \qquad \text{(II.5)}$$

where

$$Pr = \frac{C_p\eta}{k} \qquad \text{(the Prandtl Number)} \qquad \text{(II.6)}$$

η = viscosity of the fluid; C_p = its specific heat at constant pressure; and the Reynolds Number is defined in Appendix I.1.

Values of the constants a, b and c suitable for use with liquids of low viscosity are given in Table II.1.

TABLE II.1
Values of the constants a, b and c in equation (II.5)[1]

System	a	b	c
Fluid flowing inside a circular tube:			
(i) fluid heated	0·023	0·8	0·4
(ii) fluid cooled	0·023	0·8	0·3
Fluid flowing at right-angles to a circular cylinder	0·26	0·6	0·3
Fluid flowing over tube banks	See reference 1		

II.1.3. NATURAL CONVECTION

Here the Nusselt Number can be expressed approximately as a function of the Prandtl and Grashof Numbers:[1]

$$Nu = a(Pr \cdot Gr)^b \qquad \text{(II.7)}$$

where

$$Gr = \frac{D^3\rho^2 g\beta(\theta_1 - \theta_2)}{\eta^2} \qquad \text{(the Grashof Number)} \qquad \text{(II.8)}$$

ρ = density of the fluid; g = acceleration due to gravity; β = coefficient of volumetric expansion of fluid.

TABLE II.2
Values of the constants a and b in equation (II.7)

System	D	Value of Pr . Gr	a	b
Horizontal or vertical cylinders	diameter	10^3–10^8	0·47	0·25
		$> 10^9$	0·10	0·33
Vertical planes	height	10^3–10^8	0·56	0·25
		$> 10^9$	0·12	0·33
Horizontal square planes facing upwards	side	10^3–10^8	0·54	0·25
		$> 10^9$	0·14	0·33
Fluid between parallel vertical planes	gap width	$< 10^3$	1	0
		10^4–10^6	0·15	0·25
		$> 10^6$	heat transfer takes place independently at each face	

Suitable values of the constants a and b for fluid of low viscosity and the appropriate dimension D to be used in Nu and Gr are given in Table II.2.

II.2.   THERMAL CONDUCTION

II.2.1. THE STEADY STATE

If heat is transferred by conduction between the parallel faces of an infinitely large slab of thickness d, one face being held at temperature θ_1 and the other at θ_2, the rate of heat transfer per unit area of the slab

$$= \frac{k}{d}(\theta_1 - \theta_2) \qquad (II.9)$$

where k is the thermal conductivity of the material of the slab.

In the case of a complex thermal barrier composed of a series of such infinite slabs (thickness $d_1, d_2, \ldots$ and thermal conductivities $k_1, k_2, \ldots$) either in contact or separated by parallel-sided fluid-filled spaces (there existing convective resistances at fluid–solid boundaries defined by a series of heat transfer coefficients $h_1, h_2, \ldots$) an overall heat transfer coefficient (U) may be defined by:

$$\frac{1}{U} = \frac{d_1}{k_1} + \frac{d_2}{k_2} + \cdots + \frac{1}{h_1} + \frac{1}{h_2} + \cdots \qquad (II.10)$$

and the rate of heat flow per unit area across the barrier

$$= U(\theta_1 - \theta_2) \tag{II.11}$$

If a hollow cylinder (inside radius r_1, outside radius r_2) of material of thermal conductivity k is immersed in a fluid at temperature θ_2, the heat transfer coefficient at the solid–fluid interface being h, and if the inside face of the cylinder is maintained at temperature θ_1, then the rate of heat flow per unit length of cylinder

$$= \frac{2\pi(\theta_1 - \theta_2)}{\dfrac{1}{k} \ln\left(\dfrac{r_2}{r_1}\right) + \dfrac{1}{r_2 h}} \tag{II.12}$$

N.B. The rate of heat transfer increases with r_2 when $r_2 < k/h$; thus lagging pipes with poor insulation may increase the heat loss from them.

II.2.2. THE UNSTEADY STATE

When a solid body changes temperature from θ_1 to θ_2 it is convenient to express the temperature θ of a point within it at time t during the change as a dimensionless temperature (V):

$$V = \frac{\theta - \theta_2}{\theta_1 - \theta_2} \tag{II.13}$$

Clearly V will have an initial value of 1 and will tend to zero as the change progresses. Formulae for V are conveniently expressed in terms of the Biot (Bi) and Fourier (Fo) Numbers:

$$Bi = \frac{hl}{k} \tag{II.14}$$

$$Fo = \frac{Kt}{l^2} \tag{II.15}$$

where h = heat transfer coefficient at the surface of the body; l = characteristic dimension of the body—this is taken to be the shortest distance between the surface of the body and the thermal centre (*i.e.* the location that heats or cools slowest). For a sphere or infinite cylinder, this distance is the radius. For an infinite slab it is half the thickness. K = thermal diffusivity of the body.

Expressions giving V as a function of time are available in a number of instances[2] but are cumbersome. Charts are available for

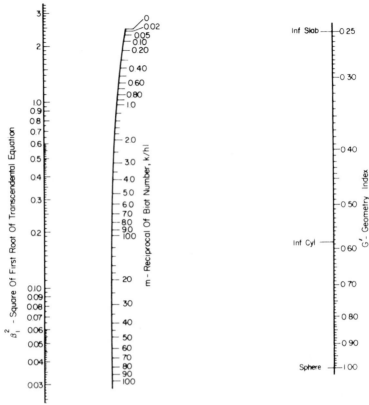

FIG. II.1.   Nomograph for the evaluation of temperature distributions in bodies of
arbitrary shape. (From Smith *et al.*[4] by permission.)

determining V at certain points in slabs, rods, cylinders, spheres and
brick-shaped bodies.[3]

It is often important to determine the temperature at the centre of a
body in the final stages of heating and cooling. Under these conditions
the formulae mentioned above can be considerably simplified. For a
body of arbitrary shape, Smith *et al.*[4] suggest an approximate method
of calculation as follows:

First a Geometrical Index G' is estimated for the body by
approximating its shape to one of those given below and using the
appropriate formula.

(i) For a brick-shaped body, $2l \times 2A_1 l \times 2A_2 l$ $(A_1, A_2 \geq 1)$

$$G' = \frac{1}{4} + \frac{1}{4A_1^2} + \frac{1}{4A_2^2} \tag{II.16}$$

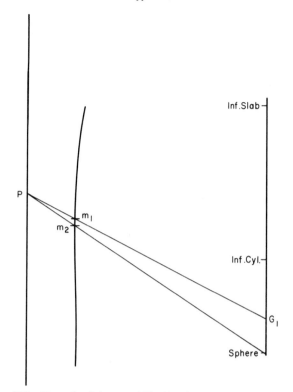

FIG. II.2. Example of the use of Fig. II.1 (for explanation, *see* text).

(ii) for an ellipsoid with semi-axes l, $B_1 l$ and $B_2 l$ $(B_1, B_2 \geq 1)$

$$G' = \frac{1}{4} + \frac{3}{8B_1^2} + \frac{3}{8B_2^2} \tag{II.17}$$

(iii) for a finite cylinder radius l, length $2lC_1$ $(C_1 > 1)$

$$G' = 0 \cdot 586 + \frac{1}{4C_1^2} \tag{II.18}$$

Then, referring to the nomograph in Fig. II.1 and the explanatory example in Fig. II.2, knowing the Biot Number $(Bi)_1$ for the arbitrary body, a value m_1 is calculated where:

$$m_1 = \frac{1}{(Bi)_1} \tag{II.19}$$

and a line is drawn from the point indicating the geometrical index of the arbitrary body (G'_1) through the point corresponding to m_1 to cut the left hand line at the point P as shown. Taking the nearest regular solid to the point G'_1 (in the example, this is the sphere) a line is drawn to P, cutting the m-line at m_2. Then, for $Fo > 0.2$, the relationship between Fo and V at the centre of the arbitrary body will be approximately the same as that at the centre of the regular body chosen (in the example, the sphere) when the Biot number for the regular body is $1/m_2$.

Again, for the infinite slab, infinite cylinder and sphere, with infinite Biot Number (*i.e.* infinite heat transfer coefficient, so that the surface is held at the temperature of the heating and cooling medium) for $Fo > 0.2$

$$V \simeq a \exp(-b.Fo) \qquad (II.20)$$

where the values of the constants a and b are given in Table II.3.

TABLE II.3
Values of the constants a and b in equation (II.20)

Body	a	b
Infinite slab	1·27	2·47
Infinite cylinder	1·60	5·78
Sphere	2·00	9·87

II.3. RADIATION TRANSFER[5]

Matter, as a consequence of its temperature, emits radiation at wavelengths and with intensities that depend on the nature of the radiator. Radiation can also be absorbed by bodies and thus its interchange provides a method of heat exchange. The radiating surfaces may be characterised as 'black body', 'grey body' or 'selective emitters'.

II.3.1. BLACK BODY RADIATORS

Black body radiators are conceived to be perfect radiators. They emit the greatest amount of thermal radiation possible at any given temperature. They absorb all energy incident upon them, reflecting nothing. Dark dull surfaces approximate to black body radiators.

The total energy emitted per unit area from a black body at *absolute* temperature T in unit time is:

$$\sigma T4 \qquad (II.21)$$

where $\sigma = 5.775 \times 10^{-8} \text{ W/m}^2 \text{ K}^4$.

If two black body radiators at absolute temperatures T_1 and T_2 ($T_1 > T_2$) radiate to each other, the net rate of exchange of heat

$$= E = C\sigma(T_1^4 - T_2^4) \tag{II.22}$$

where C is a constant depending on the geometry of the system.

If $T_1 - T_2$ ($= \Delta T$) is small compared with T_1 equation (II.22) can be re-written:

$$E \simeq 4C\sigma T_1^3 \Delta T \tag{II.23}$$

thus the energy transfer in this case is approximately proportional to the temperature difference (*cf.* convective transfer).

The thermal energy radiated by a black body is not uniformly distributed over the whole spectrum but has a maximum intensity at wavelength λ given by

$$\lambda T = 0 \cdot 2896 \, \text{cm K} \tag{II.24}$$

II.3.2. GREY BODY RADIATORS

The radiation from grey bodies is spectrally distributed in a manner similar to that from a black body, but with the intensity at any wavelength reduced by a factor ε (the 'emissivity' of the body) which is constant over the whole spectrum. Thus equation (II.21) holds for grey bodies if its right-hand side is multiplied by ε, equations (II.22) and (II.23) hold without modification, though C is now also a function of the emissivities of the surfaces, and equation (II.24) stands unchanged.

Most electrical insulators and semi-conductors can, in practice, be regarded as grey bodies. The emissivity of unpolished surfaces of such materials is usually of the order of $0 \cdot 9$.

II.3.3. SELECTIVE EMITTERS

Some materials, particularly metals, metal oxides and certain gases and vapours, show an irregular distribution of radiant intensity, the emissivity of their surfaces varying over the spectrum.

Since the emissivity of a body is equal to its absorptivity, a body which reflects much radiation radiates little. Thus the emissivity of clean metal surfaces is low. Moreover if a body is perfectly transparent, neither absorbing nor reflecting radiation, it will not emit radiation (*i.e.* $\varepsilon = 0$). This behaviour is approximated by certain gases such as hydrogen, oxygen and nitrogen. Gases and vapours consisting of polar molecules (*e.g.* steam and carbon dioxide) are selective emitters with a complex emission spectrum.

REFERENCES

1. Fishenden, M., and Saunders, O. A., 'An Introduction to Heat Transfer'. (Oxford: 1950.)
2. Carslaw, H. S., and Jaeger, J. C., 'Conduction of Heat in Solids', 2nd ed. (Oxford: 1958).
3. Dalgleish, N., and Ede, A. J., 'Charts for Determining Centre, Surface and Mean Temperatures in Regular Geometric Solids during Heating or Cooling'. NEL Report No. 192 (1965).
4. Smith, R. E., Nelson, G. L., and Henrickson, R. L., Transactions of the American Society of Agricultural Engineers, **10,** 236 (1967).
5. Gröber, H., and Erk, S., 'Fundamentals of Heat Transfer'. 3rd ed., *revised by* Grigull, U., *translated by* Moszynski, J. R. (McGraw-Hill: 1961).

PSYCHROMETRICS

Psychrometrics is the study of the properties of gas–vapour mixtures. The mixture most commonly encountered in food processing is air–water vapour and this appendix is restricted to that system.

III.1. DEFINITIONS

The 'absolute' (or specific) humidity, H, is the weight of water present in the mixture, per unit weight of dry air. Assuming 'perfect gas' behaviour:

$$H = \frac{M_w p_v}{M_A(P - p_v)} \qquad \text{(III.1)}$$

where M_w = the molecular weight of water; M_A = the molecular weight of air; P = the total pressure of the system; p_v = the partial pressure of water vapour in the system.

The saturation humidity, H_s, is the absolute humidity of saturated air. In saturated air the water vapour pressure equals the vapour pressure of water at air temperature.

$$H_s = \frac{M_w p_w}{M_A(P - p_w)} \qquad \text{(III.2)}$$

where p_w = the vapour pressure of water at air temperature.

The percentage absolute humidity, H_p, is the ratio of the absolute humidity of a mixture at a given temperature to the saturation humidity at the same temperature (expressed as a percentage)

$$H_p = 100 \frac{H}{H_s} = 100 \frac{p_v (P - p_w)}{p_w (P - p_v)} \qquad \text{(III.3)}$$

The percentage relative humidity, H_R, is the ratio of the partial pressure of water vapour in a mixture at a given temperature to the vapour pressure of water at that temperature (expressed as a percentage)

$$H_R = 100 \frac{p_v}{p_w} \qquad \text{(III.4)}$$

The dewpoint (or saturation temperature) is the temperature at which a given air–water vapour mixture becomes saturated, if cooled at constant humidity.

The humid heat, C_H, is the heat necessary to raise the temperature of a mass of mixture containing unit mass of dry air, by unit amount.

$$C_H = C_A + C_v H \qquad \text{(III.5)}$$

where C_A = the specific heat of dry air; C_v = the specific heat of water vapour.

The humid volume, V_H, is the volume of a mass of mixture containing unit mass of dry air, at one atmosphere pressure and a given temperature. Assuming the perfect gas law applies, in SI units:

$$V_H = \frac{22 \cdot 4}{273} (\theta + 273) \left(\frac{1}{M_A} + \frac{H}{M_w} \right) \qquad \text{(III.6)}$$

where θ = the temperature of the mixture, °C; when $H = 0$, V_H = the specific volume of dry air; when $H = H_s$, V_H = the specific volume of saturated air.

Adiabatic saturation temperature: If a stream of moist air passes co-currently through water sprays at temperature θ_s, under adiabatic conditions, so that the air leaves the system in equilibrium with the water (saturated) and at temperature θ_s, the temperature θ_s is known as the adiabatic saturation temperature. The line relating the temperature and humidity of the air during the adiabatic cooling is known as the adiabatic cooling (or saturation) line. The equation to this line is

$$H_s - H = \frac{C_H}{L_s} (\theta - \theta_s) \qquad \text{(III.7)}$$

where L_s = the latent heat of vaporisation of water at θ_s.

The wet-bulb temperature, θ_w, is the steady state (dynamic equilibrium) temperature attained by a small quantity of water evaporating under adiabatic conditions in an air stream. Wet-bulb temperature is measured by means of a temperature-sensing element covered by a wick which is maintained saturated with water. The conditions are such that changes in the properties of the moist air mass passing the wick are negligible. The rate of heat transfer from the air exactly balances the rate of evaporation, therefore:

$$H_w - H = \frac{h_c}{L_w k} (\theta - \theta_w) \qquad \text{(III.8)}$$

where H_w = the saturation humidity at θ_w; L_w = the latent heat of vaporisation at θ_w; h_c = heat transfer coefficient; k = mass transfer coefficient.

Relationship between wet-bulb and adiabatic saturation temperature: It has been shown experimentally that for air–water vapour mixtures θ_w and θ_s are approximately equal and may be used interchangeably for most engineering calculations.

III.2. THE PSYCHROMETRIC (OR HUMIDITY) CHART

The properties of air–water vapour mixtures may be displayed on a diagram, or chart, such as that shown in Fig. III.1. This chart is for air–water vapour mixtures at one atmosphere pressure.

The use of the humidity chart is illustrated in Fig. III.2. The point 'b' on the chart represents a sample of moist air at a temperature θ_1 and absolute humidity H_1. The percentage absolute humidity of this air, $H_{p1}\%$ is obtained from the curve of constant percentage absolute humidity passing through point 'b'. Interpolation between such lines may be necessary. The abscissa 'd' of point 'c' on the 100% absolute humidity line represents the dewpoint of the air sample. The line a–b represents the locus of points denoting air samples with the same adiabatic saturation temperature. Since the adiabatic saturation temperature of saturated air is equal to the temperature of that air, the

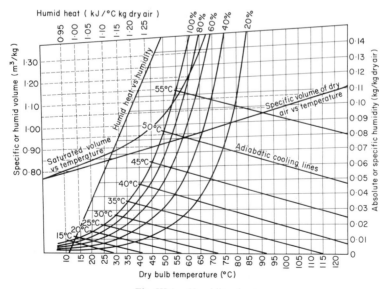

Fig. III.1. Humidity chart.

abscissa of the point 'a' (where the line a–b cuts the 100 % absolute humidity line) indicates the value, θ_{s1}, of the adiabatic saturation temperature for which the line a–b is drawn. The saturation humidity H_{s1} corresponding to this adiabatic saturation temperature is given by the ordinate of the point 'a'. The humid heat and humid volume of the moist air represented by point 'b' can be obtained from auxiliary

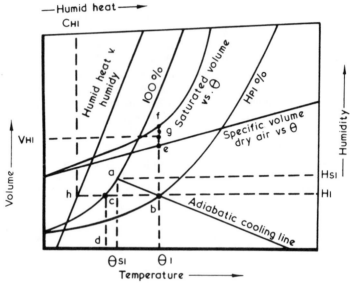

FIG. III.2. Use of humidity chart.

curves on the chart. The humid heat C_{H1} is the abscissa of the point 'h' on the humid heat v. humidity line having an ordinate H_1. The ordinates of points 'e' and 'f' are the specific volumes of dry and saturated air at θ_1 respectively. The humid volume is the ordinate of the point 'g' which is located so that:[1,2]

$$\frac{eg}{ef} = \frac{H_{p1}}{100}$$

REFERENCES

1. McCabe, W. L., and Smith, J. C., 'Unit Operations of Chemical Engineering', 2nd ed. (McGraw-Hill: 1967).
2. Perry, R. H., and Chilton, C. H., (Eds) 'Chemical Engineers' Handbook', 5th ed. (McGraw-Hill: 1973).

INTERNATIONAL (SI) SYSTEM OF UNITS

This system is based on the following seven *fundamental units:* metre (m); kilogram (kg); second (s); ampere (A); kelvin (K); candela (cd); mole (mol).

In addition the following *derived units* are relevant to this text: newton (N) = kg m/s^2; joule (J) = Nm; watt (W) = J/s.

The following *multiples* and *submultiples* of each unit are also relevant: 10^9, giga (G); 10^6, mega (M); 10^3, kilo (k); 10^2, hecto (h); 10, deca (da); 10^{-1}, deci (d); 10^{-2}, centi (c); 10^{-3}, milli (m); 10^{-6}, micro (μ); 10^{-9}, nano (n).

USEFUL CONVERSION FACTORS

Quantity	Non-SI Unit	Conversion Factor	SI Unit
Length	1 foot (ft)	= 0·3048	m
Mass	1 pound (lb)	≃ 0·454	kg
	1 ton (ton)	≃ 1·02 × 10^3	kg
Temperature	1 degree Fahrenheit (°F)	≃ 0·556	K (or °C)
	[492R ≃ 32°F	= 0°C ≃ 273K]	
Volume	1 ft^3	≃ 2·83 × 10^{-2}	m^3
	1 UK gallon (gal)	≃ 4·46 × 10^{-3}	m^3
Specific volume	1 ft^3/lb	≃ 6·24 × 10^{-2}	m^3/kg
Force	1 pound force (lb force)	≃ 4·45	N
Pressure, stress	1 lb force/in^2 (p.s.i.)	≃ 6·90	kN/m^2
	1 in Hg	≃ 3·39	kN/m^2
	1 mm Hg (≃ 1.00 Torr)	≃ 0·133	kN/m^2
	1 ft H20	≃ 2·99	kN/m^2
	1 bar (bar)	= 1 × 10^2	kN/m^2
Dynamic viscosity	1 lb/ft s	≃ 1·49	kg/m s
	1 poise (P)	= 0·1	kg/m s
Energy	1 British thermal unit (Btu)	≃ 1·06·	kJ
	1 kWh	= 3·6	MJ
	1 erg (erg)	= 0·1	J
Specific energy	1 Btu/lb	≃ 2·33	kJ/kg
Specific heat capacity	1 Btu/lb °F	≃ 4·19	kJ/kg K
Thermal conductivity	1 Btu/h ft °F	≃ 1·73	W/mK
Heat transfer coefficient	1 Btu/h ft^2 °F	≃ 5·68	W/m^{2}K

INDEX